ANALYTIC GEOMETRY

HARCOURT BRACE JOVANOVICH COLLEGE OUTLINE SERIES

ANALYTIC GEOMETRY

Peter H. Selby

Director, Educational Technology
Man Factors Associates
San Diego, California

Books for Professionals
Harcourt Brace Jovanovich, Publishers
San Diego New York London

Printed in the United States of America

Library of Congress Cataloging in Publication Data

Selby, Peter H.
Analytic geometry.

(Harcourt Brace Jovanovich college outline series) (Books for professionals)
Includes index.
1. Geometry, Analytic. I. Title. II. Series. III. Series: Books for professionals.
QA551.S45 1986 516.3 84-22542
ISBN 0-15-601525-0

First edition

A B C D E

PREFACE

Do not *read* this Outline—*use* it. You can't learn analytic geometry simply by reading it: You have to ***do*** it. Solving specific, practical problems is the best way to master—and to demonstrate your mastery of—the geometric and algebraic principles upon which the mathematical techniques of analytic geometry are based. Outside the classroom, you need three tools to do analytic geometry: a pencil, paper (including two kinds of graph paper), and a calculator. Add a fourth tool, this Outline, and you're all set.

This HBJ College Outline has been designed as a tool to help you sharpen your problem-solving skills in analytic geometry. Each chapter covers a single topic, whose fundamental principles are broken down in outline form for easy reference. The outline text is heavily interspersed with worked-out examples, so you can see immediately how each new idea is applied in problem form. Each chapter also contains a Summary and a Raise Your Grades section, which (taken together) give you an opportunity to review the primary principles of a topic and the problem-solving techniques implicit in those principles.

Most important, this Outline gives you plenty of problems to practice on. Work the Solved Problems, and check yourself against the step-by-step solutions provided. Test your mastery of the material in each chapter by doing the Supplementary Exercises. (In the Supplementary Exercises, you're given answers only—the details of the solution are up to you.) Then quiz yourself by working the problems in the periodic Exams. Finally, you can review all the topics covered in the Outline by working the problems in the Midterm and Final Exams. (The solution to each Exam question includes critical intermediate steps so you can diagnose your own strengths and weaknesses.) [*Warning*: You can't do analytic geometry unless you have a working knowledge of algebra, geometry, and trigonometry. If you can't follow the problem-solving steps in this Outline, you might want to refresh your skills in these areas.]

Having the tools is one thing; knowing how to use them is another. The study of analytic geometry gives you the basic conceptual tool that integrates several branches of mathematics. Analytic geometry is, in essence, an algebraic treatment of plane and solid Euclidean, or synthetic, geometry—with trigonometry thrown in for good measure. A knowledge of this subject can be valuable to anyone anticipating a career in physics, engineering, architecture, in fact a whole range of technical fields. It is also an *essential preliminary to the study of calculus*, since it provides the foundation on which much of the calculus is based.

This Outline contains a comprehensive exposition of the concepts of analytic geometry you'll need to begin (and to understand) differential and integral calculus. The analytic and problem-solving skills required to manipulate and graph the equations of planar curves and quadric surfaces—mentioned and used, but not fully developed, in calculus textbooks—are presented in a series of concise, self-contained chapters, each of which is devoted to a specific analytic topic. The conic sections, for example, are explained one-by-one in Chapters 4 through 7, and as a group in Chapter 8. And, in Part II (Solid Analytic Geometry), the point, the plane, and the line are covered individually in Chapters 13, 14, and 15, respectively. Finally, the three Appendices give you a quick review of the symbols, abbreviations, and mathematical subjects used in analytic geometry.

San Diego, California PETER H. SELBY

CONTENTS

PART I

Planar Analytic Geometry

FUNDAMENTAL CONCEPTS

THIS CHAPTER IS ABOUT

- ☑ Rectangular Coordinates
- ☑ Directed Line Segments
- ☑ Distance between Two Points
- ☑ Division Point of a Line Segment
- ☑ Inclination and Slope
- ☑ Parallel and Perpendicular Lines
- ☑ Angle between Two lines
- ☑ Applications to Elementary Geometry

1-1. Rectangular Coordinates

The system of coordinates we use in analytic geometry is defined by the familiar *Cartesian plane* used in algebra and trigonometry. As shown in Figure 1-1, the plane is divided into four **quadrants** (I, II, III, and IV) by the two perpendicular lines (axes X and Y) intersecting at the origin O. The arrowheads at the right end of the X-axis and at the top of the Y-axis indicate the positive direction of these axes. Any point on the plane can be defined by its position relative to the X- and Y-axes.

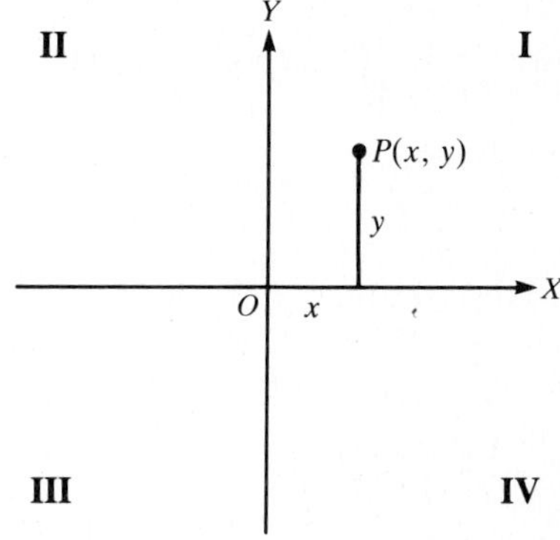

Figure 1-1. The rectangular coordinate system.

The distance of a point from the Y-axis is called the *x-coordinate* or *abscissa* of the point, while the distance from the X-axis is called the *y-coordinate* or *ordinate*. The two distances taken together and enclosed in parentheses (x, y) are called the **Cartesian** or **rectangular coordinates** of the point. Thus, (x, y) is considered an *ordered pair*: The abscissa is always written first, followed by the ordinate. The origin O corresponds to the zero of the real number system. Points to the right of the Y-axis have positive abscissas, while those to the left have negative abscissas. Similarly, points above and below the X-axis have, respectively, positive and negative ordinates.

- There is a one-to-one correspondence between ordered number pairs and points in the plane: To each pair of numbers there corresponds one and only one point; and, conversely, to each point in the plane there corresponds one and only one ordered pair of numbers.

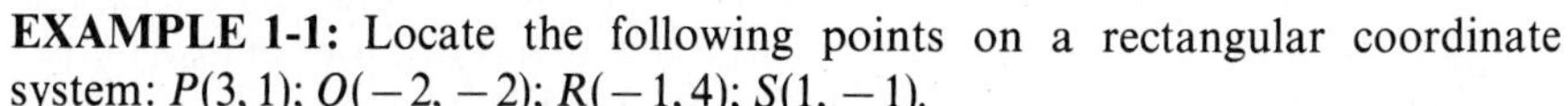

EXAMPLE 1-1: Locate the following points on a rectangular coordinate system: $P(3, 1)$; $Q(-2, -2)$; $R(-1, 4)$; $S(1, -1)$.

Solution: Using a piece of graph paper (cross-section or quadrille), draw a pair of X- and Y-axes, establishing some convenient scale, as shown in Figure 1-2. Then plot the four points, remembering that the x-coordinate is always given first and the y-coordinate second. Thus, point P is plotted three units to the right of the Y-axis and one unit above the X-axis, point Q is plotted two units to the left of the Y-axis and two units below the X-axis, and so on.

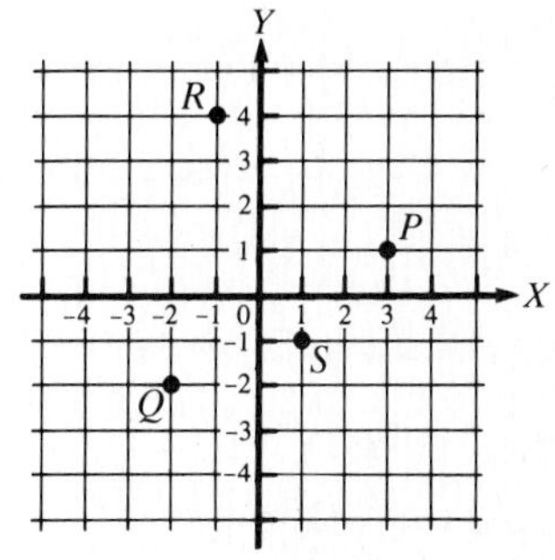

Figure 1-2

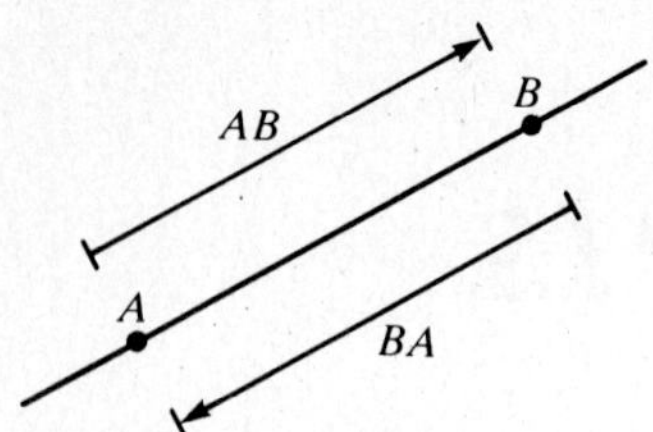

Figure 1-3. Directed line segment.

1-2. Directed Line Segments

A line segment to which positive or negative direction has been assigned is called a **directed line segment**. Thus, if AB in Figure 1-3 represents the length of the segment from A to B, then BA will represent the length of the segment measured in the opposite direction, from B to A. That is,

$$BA = -AB \qquad \text{or} \qquad AB + BA = 0$$

We used this idea in setting up our coordinate system: By definition, an abscissa has a positive direction when it is measured to the right of the Y-axis, and has a negative direction when it is measured to the left of the Y-axis. Similarly, an ordinate is positive when measured up from the X-axis and negative when measured down.

Given that any line drawn parallel to one of the coordinate axes has the same direction as that axis, we can derive an important relationship describing the addition of line segments. Figure 1-4 shows two arrangements of three points A, B, and C on a line parallel to the X-axis, so that line segments AB and BC are added:

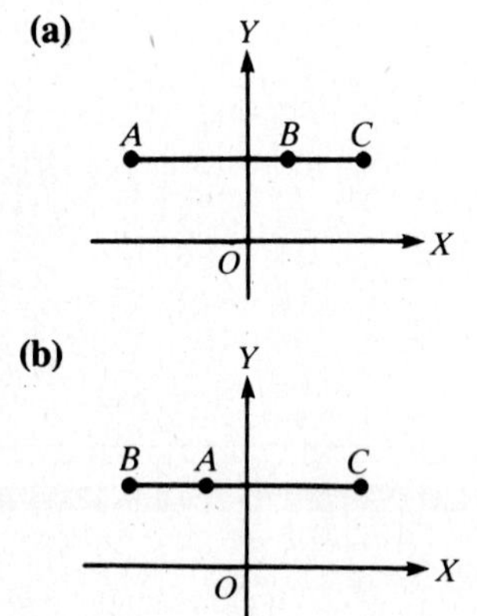

Figure 1-4. Addition of line segments: $AB + BC = AC$.

ADDITION OF LINE SEGMENTS

$$AB + BC = AC \tag{1-1}$$

This relationship is always true.

In Figure 1-4a the segments AB and BC have the same (positive →) sign, and their sum is the positive number AC. In Figure 1-4b, AB (←) and BC (→) are different in sign; but BC, which is positive, is larger than the negative AB, so again the sum is positive (AC). If the line is revolved 90°, the points lie on a line parallel to the Y-axis and eq. (1-1) is still true. Therefore, we can say that the relation $AB + BC = AC$ is true for ALL relative positions of A, B, and C on a line parallel to either of the coordinate axes.

EXAMPLE 1-2: The points A, B, and C lie on a line parallel to the Y-axis. Point A is four units below the X-axis, point B is five units above the X-axis, and point C is one unit below the X-axis. Show that $AB + BC = AC$.

Solution: Segment AB (the directed distance from A to B) is $+9$ because it is measured in a positive direction; BC is -6 (measured in a negative direction), and AC is $+3$ (measured in a positive direction). Then, $AB(9) + BC(-6) = AC(3)$, or $9 - 6 = 3$, and $3 = 3$, so $AB + BC = AC$.

1-3. Distance between Two Points

In finding the distance between two points P_1 and P_2, there are two cases to consider: points on a line parallel to an axis, and points on a line not parallel to an axis.

A. Points on a line parallel to an axis

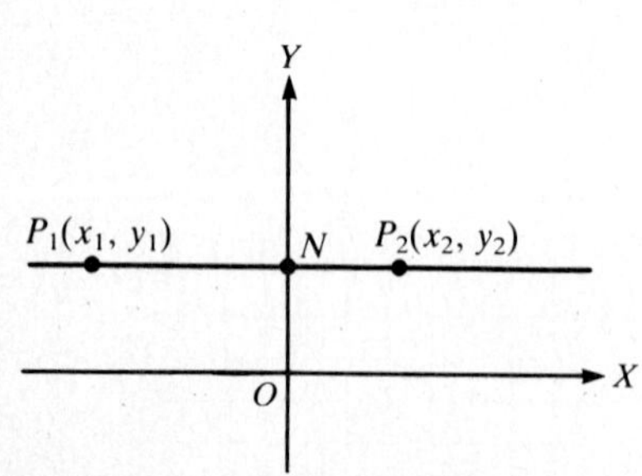

Figure 1-5. Distance between two points on a line parallel to a coordinate (X) axis: $d = P_1P_2 = x_2 - x_1$.

When P_1 and P_2 are on a line parallel to the X-axis and point N is the Y-intercept of the line (as shown in Figure 1-5), we know that $y_1 = y_2$. Therefore, using eq. (1-1), the distance from P_1 to P_2 is

$$AC = AB + BC$$

$$P_1P_2 = P_1N + NP_2 = NP_2 - NP_1$$

for all positions of P_1 and P_2. But $NP_2 = x_2$ and $NP_1 = x_1$, so $P_1P_2 = x_2 - x_1$. Similarly, if the points are on a line parallel to the Y-axis, $P_1P_2 = y_2 - y_1$.

- The distance between two points on a line parallel to the X-axis is the abscissa of the terminal point minus the abscissa of the initial point: $P_1P_2 = x_2 - x_1$.
- The distance between two points on a line parallel to the Y-axis is the ordinate of the terminal point minus the ordinate of the initial point: $P_1P_2 = y_2 - y_1$.

EXAMPLE 1-3: Find the directed distance from $P_1(-5, 2)$ to $P_2(3, 2)$.

Solution: The fact that the y-coordinate 2 is the same for both points tells us that the points lie on a line parallel to the X-axis. Therefore,

$$\begin{aligned} P_1P_2 &= x_2 - x_1 \\ &= 3 - (-5) = 8 \end{aligned}$$

B. Points on a line not parallel to an axis

When the points P_1 and P_2 are located *anywhere* in the plane, we can use elementary geometry to find the distance d between the two points. Draw a line through P_1 parallel to the X-axis, and a second line through P_2 parallel to the Y-axis (see Figure 1-6). These lines meet at the point Q whose coordinates are (x_2, y_1). Using the formulas for lines parallel to an axis, we have $P_1Q = x_2 - x_1$ and $QP_2 = y_2 - y_1$. Then we apply the Pythagorean theorem to get

$$(P_1P_2)^2 = d^2 = (P_1Q)^2 + (QP_2)^2 = (x_2 - x_1)^2 + (y_2 - y_1)^2$$

which reduces to a general formula for the distance d between two points:

DISTANCE BETWEEN TWO POINTS

$$d = \sqrt{(x_2 - x_1)^2 + (y_2 - y_1)^2} \tag{1-2}$$

Because we are interested only in the numerical value of the distance, only the positive value of the radical is considered. Also, the quantities $(x_2 - x_1)^2$ and $(y_2 - y_1)^2$ are always positive (because they are squared); therefore, either (x_1, y_1) or (x_2, y_2) may be taken as the initial point when using this formula.

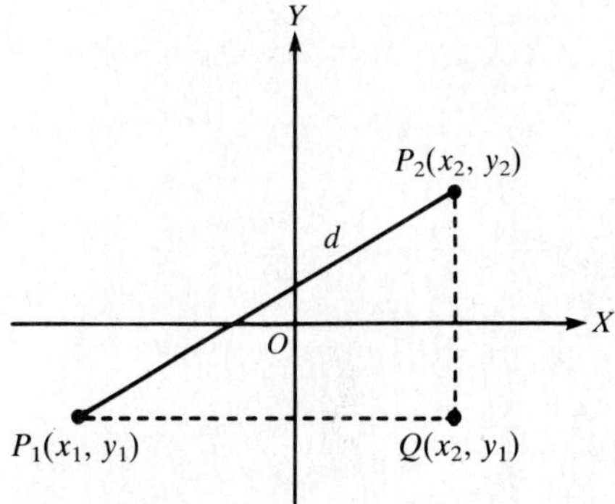

Figure 1-6. Distance between two points on a line not parallel to a coordinate axis: $d = P_1P_2 = \sqrt{(x_2 - x_1)^2 + (y_2 - y_1)^2}$.

EXAMPLE 1-4: Find the distance between the points $(3, -8)$ and $(-6, 4)$.

Solution: Using eq. (1-2), we get

$$\begin{aligned} d &= \sqrt{(x_2 - x_1)^2 + (y_2 - y_1)^2} \\ &= \sqrt{(3 + 6)^2 + (-8 - 4)^2} = \sqrt{81 + 144} = \sqrt{225} \\ &= 15 \end{aligned}$$

EXAMPLE 1-5: Find the distance between the points $(4, 4)$ and $(8, 7)$.

Solution: Again, using eq. (1-2),

$$\begin{aligned} d &= \sqrt{(8 - 4)^2 + (7 - 4)^2} \\ &= \sqrt{(4)^2 + (3)^2} = \sqrt{16 + 9} = \sqrt{25} \\ &= 5 \end{aligned}$$

1-4. Division Point of a Line Segment

The coordinates of the point dividing a line segment P_1P_2 in the ratio r_1/r_2 can be found with a little geometric manipulation. We begin by drawing the line segment.

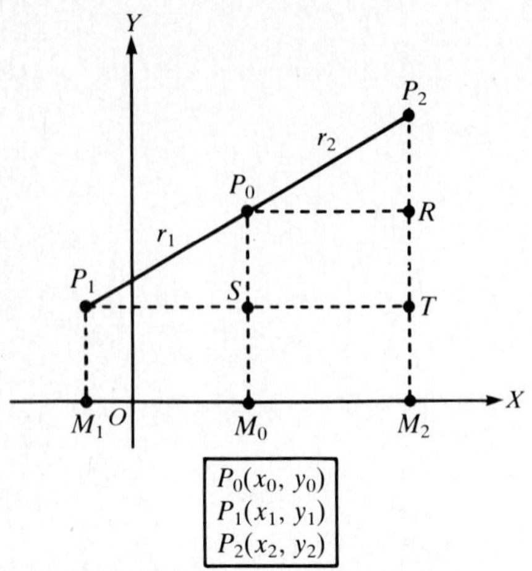

Figure 1-7. Coordinates of a point dividing a line segment: $x_0 = \dfrac{x_1r_2 + x_2r_1}{r_1 + r_2}$; $y_0 = \dfrac{y_1r_2 + y_2r_1}{r_1 + r_2}$.

In Figure 1-7, for example, P_1 is the initial point and P_2 is the terminal point, with coordinates as shown. Point P_0, with coordinates (x_0, y_0), is the point on the line joining P_1 and P_2, such that

$$\frac{P_1P_0}{P_0P_2} = \frac{r_1}{r_2}$$

We draw in the segments M_1P_1, M_0P_0, and M_2P_2 perpendicular to the X-axis. Then through P_1 and P_0 we draw the lines P_1ST and P_0R parallel to the X-axis. Now we have some line segments parallel to the axes, so we can write their coordinates:

$$P_1S = x_0 - x_1 \qquad SP_0 = y_0 - y_1$$

$$P_0R = x_2 - x_0 \qquad RP_2 = y_2 - y_0$$

Then, since triangles P_1SP_0 and P_0RP_2 are similar, we can write

$$\frac{P_1S}{P_0R} = \frac{P_1P_0}{P_0P_2} \quad \text{or} \quad \frac{x_0 - x_1}{x_2 - x_0} = \frac{r_1}{r_2}$$

Solving for x_0 gives us the x-coordinate of the division point:

x-COORDINATE OF DIVISION POINT

$$x_0 = \frac{x_1r_2 + x_2r_1}{r_1 + r_2} \tag{1-3}$$

And solving for y_0 gives the y-coordinate of the division point:

y-COORDINATE OF DIVISION POINT

$$y_0 = \frac{y_1r_2 + y_2r_1}{r_1 + r_2} \tag{1-4}$$

In Figure 1-7, P_0 lies between P_1 and P_2; that is, P_1P_0 and P_0P_2 have the same sign. If P_0 did not lie between P_1 and P_2 but fell on an extension of the line P_1P_2, thus dividing it externally, P_1P_0 and P_0P_2 would differ in sign and the ratio r_1/r_2 would be negative.

When the division point P_0 is the **midpoint** of the segment P_1P_2, so that $r_1 = r_2$, eqs. (1-3) and (1-4) reduce to

MIDPOINT COORDINATES

$$x_0 = \frac{x_1 + x_2}{2} \quad \text{and} \quad y_0 = \frac{y_1 + y_2}{2} \tag{1-5}$$

EXAMPLE 1-6: Find the coordinates of the point that is two-thirds of the way from $(-3, 5)$ to $(6, -4)$.

Solution: Let P_1 be $(-3, 5)$ and P_2 be $(6, -4)$. If P_0 is the desired point, then

$$\frac{P_1P_0}{P_0P_2} = \frac{r_1}{r_2} = \frac{2}{1}$$

where $r_1 = 2$ (two-thirds of the distance from P_1 to P_2) and $r_2 = 1$ (one-third of the distance from P_1 to P_2). Thus, from eq. (1-3)

$$x_0 = \frac{x_1r_2 + x_2r_1}{r_1 + r_2} = \frac{(-3)(1) + (6)(2)}{2 + 1} = 3$$

and from eq. (1-4)

$$y_0 = \frac{y_1r_2 + y_2r_1}{r_1 + r_2} = \frac{(5)(1) + (-4)(2)}{2 + 1} = -1$$

So the coordinates of the point P_0 are $(3, -1)$.

EXAMPLE 1-7: Find the coordinates of the point that lies three-fifths of the way from the point $(-7, -5)$ to the point $(-4, 2)$.

Solution: Let P_1 be $(-7, -5)$ and P_2 be $(-4, 2)$. If P_0 is the desired point, the ratio is $3/2$ (3 parts of 5 to 2 parts of 5). Hence, $r_1 = 3$ and $r_2 = 2$. From eq. (1-3)

$$x_0 = \frac{(-7)(2) + (-4)(3)}{3 + 2} = -\frac{26}{5}$$

and from eq. (1-4)

$$y_0 = \frac{(-5)(2) + (2)(3)}{3 + 2} = -\frac{4}{5}$$

The coordinates of P_0 are $(-\frac{26}{5}, -\frac{4}{5})$.

EXAMPLE 1-8: Find the coordinates of the midpoint of the segment joining $(2, 6)$ and $(8, -4)$.

Solution: From eq. (1-5),

$$x_0 = \frac{x_1 + x_2}{2} = \frac{2 + 8}{2} = 5$$

$$y_0 = \frac{y_1 + y_2}{2} = \frac{6 + (-4)}{2} = 1$$

The coordinates of the midpoint are $(5, 1)$.

EXAMPLE 1-9: Find the coordinates of the midpoint between the points $(3, -4)$ and $(-5, 6)$.

Solution: From eq. (1-5),

$$x_0 = \frac{3 + (-5)}{2} = -1$$

$$y_0 = \frac{-4 + 6}{2} = 1$$

The coordinates of the midpoint are $(-1, 1)$.

1-5. Inclination and Slope

In everyday language, we often use the terms "slope" and "inclination" interchangeably. We say, for example, that a road has a "steep slope" or a "high angle of inclination." But in analytic geometry these terms have precise meanings.

- **Inclination** is the angle (α), less than 180° measured counterclockwise, that a line makes with the positive X-axis.
- **Slope** (m) is the tangent of the angle of inclination; i.e., $m = \tan \alpha$.

Slope can be positive or negative. For example, in Figure 1-8, line l_1 makes an acute angle α_1 with the positive direction of the X-axis. Hence $m_1 = \tan \alpha_1$ is positive, and so l_1 is said to have a positive slope. Similarly, since α_2 is obtuse, $m_2 = \tan \alpha_2$ is negative, and so l_2 has a negative slope. Therefore, we can say in general that

- a line that rises from left to right has a positive slope;
- a line that descends from left to right has a negative slope.

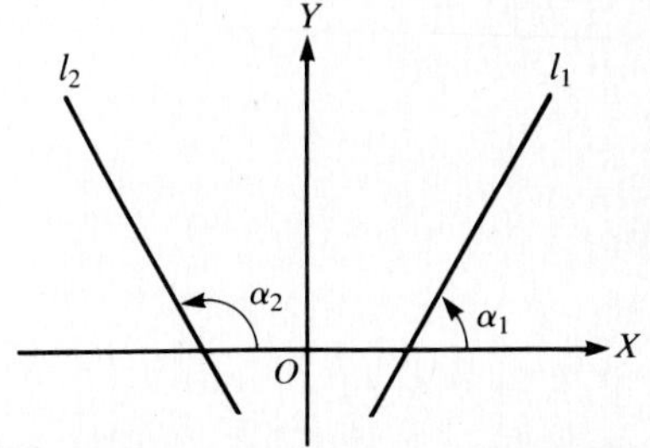

Figure 1-8. Inclination angle: acute α_1; obtuse α_2.

Slope can be zero or infinite. Since $\tan 0° = 0$ and $\tan 90°$ is undefined (as we know from trigonometry),

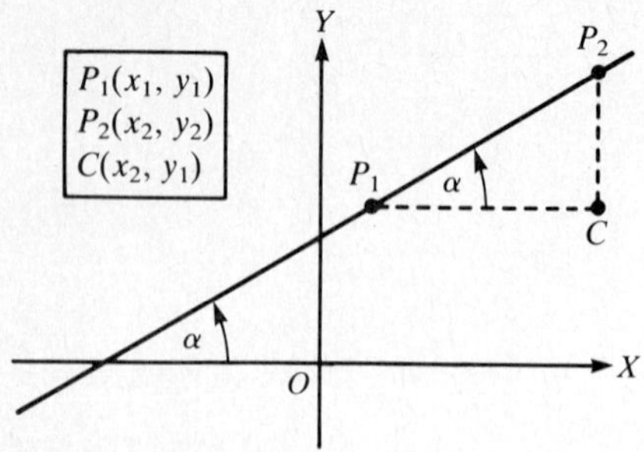

Figure 1-9. Slope of a line through two points: $m = \tan\alpha = \dfrac{CP_2}{P_1C} = \dfrac{y_2 - y_1}{x_2 - x_1}$.

- a line parallel to the X-axis has a zero slope;
- a line perpendicular to the X-axis has *no* slope, sometimes called *infinite* slope.

note: "No" slope is *not* the same as "zero" slope.

The slope of a line through two points, such as P_1 and P_2 in Figure 1-9, can be expressed in terms of the coordinates of those points as follows:

SLOPE OF A LINE THROUGH TWO POINTS

$$m = \tan\alpha = \frac{CP_2}{P_1C} = \frac{y_2 - y_1}{x_2 - x_1} \tag{1-6}$$

where $x_1 \neq x_2$.

The relation

$$\frac{y_2 - y_1}{x_2 - x_1} = \frac{y_1 - y_2}{x_1 - x_2}$$

is always true, regardless of whether the slope is positive or negative. And the slope of the line directed from P_1 to P_2 is the same as that of the line directed from P_2 to P_1. In general

- the slope of a line that is not parallel to the Y-axis is equal to the difference of the ordinates divided by the corresponding difference of the abscissas.

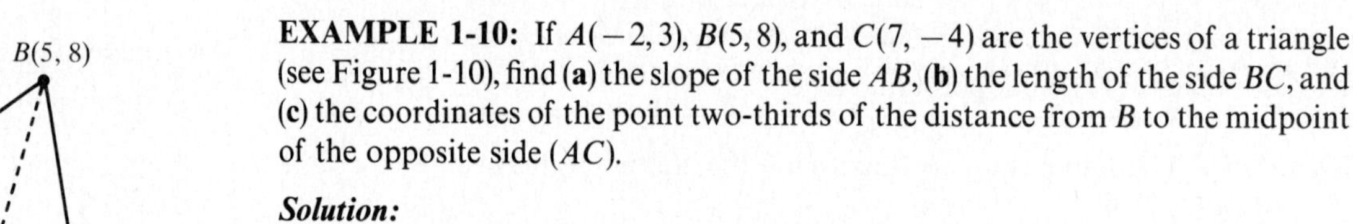
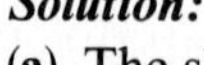

EXAMPLE 1-10: If $A(-2, 3)$, $B(5, 8)$, and $C(7, -4)$ are the vertices of a triangle (see Figure 1-10), find **(a)** the slope of the side AB, **(b)** the length of the side BC, and **(c)** the coordinates of the point two-thirds of the distance from B to the midpoint of the opposite side (AC).

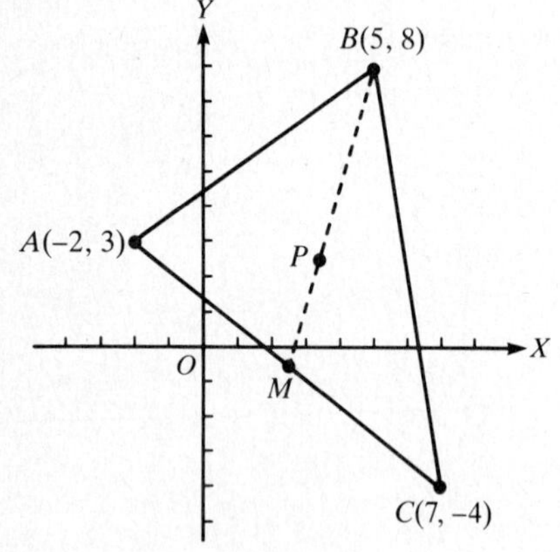

Figure 1-10

Solution:

(a) The slope m of the line AB is given by eq. (1-6):

$$m = \frac{y_2 - y_1}{x_2 - x_1} = \frac{8 - 3}{5 - (-2)} = \frac{5}{7}$$

note: Although this value was found by taking the direction from A to B, we know that the slope is the same if the direction is taken from B to A:

$$m = \frac{y_1 - y_2}{x_1 - x_2} = \frac{3 - 8}{-2 - 5} = \frac{-5}{-7} = \frac{5}{7}$$

(b) We can find the length of the side BC by using eq. (1-2) for the distance between two points:

$$\begin{aligned} BC &= \sqrt{(x_2 - x_1)^2 + (y_2 - y_1)^2} \\ &= \sqrt{(7 - 5)^2 + (-4 - 8)^2} = \sqrt{4 + 144} \\ &= 2\sqrt{37} \end{aligned}$$

(c) Before we can find the coordinates of the point two-thirds of the distance from B to the midpoint of AC, we first must find the coordinates of the midpoint (M) itself. Using the midpoint equations (1-5), we get

$$x_0 = \frac{x_1 + x_2}{2} = \frac{-2 + 7}{2} = \frac{5}{2}$$

$$y_0 = \frac{y_1 + y_2}{2} = \frac{3 - 4}{2} = -\frac{1}{2}$$

so the coordinates of M are $(\frac{5}{2}, -\frac{1}{2})$. Now if P is the point two-thirds of the way from B to M, we know that $BP/PM = 2/1$; so we can find the coordinates of P from eqs. (1-3) and (1-4):

$$x_0 = \frac{(5)(1) + (\frac{5}{2})(2)}{2+1} = \frac{10}{3}$$

$$y_0 = \frac{(8)(1) + (-\frac{1}{2})(2)}{2+1} = \frac{7}{3}$$

Thus, $P = (\frac{10}{3}, \frac{7}{3})$.

note: The line BM is a *median* of the triangle, and the point $P(\frac{10}{3}, \frac{7}{3})$ is called the *center of gravity* of the triangle.

1-6. Parallel and Perpendicular Lines

A. Parallel lines

If two lines with defined slopes m_1 and m_2 are parallel, their slopes are equal. The converse is also true: If two lines have equal slopes, they are parallel. Thus, if l_1 is parallel to l_2 (as in Figure 1-11), then $\alpha_1 = \alpha_2$, and so $m_1 = \tan\alpha_1 = \tan\alpha_2 = m_2$. Conversely, if $m_1 = m_2$, then $\alpha_1 = \alpha_2$, so the lines are parallel.

note: All lines with *undefined* (no) slopes are also parallel; i.e., all vertical lines are parallel.

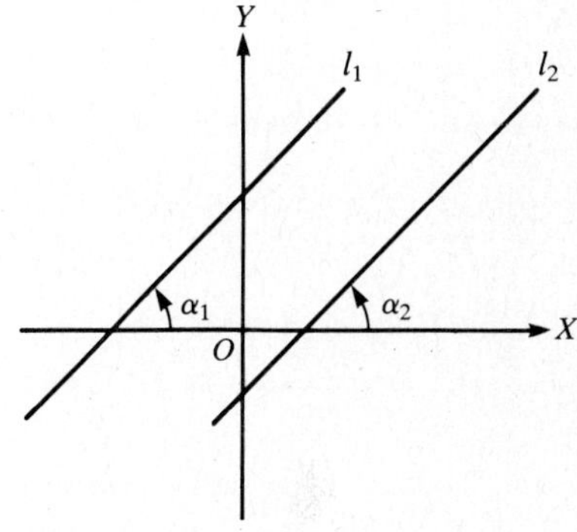

Figure 1-11. Slopes of parallel lines: $\tan\alpha_1 = \tan\alpha_2$.

EXAMPLE 1-11: Determine whether the line segment joining the points (3, 7) and (−2, 4) is parallel to the line joining (6, −5) and (1, −8).

Solution: Use eq. (1-6) to determine the slope of the first pair of points,

$$m_1 = \frac{y_2 - y_1}{x_2 - x_1} = \frac{4-7}{-2-3} = \frac{3}{5}$$

and the second pair of points,

$$m_2 = \frac{y_2 - y_1}{x_2 - x_1} = \frac{-8-(-5)}{1-6} = \frac{3}{5}$$

The slopes are the same, so the lines are parallel.

B. Perpendicular lines

If two lines with defined and nonzero slopes m_1 and m_2 are perpendicular, their slopes are negative reciprocals. Conversely, if the slopes of two lines are negative reciprocals, the lines are perpendicular. Thus, in Figure 1-12, l_1 and l_2, with slopes $m_1 = \tan\alpha_1$ and $m_2 = \tan\alpha_2$, are two lines that meet at right angles. Since we know from plane geometry that each exterior angle of a triangle equals the sum of the two opposite interior angles, we can write $\alpha_2 = 90° + \alpha_1$. Thus

$$\tan\alpha_2 = \tan(90° + \alpha_1) = -\cot\alpha_1 = -\frac{1}{\tan\alpha_1}$$

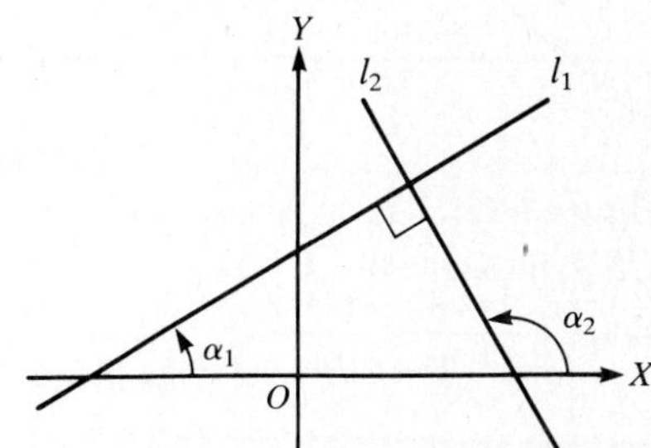

Figure 1-12. Slopes of perpendicular lines: $\tan\alpha_2 = -\dfrac{1}{\tan\alpha_1}$.

Therefore

SLOPES OF PERPENDICULAR LINES

$$m_2 = -\frac{1}{m_1} \quad \text{or} \quad m_1 m_2 = -1 \tag{1-7}$$

exception: Vertical lines (no slope) are perpendicular to horizontal lines (zero slope).

EXAMPLE 1-12: Show that the line joining the points (5, 3) and (2, −4) is perpendicular to the line joining the points (−4, 2) and (3, −1).

Solution: Use eq. (1-6) to find the slopes of the two lines:

$$m_1 = \frac{3-(-4)}{5-2} = \frac{7}{3} \quad \text{and} \quad m_2 = \frac{2-(-1)}{-4-3} = -\frac{3}{7}$$

Therefore $m_2 = -1/m_1$, and the lines are perpendicular.

EXAMPLE 1-13: Show that the line joining the points (3, 5) and (−2, 3) is perpendicular to the line joining the points (2, −1) and (−4, 14).

Solution:

$$m_1 = \frac{5-3}{3+2} = \frac{2}{5} \quad \text{and} \quad m_2 = \frac{-1-14}{2+4} = -\frac{15}{6} = -\frac{5}{2}$$

Thus $m_2 = -1/m_1$, and the lines are perpendicular.

EXAMPLE 1-14: Determine whether the line joining the points (12, 11) and (−3, 1) is parallel or perpendicular to the line joining the points (−13, 5) and (−1, −5).

Solution: From eq. (1-6),

$$m_1 = \frac{1-11}{-3-12} = \frac{2}{3} \quad \text{and} \quad m_2 = \frac{-5-5}{-1+13} = -\frac{5}{6}$$

The slopes are neither equal nor negative reciprocals, so the lines are *neither* parallel nor perpendicular to each other.

1-7. Angle between Two Lines

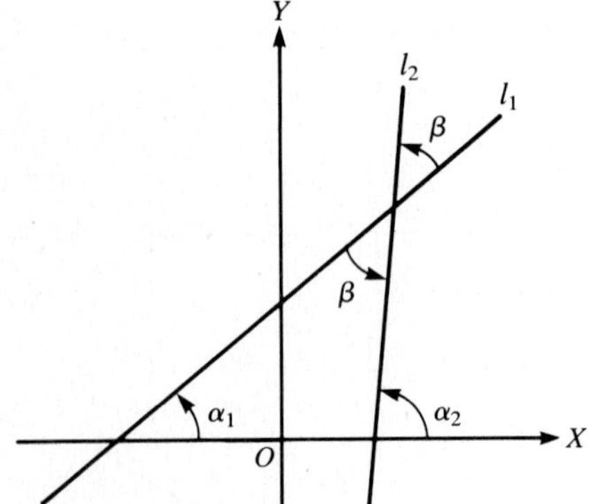

Figure 1-13. The angle between two intersecting lines: $\tan\beta = \dfrac{\tan\alpha_2 - \tan\alpha_1}{1+\tan\alpha_1\tan\alpha_2}$.

The methods of analytic geometry also make it possible to find the angle between two intersecting lines that do *not* meet at right angles.

If l_1 and l_2 are two lines and β (beta) is the angle measured counterclockwise from l_1 to l_2 (as shown in Figure 1-13), then $\alpha_2 = \alpha_1 + \beta$, or $\beta = \alpha_2 - \alpha_1$. Now we can use the trigonometric equation for the tangent of the difference of two angles to write

$$\tan\beta = \tan(\alpha_2 - \alpha_1) = \frac{\tan\alpha_2 - \tan\alpha_1}{1+\tan\alpha_1\tan\alpha_2}$$

But $\tan\alpha_1 = m_1$ and $\tan\alpha_2 = m_2$; so the equation may be written

TANGENT OF ANGLE BETWEEN TWO LINES

$$\tan\beta = \frac{m_2 - m_1}{1 + m_1 m_2} \tag{1-8}$$

The sign of $\tan\beta$ in eq. (1-8) tells us whether we have found the acute or the obtuse angle between the lines.

- If $\tan\beta$ is positive, the angle is acute; if $\tan\beta$ is negative, the angle is obtuse.

And if we know β, we can find its supplementary angle by subtracting β from 180°.

note: β is measured from l_1 to l_2, so m_2 is the slope of the line that is the terminal side of the angle. Except in specified cases, we can designate either line as l_2 if we remember that, once our choice is made, the acute angle β remains fixed.

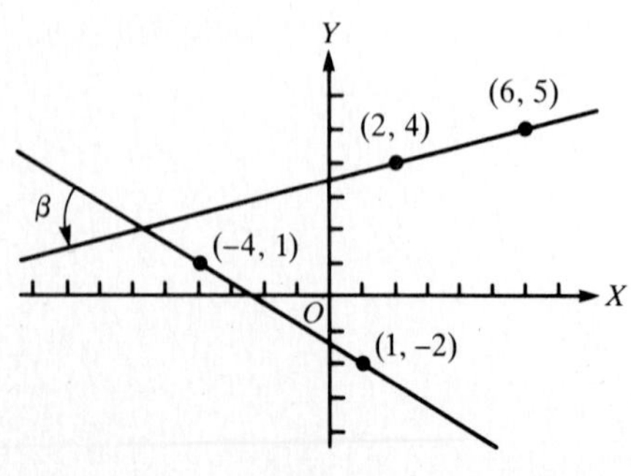

Figure 1-14

EXAMPLE 1-15: Find the acute angle made by the line joining the points (1, −2) and (−4, 1), to the line joining the points (2, 4) and (6, 5).

Solution: If we plot the points as shown in Figure 1-14, we see that m_2 is the slope of the line through the points (2, 4) and (6, 5). Therefore, from eq. (1-6)

$$m_1 = \frac{-2-1}{1+4} = -\frac{3}{5}$$

$$m_2 = \frac{5-4}{6-2} = \frac{1}{4}$$

and from eq. (1-8)

$$\tan\beta = \frac{\frac{1}{4}+\frac{3}{5}}{1-\frac{3}{20}} = \frac{17}{17} = 1$$

Therefore $\beta = 45°$. (We know from trigonometry that the tangent of an angle of 45° is 1.)

note: If we hadn't plotted the points and had chosen the line through (1, −2) and (−4, 1) as the terminal side of the angle, we'd have gotten the following result:

$$m_1 = \frac{5-4}{6-2} = \frac{1}{4}$$

$$m_2 = \frac{-2-1}{1+4} = -\frac{3}{5}$$

$$\tan\beta = \frac{-\frac{3}{5}-\frac{1}{4}}{1-\frac{3}{20}} = -1$$

so that $\beta = 135°$ (since the tangent is negative in the second quadrant). But this is not an acute angle. We can *obtain* the acute angle from the relation $180° - \beta$; that is, $180° - 135° = 45°$.

EXAMPLE 1-16: Find the acute angle made by the line joining the points (−3, 2) and (4, 4) and the line joining the points (−2, −1) and (1, 2).

Solution: Plotting the points and drawing in the lines, we get the relationship shown in Figure 1-15. Here, l_2 is defined by the points (−2, −1) and (1, 2). Therefore, from eqs. (1-6) and (1-8)

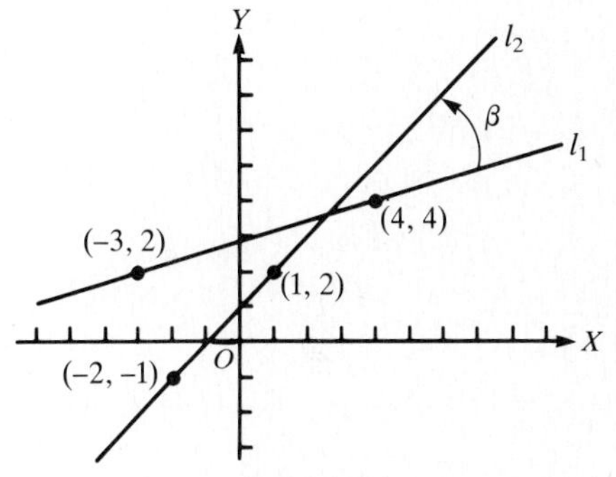

Figure 1-15

$$m_1 = \frac{4-2}{4+3} = \frac{2}{7} \quad \text{and} \quad m_2 = \frac{2+1}{1+2} = 1$$

so

$$\tan\beta = \frac{1-2/7}{1+(2/7)(1)} = \frac{(7-2)/7}{(7+2)/7} = \frac{5}{9} = 0.555\,556$$

And a calculator tells us that, for this value of the tangent, $\beta = 29°$.

1-8. Applications to Elementary Geometry

Many of the theorems of plane geometry can be proved by the analytic methods of coordinate geometry. But it is important that the proof be *general*; that is, a figure must not have any special conditions that would restrict the statement of the theorem, and the results must be expressed in terms of variables. Also, the coordinate axes should be used as parts of the figure when it is possible to do so without diminishing the generality of the proof.

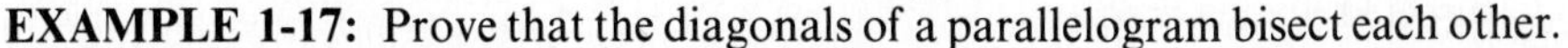

EXAMPLE 1-17: Prove that the diagonals of a parallelogram bisect each other.

Solution: We may choose the origin as a vertex and an axis as one side of the parallelogram without loss of generality. But we may not use *both* axes as sides,

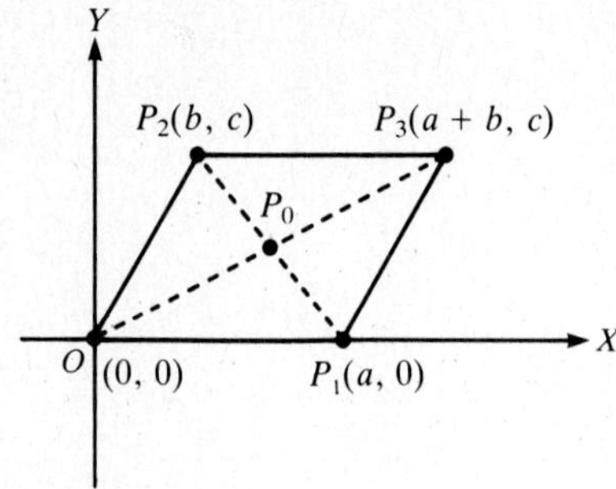

Figure 1-16

because our figure would then contain a right angle and the parallelogram would be a special type (i.e., a rectangle).

Choosing the X-axis as a side (as in Figure 1-16), we have O and P_1 with coordinates $(0, 0)$ and $(a, 0)$, respectively, as two vertices. If P_2 with coordinates (b, c) is taken as the third vertex, then the fourth vertex P_3 must have coordinates $(a + b, c)$, because the segment P_2P_3 is parallel and equal in length to the segment OP_1.

To prove the theorem, we must show that P_0 is the midpoint of both diagonals. Using the diagonal OP_3, we find that the coordinates of P_0 are $(\frac{a+b}{2}, \frac{c}{2})$. Likewise, using the diagonal P_1P_2, the coordinates of P_0 are $(\frac{a+b}{2}, \frac{c}{2})$. Hence the diagonals bisect each other, and the theorem is proved.

EXAMPLE 1-18: Prove that a triangle is isosceles if two medians of the triangle are equal.

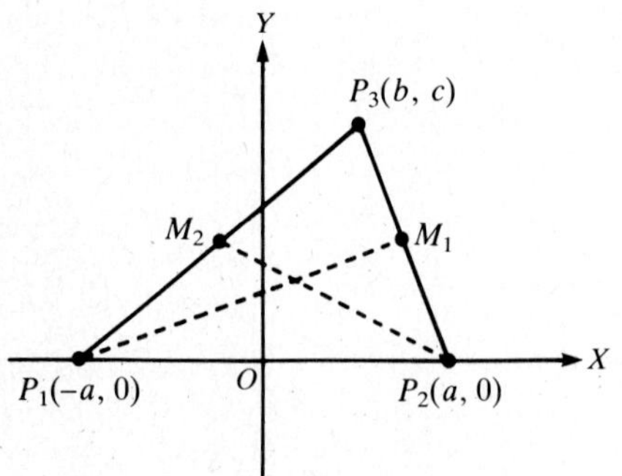

Figure 1-17

Solution: Choose a triangle that has a base length of $2a$ units and base vertices P_1 and P_2 whose coordinates are $(-a, 0)$ and $(a, 0)$, respectively, as in Figure 1-17. Then let the third vertex P_3 have coordinates (b, c), and let M_1 and M_2 be the midpoints of sides P_2P_3 and P_1P_3, respectively.

By hypothesis, the medians are equal, $P_1M_1 = P_2M_2$, so we must show that $P_1P_3 = P_2P_3$. This is equivalent to saying that P_3 falls on the Y-axis, or that $b = 0$, since P_1 and P_2 are equidistant from the origin O.

The coordinates of M_1 and M_2 are $(\frac{a+b}{2}, \frac{c}{2})$ and $(\frac{b-a}{2}, \frac{c}{2})$, respectively. Therefore

$$\begin{aligned} P_1M_1 &= \sqrt{\left(\frac{a+b}{2} + a\right)^2 + \left(\frac{c}{2} - 0\right)^2} \\ &= \sqrt{(\tfrac{1}{2})^2[(a + b + 2a)^2 + c^2]} \\ &= \tfrac{1}{2}\sqrt{(b + 3a)^2 + c^2} \\ P_2M_2 &= \sqrt{\left(\frac{b-a}{2} - a\right)^2 + \left(\frac{c}{2} - 0\right)^2} \\ &= \tfrac{1}{2}\sqrt{(b - 3a)^2 + c^2} \end{aligned}$$

Hence

$$\tfrac{1}{2}\sqrt{(b + 3a)^2 + c^2} = \tfrac{1}{2}\sqrt{(b - 3a)^2 + c^2}$$

which reduces to $12ab = 0$, or $ab = 0$. Since a is one-half the length of the base, a cannot be equal to zero, so b must be equal to zero. Therefore P_3 falls on the Y-axis, and the two sides of the triangle are equal. The theorem is proved.

SUMMARY

1. Analytic geometry is the study of geometry in which the analytic methods of algebra are employed.
2. For a point in the Cartesian plane, the first (or x) coordinate determines the distance of that point from the vertical (or Y) axis; the second (or y) coordinate determines the distance of the point from the horizontal (or X) axis.
3. The x-coordinate is called the abscissa; the y-coordinate, the ordinate.
4. A line to which positive or negative direction has been assigned is called a directed line segment.
5. If (x_1, y_1) and (x_2, y_2) are the coordinates of two points, the distance between them is given by

$$d = \sqrt{(x_2 - x_1)^2 + (y_2 - y_1)^2}$$

6. The coordinates of the point P_0 dividing a line segment P_1P_2 in the ratio r_1/r_2 are given by

$$x_0 = \frac{x_1r_2 + x_2r_1}{r_1 + r_2} \quad \text{and} \quad y_0 = \frac{y_1r_2 + y_2r_1}{r_1 + r_2}$$

7. The coordinates of the midpoint P_0 of the line segment P_1P_2 (where $r_1 = r_2$) are given by

$$x_0 = \frac{x_1 + x_2}{2} \quad \text{and} \quad y_0 = \frac{y_1 + y_2}{2}$$

8. Inclination (α) is the angle (less than 180° and measured counterclockwise) that a line makes with the positive direction of the X-axis.
9. Slope (m) is the tangent of the angle of inclination: $m = \tan\alpha$.
10. The slope of a line through two points is given by

$$m = \tan\alpha = \frac{y_2 - y_1}{x_2 - x_1}$$

11. Two lines with defined slopes m_1 and m_2 are parallel if $m_1 = m_2$.
12. If two lines with defined and nonzero slopes m_1 and m_2 are perpendicular to each other, their slopes are negative reciprocals; thus $m_2 = -1/m_1$ and $m_1m_2 = -1$.
13. If β is the angle between two lines l_1 and l_2 having slopes m_1 and m_2, respectively, then the tangent of the angle between the two lines is given by

$$\tan\beta = \frac{m_2 - m_1}{1 + m_1m_2}$$

14. Many of the theorems of elementary plane geometry can be proved by the analytic methods of coordinate geometry.

RAISE YOUR GRADES

Can you...?

- ☑ place a point with given coordinates in the Cartesian plane
- ☑ add directed line segments
- ☑ find the directed distance between two points
- ☑ find the coordinates of the division point of a line segment
- ☑ find the slope of a line through two points
- ☑ show that two lines are parallel with or perpendicular to each other, given the coordinates of two points on each line
- ☑ find the acute angle between two intersecting lines that do not meet at a right angle
- ☑ prove that the diagonals of a rectangle are equal

SOLVED PROBLEMS

Rectangular Coordinates

PROBLEM 1-1 Plot the following points on a rectangular coordinate system: **(a)** $P(2,3)$; **(b)** $Q(-5,8)$; **(c)** $R(6,-2)$; **(d)** $S(-8,-2)$; **(e)** $T(4,-3)$; **(f)** $U(-5,2)$.

Solution: See Figure 1-18.

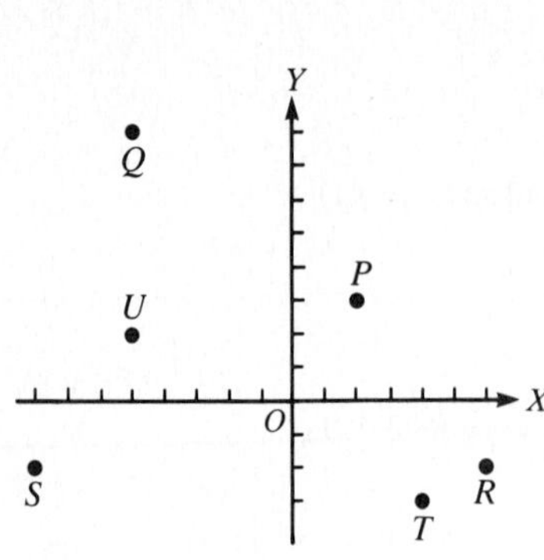

Figure 1-18

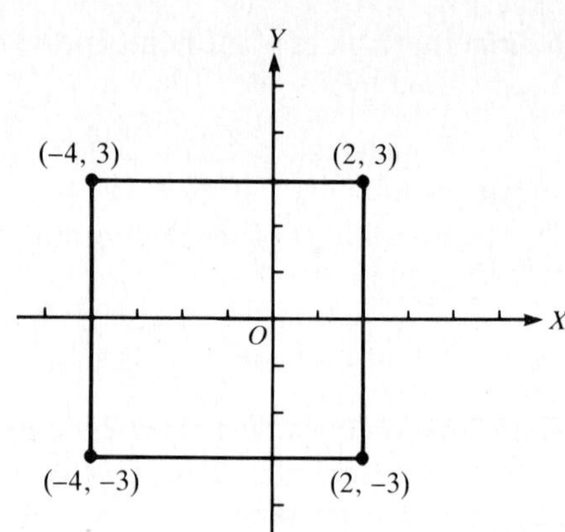

Figure 1-19

PROBLEM 1-2 (**a**) Plot the points $(-4, 3)$, $(2, 3)$, $(2, -3)$, and $(-4, -3)$, and connect them in the given order by straight lines. (**b**) What figure is obtained?

Solution: (**a**) See Figure 1-19. (**b**) A square.

Directed Line Segments

PROBLEM 1-3 Explain why $AB + BC = AC$ in Figure 1-20.

Solution: AB and BC are different in sign, but BC is greater, so their sum is AC:

$$AB + BC = AC$$
$$3 + (-9) = -6$$
$$-6 = -6$$

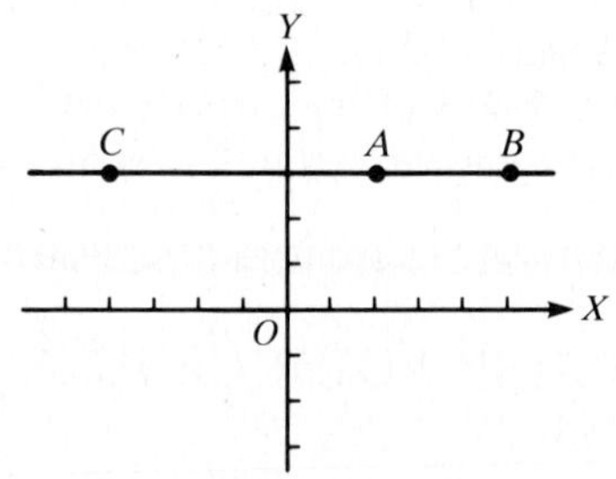

Figure 1-20

Distance between Two Points

PROBLEM 1-4 Find the directed distance from $P_1(-3, 3)$ to $P_2(3, 3)$.

Solution: The fact that the y-coordinate is the same for both points tells you that the points lie on a line parallel to the X-axis. Therefore

$$\begin{aligned} P_1P_2 &= x_2 - x_1 \\ &= 3 - (-3) = 6 \end{aligned}$$

PROBLEM 1-5 Find the directed distance from $(4, 0)$ to $(4, 4)$.

Solution: The fact that the x-coordinate is the same for both points tells you that the points lie on a line parallel to the Y-axis. Therefore

$$\begin{aligned} P_1P_2 &= y_2 - y_1 \\ &= 4 - 0 = 4 \end{aligned}$$

PROBLEM 1-6 Find the directed distance from $(4, 2)$ to $(-2, 2)$.

Solution: The y-coordinates are the same, so the points lie on a line parallel to the X-axis. Thus

$$x_2 - x_1 = -2 - 4 = -6$$

PROBLEM 1-7 Find the directed distance from $(6, 5)$ to $(2, 5)$.

Solution: The y-coordinates are the same, so the points lie on a line parallel to the X-axis. Thus

$$x_2 - x_1 = 2 - 6 = -4$$

PROBLEM 1-8 Find the distance between the points $(5, -3)$ and $(2, 8)$.

Solution: Using the distance formula (1-2), we get

$$\begin{aligned} d &= \sqrt{(x_2 - x_1)^2 + (y_2 - y_1)^2} \\ &= \sqrt{(2-5)^2 + (8+3)^2} = \sqrt{9 + 121} \\ &= \sqrt{130} \end{aligned}$$

PROBLEM 1-9 Find the distance between the points $(-7, 4)$ and $(1, -11)$.

Solution: From formula (1-2) we get

$$\begin{aligned} d &= \sqrt{(1+7)^2 + (-11-4)^2} = \sqrt{64 + 225} \\ &= \sqrt{289} = 17 \end{aligned}$$

Division Point of a Line Segment

PROBLEM 1-10 Find the coordinates of the midpoint of the line segment joining $(-5, 8)$ and $(2, -4)$.

Solution: From eqs. (1-5)

$$x_0 = \frac{x_1 + x_2}{2} \quad \text{and} \quad y_0 = \frac{y_1 + y_2}{2}$$

$$x_0 = \frac{-5 + 2}{2} \quad \text{and} \quad y_0 = \frac{8 - 4}{2}$$

$$x_0 = -\frac{3}{2} \quad \text{and} \quad y_0 = 2$$

So the coordinates of the midpoint are $(-\frac{3}{2}, 2)$.

PROBLEM 1-11 Find the coordinates of the point that is three-fifths of the way from $(-4, -2)$ to $(4, 4)$.

Solution: Let P_1 be $(-4, -2)$ and P_2 be $(4, 4)$. Therefore, since P_0 is the point you want, you can write the ratio

$$\frac{P_1P_0}{P_0P_2} = \frac{r_1}{r_2} = \frac{3}{2} \qquad \begin{array}{l} (r_1 = 3 \text{ is } \frac{3}{5} \text{ the distance from } P_1 \text{ to } P_2) \\ (r_2 = 2 \text{ is } \frac{2}{5} \text{ the distance from } P_1 \text{ to } P_2) \end{array}$$

Now you can find the x- and y-coordinates from eqs. (1-3) and (1-4), respectively:

$$\begin{aligned} x_0 &= \frac{x_1 r_2 + x_2 r_1}{r_1 + r_2} & y_0 &= \frac{y_1 r_2 + y_2 r_1}{r_1 + r_2} \\ &= \frac{(-4)(2) + (4)(3)}{3 + 2} & &= \frac{(-2)(2) + (4)(3)}{3 + 2} \\ &= \frac{4}{5} & &= \frac{8}{5} \end{aligned}$$

So the coordinates of the point are $(\frac{4}{5}, \frac{8}{5})$.

PROBLEM 1-12 Find the coordinates of the point that is three-fourths of the distance from $(6, -2)$ to $(2, 6)$.

Solution: The required point P_0 is three-fourths the distance from P_1 to P_2, so $r_1/r_2 = 3/1$. From eqs. (1-3) and (1-4) you get

$$x_0 = \frac{(6)(1) + (2)(3)}{4} = 3$$

$$y_0 = \frac{(-2)(1) + (6)(3)}{4} = 4$$

So the coordinates are (3, 4).

Inclination and Slope

PROBLEM 1-13 Find the slope of the lines joining the following pairs of points: **(a)** (3, 4) and (5, 9); **(b)** (−3, 2) and (2, −4); **(c)** (1, −2) and (6, 8); **(d)** (2, 5) and (3, −6); **(e)** (−5, −4) and (2, −3).

Solution: Use eq. (1-6) to express the slope m in coordinates:

$$m = \frac{y_2 - y_1}{x_2 - x_1}$$

(a) $m = \dfrac{9 - 4}{5 - 3} = \dfrac{5}{2}$

(b) $m = \dfrac{-4 - 2}{2 + 3} = -\dfrac{6}{5}$

(c) $m = \dfrac{8 + 2}{6 - 1} = 2$

(d) $m = \dfrac{-6 - 5}{3 - 2} = -11$

(e) $m = \dfrac{-3 + 4}{2 + 5} = \dfrac{1}{7}$

PROBLEM 1-14 Find the slope and inclination of the line joining (a, b) to (c, b).

Solution: Substituting into eq. (1-6), you get

$$m = \frac{y_2 - y_1}{x_2 - x_1} = \frac{b - b}{c - a} = 0$$

Since the slope $m = 0$ represents the tangent of the angle α of inclination (i.e., arc tan $\alpha = 0$) you can write $\alpha = 0°$. (That is, the angle whose tangent function value is 0 is the angle 0°.)

PROBLEM 1-15 Use slopes to prove that the points (0, 3), (2, 6), and (−2, 0) lie on the same straight line.

Solution: To prove that these points lie on the same straight line, you have to show that each pair of points has the same slope. So you use eq. (1-6) to find each slope:

$$m_1 = \frac{6 - 3}{2 - 0} = \frac{3}{2} \qquad m_2 = \frac{6 - 0}{2 + 2} = \frac{6}{4} = \frac{3}{2} \qquad m_3 = \frac{3 - 0}{0 + 2} = \frac{3}{2}$$

Since $m_1 = m_2 = m_3 = \frac{3}{2}$, the points must lie on the same straight line.

Parallel and Perpendicular Lines

PROBLEM 1-16 Show that the line through (1, 1) and (−2, 3) is parallel to the line through (3, 2) and (−3, 6).

Solution: To prove that the lines are parallel, you have to show that the two lines have the same slope, i.e., that $m_1 = m_2$. Using eq. (1-6), you get

$$m_1 = \frac{3 - 1}{-2 - 1} = -\frac{2}{3} \quad \text{and} \quad m_2 = \frac{6 - 2}{-3 - 3} = -\frac{4}{6} = -\frac{2}{3}$$

So the lines are parallel.

PROBLEM 1-17 Show that the line joining the points $(-2, 3)$ and $(3, 5)$ is perpendicular to the line joining $(-4, 14)$ and $(2, -1)$.

Solution: To prove the two lines are perpendicular to each other, you have to show that their slopes are negative reciprocals. Using eq. (1-6), you get

$$m_1 = \frac{5-3}{3+2} = \frac{2}{5} \quad \text{and} \quad m_2 = \frac{-1-14}{2+4} = -\frac{15}{6} = -\frac{5}{2}$$

So $m_2 = -1/m_1$, and the lines are perpendicular.

PROBLEM 1-18 Is the line segment that joins the two points $(13, 7)$ and $(-7, -3)$ parallel or perpendicular to the line that joins $(10, 6)$ and $(2, -2)$?

Solution: Examine the slopes of the two lines. From eq. (1-6), you get

$$m_1 = \frac{-3-7}{-7-13} = \frac{10}{20} = \frac{1}{2} \quad \text{and} \quad m_2 = \frac{-2-6}{2-10} = \frac{-8}{-8} = 1$$

Since their slopes are not the same, the two lines cannot be parallel; and since their slopes are not negative reciprocals, the two lines cannot be perpendicular.

Angle between Two Lines

PROBLEM 1-19 Find the acute angle made by the line joining the points $(-3, 7)$ and $(1, 6)$ with the line joining the points $(-2, -2)$ and $(3, 3)$ (see Figure 1-21).

Solution: The points are plotted, so you see that the terminal side l_1 is defined by the points $(-3, 7)$ and $(1, 6)$ and that l_2 is defined by $(-2, -2)$ and $(3, 3)$. Now you can find the slope m_1 of line l_1 and the slope m_2 of line l_2 by eq. (1-6):

$$m_1 = \frac{6-7}{1+3} = -\frac{1}{4} \quad \text{and} \quad m_2 = \frac{3+2}{3+2} = 1$$

Use the slopes to find the tangent of the acute angle β between the two lines by eq. (1-8):

$$\tan\beta = \frac{m_2 - m_1}{1 + m_1 m_2} = \frac{1+\frac{1}{4}}{1-\frac{1}{4}} = \frac{\frac{5}{4}}{\frac{3}{4}} = \frac{5}{3}$$

$$= 1.666\,67$$

and so (using your calculator) $\beta = 59°$.

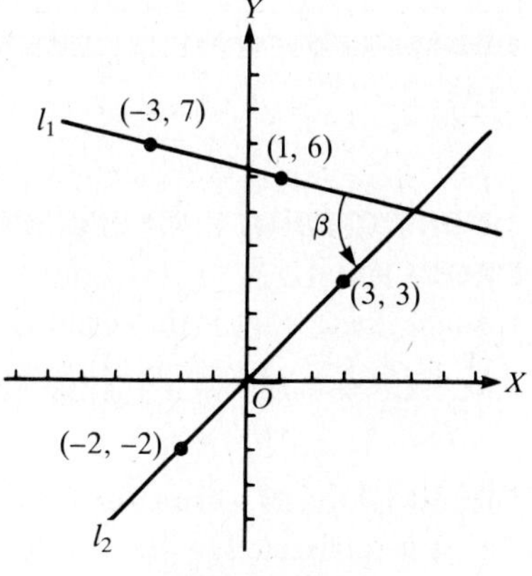

Figure 1-21

PROBLEM 1-20 Find the acute angle made between the line joining the points $(-1, 3)$ and $(3, 5)$ with the line joining $(-2, 8)$ and $(-3, 5\sqrt{3})$.

Solution: Designate l_1 as the line defined by the points $(-1, 3)$ and $(3, 5)$, and l_2 as the line defined by the points $(-2, 8)$ and $(-3, 5\sqrt{3})$. So the respective slopes are

$$m_1 = \frac{5-3}{3+1} = \frac{1}{2} \quad \text{and} \quad m_2 = \frac{8-5\sqrt{3}}{-2+3} = 8 - 5\sqrt{3}$$

Then if you substitute into eq. (1-8)

$$\tan\beta = \frac{(8-5\sqrt{3}) - \frac{1}{2}}{1 + \frac{1}{2}(8-5\sqrt{3})} = \frac{2(8-5\sqrt{3}) - 1}{2 + (8-5\sqrt{3})}$$

$$= \frac{3-2\sqrt{3}}{2-\sqrt{3}}$$

and rationalize the denominator, you get

$$\tan \beta = -\sqrt{3}$$

from which you find that $\beta = 120°$. Now you can find the acute angle by subtracting:

$$180° - \beta = 60°$$

Applications to Elementary Geometry

PROBLEM 1-21 Prove that the diagonals of a rectangle are equal.

Solution: First draw a rectangle $ABCD$ and choose the X- and Y-axes as sides, as shown in Figure 1-22. Then write down the general coordinates of the vertices:

$$A(0,0) \qquad B(a,0) \qquad C(a,b) \qquad D(0,b)$$

Use eq. (1-2) to find the length of each diagonal AC and BD:

$$AC = \sqrt{(a-0)^2 + (b-0)^2}$$

$$BD = \sqrt{(0-a)^2 + (b-0)^2}$$

The length of each diagonal reduces to $\sqrt{a^2 + b^2}$, which proves the proposition.

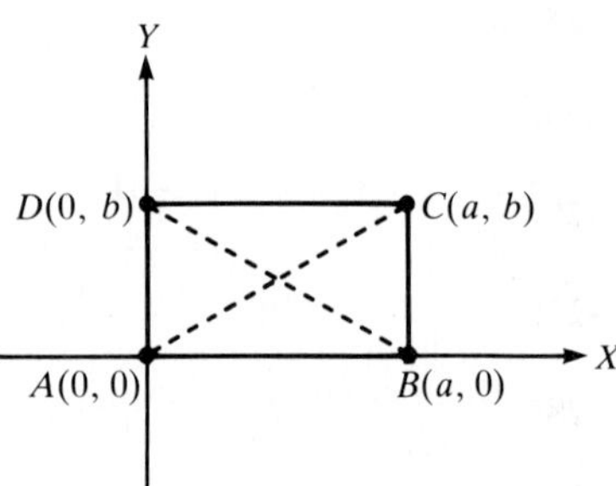

Figure 1-22

Supplementary Exercises

PROBLEM 1-22 If you connect the points (0, 0), (0, 2), (8, 2), and (8, 0) in the given order by straight lines, what is the resulting figure?

PROBLEM 1-23 What is the abscissa of a point on the Y-axis? the ordinate of a point on the X-axis?

PROBLEM 1-24 One end of a line segment drawn parallel to the X-axis is (3, −4). If the segment is trisected by the Y-axis, what are the coordinates of the other end? [*Hint:* This problem has two answers.]

PROBLEM 1-25 Three vertices of a rectangle are (0, 0), (5, 0), and (0, 3). What are the coordinates of the fourth vertex?

PROBLEM 1-26 Find the distance between the pairs of points whose coordinates are **(a)** (−3, 0) and (−4, 7); **(b)** (−1, −5) and (2, −3); **(c)** (−3, 1) and (3, −1).

PROBLEM 1-27 Find the coordinates of the midpoint of the segment joining (8, 6) and (−1, 1).

PROBLEM 1-28 A line segment joins the points (2, 8) and (5, −3). What is its length? What are the coordinates of its midpoint?

PROBLEM 1-29 Find the coordinates of the point that divides the segment from (−4, −5) to (5, −1) in the ratio 5:3.

PROBLEM 1-30 Find the slopes of the lines passing through the following pairs of points: **(a)** (3, 4) and (1, −2); **(b)** (−5, 3) and (2, −3); **(c)** (1, 3) and (7, 1); **(d)** (2, 4) and (−2, 4).

PROBLEM 1-31 Find the inclination of the lines passing through the following pairs of points: **(a)** (4, 6) and (1, 3); **(b)** (2, 3) and (1, 0); **(c)** (2, 3) and (1, 4); **(d)** (3, −2) and (3, 5).

PROBLEM 1-32 Using slopes, show that the following set of points are the vertices of a right triangle: (6, 5), (1, 3), and (5, −7).

PROBLEM 1-33 Prove that the line passing through (−2, 0) and (3, 4) is parallel to the line through (−3, 1) and (2, 5).

Answers to Supplementary Exercises

1-22: rectangle

1-23: $x = 0$; $y = 0$

1-24: $(-6, -4)$ and $(-\frac{3}{2}, -4)$

1-25: $(5, 3)$

1-26: **(a)** $5\sqrt{2}$ **(b)** $\sqrt{13}$ **(c)** $2\sqrt{10}$

1-27: $(\frac{7}{2}, \frac{7}{2})$

1-28: $\sqrt{130}$; $(\frac{7}{2}, \frac{5}{2})$

1-29: $(\frac{37}{2}, 5)$

1-30: **(a)** 3 **(b)** $-\frac{6}{7}$ **(c)** $-\frac{1}{3}$ **(d)** 0

1-31: **(a)** $\alpha = \arctan 1 = 45°$
(b) $\alpha = \arctan 3 = 72°$
(c) $\alpha = \arctan -1 = 135°$
(d) $\alpha = \arctan \infty = 90°$

1-32: The slope of $m_1 = \frac{2}{5}$ and the slope of $m_2 = -\frac{5}{2}$. Since the slopes of these two lines are negative reciprocals of each other, the angle between them is 90° and the triangle defined by the three points is a right triangle.

1-33: The slope of both lines is $\frac{4}{5}$, so they are parallel.

2 EQUATIONS AND LOCI

THIS CHAPTER IS ABOUT

☑ **Locus of an Equation**
☑ **Using Properties of Equations to Specify Points on Curves**
☑ **Intersections of Curves**
☑ **Equation of a Locus**

In analytic geometry the curve traced by a moving point is called the *locus* (position) of that point. The concept of locus is fundamental to analytic geometry, which solves problems that deal with the *locus of an equation* and the *equation of a locus*. Specifically, these problems take two forms:

(1) Given an equation, find the corresponding locus and its properties.
(2) Given a geometrically defined locus, find the corresponding equation.

Algebra introduces you to the technique of plotting points to draw the graph of a simple equation, either linear (first-degree) or quadratic (second-degree). This familiar technique can be expanded and redefined in analytic terms.

2-1. Locus of an Equation

By definition, a locus is a curve:

- The **locus** (or *graph*) of an equation in two variables is the curve (including straight lines) that contains all of the points (and no others) whose coordinates satisfy the given equation.

note: By "satisfy" we mean, as in algebra, that the coordinates reduce the equation to an *identity* (that is, an equation that has the same value on both sides of the equals sign).

While this definition is correct, it is equally correct—and helpful—to think of a curve as the path traced by a moving point, in which case we can define the locus of an equation as follows:

- If a variable point $P(x, y)$ moves in such a way that its coordinates must always satisfy a given equation, then the curve traced by P is called the **locus of the equation**; that is, the curve is the locus, or place, of all points (and no others) whose coordinates satisfy the equation.

EXAMPLE 2-1: Suppose we decide to choose coordinates that satisfy the equation $x = 2$, with the value of y being unrestricted. What will the curve look like?

Solution: The points of this locus will lie on a straight line two units to the right of, and parallel to, the Y-axis. No points other than those on this line will satisfy the equation. The line is the locus of the equation, and $x = 2$ is the equation of the line.

EXAMPLE 2-2: Plot the locus of the equation $x - 2y + 2 = 0$.

Solution: For each arbitrary choice of a value for x, the value for y is uniquely determined. Thus, if we write the equation in the form $y = \frac{1}{2}x + 1$ and substitute $x = 2$, we find that $y = \frac{1}{2}(2) + 1 = 2$. We choose several arbitrary x values, find the corresponding unique y values, and tabulate the points as in the box in Figure 2-1. When we plot these points, we find that they lie on a definite curve, which appears to be a straight line. This curve is the locus of the equation $x - 2y + 2 = 0$.

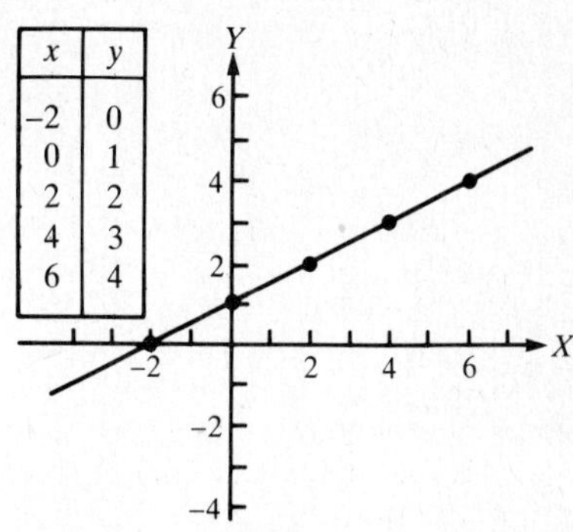

x	y
−2	0
0	1
2	2
4	3
6	4

Figure 2-1. Locus of $x - 2y + 2 = 0$.

EXAMPLE 2-3: Plot the locus of the equation $4y^2 - 9x - 18 = 0$.

Solution: Solving the equation for y, we get

$$y = \pm\tfrac{3}{2}\sqrt{x + 2}$$

Assigning arbitrary values to x, we get the y values shown in the box in Figure 2-2. Plotting these points, we connect them by a smooth curve, which is the locus of the equation.

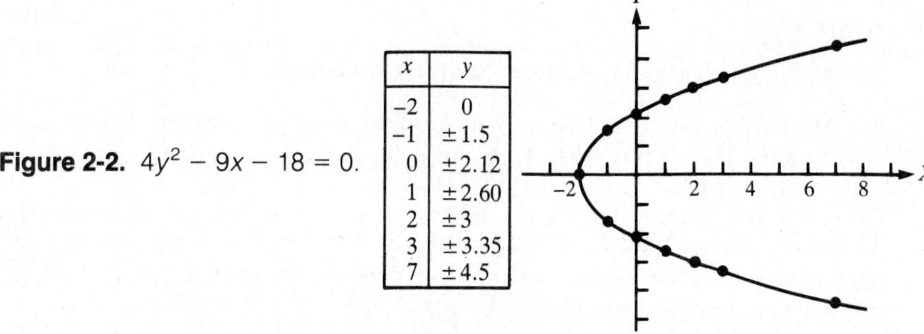

x	y
−2	0
−1	±1.5
0	±2.12
1	±2.60
2	±3
3	±3.35
7	±4.5

Figure 2-2. $4y^2 - 9x - 18 = 0$.

2-2. Using Properties of Equations to Specify Points on Curves

The graph of an equation drawn by plotting separate points is usually an approximation—we can't possibly plot all the points, and the position of a point can't be drawn precisely. But there are a few ways to verify a graph of a particular equation by checking the geometric properties of the curve defined by that equation. Certain points on a curve can be found precisely by analytic methods.

A. Intercepts

The **intercept** of a curve is the directed distance from the origin to the point at which the curve crosses a coordinate axis. To find the X-intercept, we substitute $y = 0$ in the equation of the curve and solve algebraically for x; this gives us the x-coordinate of the point at which the curve crosses the X-axis. To find the Y-intercept, we substitute $x = 0$ in the equation and solve for y; this gives us the y-coordinate of the point at which the curve crosses the Y-axis.

note: Of course, in order for a curve to cross an axis, the intercept on that axis must be real; that is, it must have real roots (i.e., not be imaginary), as you know from algebra.

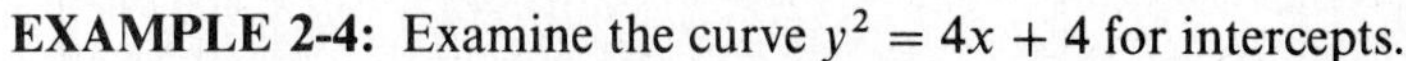

EXAMPLE 2-4: Examine the curve $y^2 = 4x + 4$ for intercepts.

Solution: For $x = 0$, we get $y = \pm 2$ as the Y-intercepts. For $y = 0$, we get $x = -1$ as the X-intercept (see Figure 2-3).

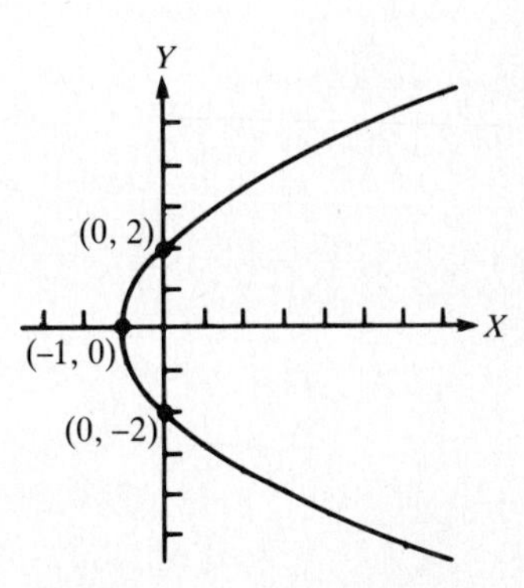

Figure 2-3. $y^2 = 4x + 4$.

EXAMPLE 2-5: What are the X- and Y-intercepts of $x^2 = 2y + 2$?

Solution: When $x = 0$, we get $y = -1$; when $y = 0$, we get $x = \pm\sqrt{2}$ (see Figure 2-4).

Figure 2-4. $x^2 = 2y + 2$.

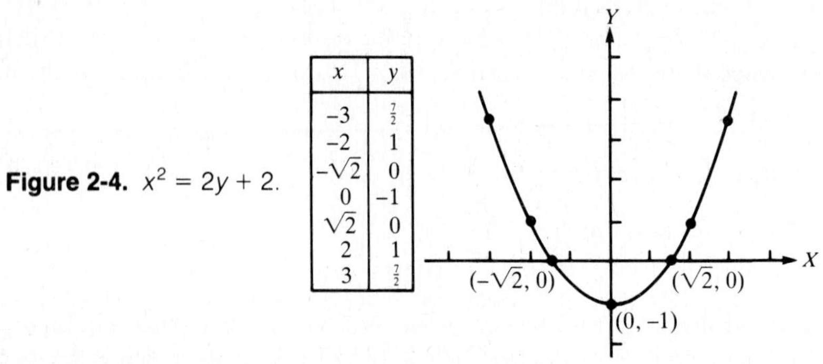

x	y
−3	$\frac{7}{2}$
−2	1
$-\sqrt{2}$	0
0	−1
$\sqrt{2}$	0
2	1
3	$\frac{7}{2}$

B. Symmetry

Symmetry is a property often associated with curves.

- Two points are symmetric with respect to a line, called the **axis of symmetry**, if that line is the perpendicular bisector of the segment joining the two points.

Thus, the points P and P' in Figure 2-5 are considered to be symmetric with respect to a line, the Y-axis, because the Y-axis is the perpendicular bisector of PP', the segment joining the two points.

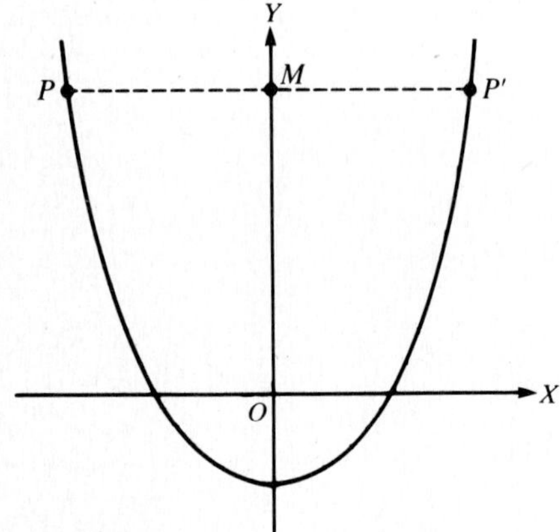

Figure 2-5. Symmetry with respect to the Y-axis.

- Two points are symmetric with respect to a third point, called the **center of symmetry**, if the third point is the midpoint of the segment joining the two points.

Thus, P and P' are symmetric with respect to the midpoint M in Figure 2-5.

- A curve is symmetric with respect to a line as an axis of symmetry, or with respect to a point as a center of symmetry, if each point on the curve has a symmetric point with respect to the axis or center that is also on the curve.

Thus, in Figure 2-5, the entire curve is symmetric about (or with respect to) the Y-axis, because for every point on the right side of the curve there is a symmetrically positioned opposite point on the left side of the curve. In general then, a curve is symmetric about the Y-axis, for example, if for each point of the curve in the first or in the fourth quadrant there is a symmetric point in the second or third quadrant that is also on the curve.

Equations that define symmetric curves have certain earmarks, which can be used as tests for types of symmetry:

(1) If an equation remains unchanged when x is replaced by $-x$, the locus (curve) is symmetric with respect to the Y-axis.
(2) If an equation remains unchanged when y is replaced by $-y$, the locus (curve) is symmetric with respect to the X-axis.
(3) If an equation remains unchanged when x is replaced by $-x$ and y is replaced by $-y$ at the same time, the locus (curve) is symmetric with respect to the origin.

Thus, for example, $x^2 + y = 5$, $x + y^2 = 5$, and $x^3 + y = 0$ are symmetric with respect to the Y-axis, the X-axis, and the origin, respectively.

EXAMPLE 2-6: Apply the three tests for symmetry to the equation $y^2 = 4x + 4$ and state your conclusions.

Solution: If we replace x by $-x$, we have $y^2 = -4x + 4$, which is not the same equation as the original. So the curve is not symmetric about the Y-axis. Replacing y by $-y$ gives us $(-y)^2 = y^2 = 4x + 4$, leaving the equation unchanged. So the curve is symmetric about the X-axis. if both x and y are replaced by their negatives, the equation is not the same, which tells us that the curve is not symmetric about the origin.

C. Extent

1. Excluded values

When considering an equation in two variables, we need to know if one of the variables is *bounded*; i.e., we need to ask if there are values of one of the variables that will cause the other variable to become imaginary. Such values are called **excluded values** because they do not give points on the curve. To test for excluded values, we begin by solving the equation for y in terms of x, and for x in terms of y. Then, if either solution produces radicals of even order, we look for values of the variable that would make the expression under the radical sign negative. Any such values must be excluded, since the corresponding values of the other variable will be imaginary.

EXAMPLE 2-7: Test the equation $y^2 - x + 4 = 0$ for excluded values.

Solution: Solving the equation for y gives us $y = \sqrt{x - 4}$—a square root, which is an even-order radical. Now we can see that values of x less than 4 would result in a negative value under the radical. So values of $x < 4$ must be excluded because corresponding values of y would be imaginary.

EXAMPLE 2-8: Figure 2-6 shows the graph of the equation $y^2 = 4x + 4$, which is the equation we examined for intercepts in Example 2-4. Examine this curve for excluded values.

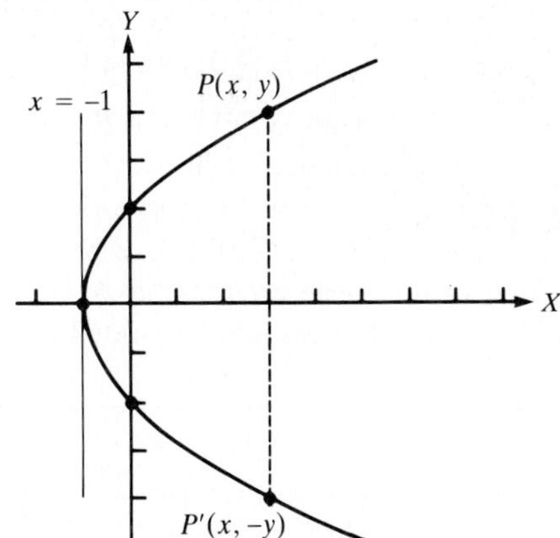

Figure 2-6. $y^2 = 4x + 4$: $x < -1$ excluded.

Solution: Solving the equation for y gives us $y = \pm 2\sqrt{x + 1}$, which shows that the expression under the radical is positive or zero for $x \geq -1$. This means that y is real for any value of $x \geq -1$, so that the curve lies entirely to the right of the line $x = -1$ and values of $x < -1$ are excluded.

EXAMPLE 2-9: Examine the curve $9x^2 + 25y^2 = 225$ for **(a)** intercepts, **(b)** symmetry, and **(c)** excluded values. **(d)** Draw the curve.

note: If a curve is symmetric about both axes *and* the origin, it is a *closed* curve.

Solution:

(a) **(1)** Set $y = 0$ and solve for x:

$$9x^2 + 25y^2 = 225$$

$$9x^2 + 25(0) = 225$$

$$x = \pm 5$$

So $x = \pm 5$ are the X-intercepts.

(2) Set $x = 0$ and solve for y:

$$9(0) + 25y^2 = 225$$

$$y = \pm 3$$

So $y = \pm 3$ are the Y-intercepts.

(b) Apply the tests for symmetry:

(1) Replace x by $-x$:

$$9(-x)^2 + 25y^2 = 225$$

Since the equation is unchanged, the curve is symmetric about the Y-axis.

(2) Replace y by $-y$:

$$9x^2 + 25(-y)^2 = 225$$

Since the equation is unchanged, the curve is symmetric about the X-axis.

(3) Replace x and y by $-x$ and $-y$ simultaneously:

$$9(-x)^2 + 25(-y)^2 = 225$$

Since the equation is unchanged, the curve is symmetric about the origin.

(c) **(1)** Solve the equation for y:

$$25y^2 = 225 - 9x^2$$

$$y^2 = \frac{225 - 9x^2}{25}$$

$$= \frac{9(25 - x^2)}{25}$$

$$y = \sqrt{\tfrac{9}{25}}\sqrt{25 - x^2}$$

$$y = \pm \tfrac{3}{5}\sqrt{25 - x^2}$$

So values of $x > 5$ and $x < -5$ are excluded.

(2) Solve the equation for x:

$$9x^2 = 225 - 25y^2$$

$$x = \sqrt{\tfrac{25}{9}}\sqrt{9 - y^2}$$

$$x = \pm \tfrac{5}{3}\sqrt{9 - y^2}$$

So values of $y > 3$ and $y < -3$ are excluded.

(d) Putting everything you know together, you can draw the curve shown in Figure 2-7: The curve's X- and Y-intercepts are at ± 5 and ± 3, respectively; the curve is closed because it is symmetric about the X- and Y-axes and the origin; and the curve must lie entirely within the rectangle bounded by the lines $x = \pm 5$ and $y = \pm 3$.

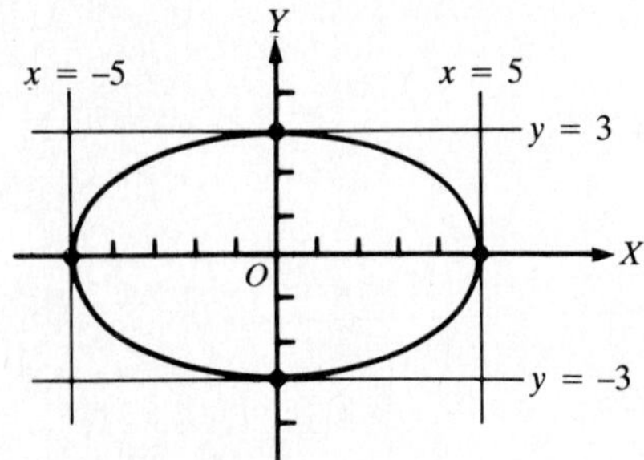

Figure 2-7. $9x^2 + 25y^2 = 225$.

2. *Infinite extent*

If the value of one of the variables, say x, of an equation becomes infinite for a finite value of the other variable y, the tracing point of the described curve will recede into infinity; i.e., the curve will have **infinite extent**, and there will usually be two or more branches of the curve. The infinite extent of a curve can generally be found from the equation by a simple procedure:

(1) Solve the equation for x. If the result is a fraction, find the finite value of y that sets the denominator equal to zero.

(2) Solve the equation for y. If the result is a fraction, find the finite value of x that sets the denominator equal to zero.
(3) Draw the y and x values that make the denominators equal to zero as straight lines parallel to the X- and Y-axes, respectively.
(4) Compute a table of x and y values by solving the equation for x in terms of y, and y in terms of x.
(5) Sketch the curve. FOR THE MOST PART, the lines that make the denominators equal to zero will be *asymptotes*, or boundaries, along which the branches of the curve will recede to infinity.

EXAMPLE 2-10: Draw the graph of the equation $xy + x - 3y - 4 = 0$.

Solution: Solve the equation for y in terms of x and for x in terms of y:

$$\textbf{(1)}\quad x = \frac{3y+4}{y+1} \qquad \text{and} \qquad \textbf{(2)}\quad y = \frac{4-x}{x-3}$$

In **(1)**, as y approaches -1, the denominator approaches zero and x becomes infinite; so the tracing point of the curve recedes to infinity at $y = -1$. Likewise, in **(2)**, as x approaches $+3$, the denominator approaches zero and y becomes infinite; so the curve recedes to infinity at $x = 3$. Now you can draw the asymptotic lines $x = 3$ and $y = -1$ (parallel to the Y- and X-axes, respectively), where each branch of the curve recedes to infinity. Finally, solve the equation, computing a table of x and y values that give you the curve shown in Figure 2-8.

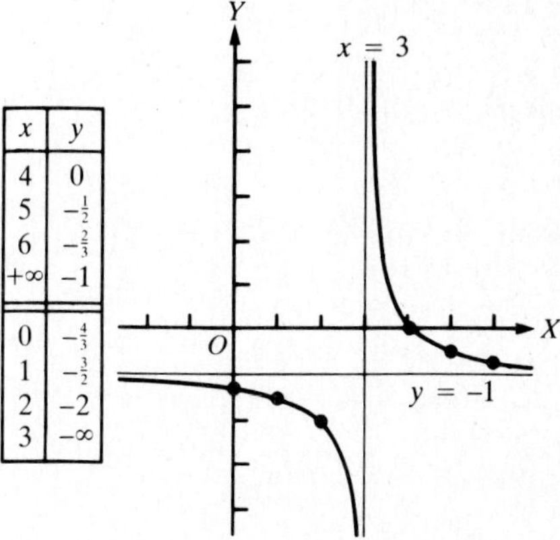

Figure 2-8. Infinite extent: $xy + x - 3y - 4 = 0$.

2-3. Intersections of Curves

A point lies on a curve if its coordinates satisfy the equation of that curve; the converse is also true. Hence

- If two curves intersect, the coordinates of their common points must satisfy *both* equations.

To find the coordinates of such common points, we solve the equations of the two curves simultaneously. If the solutions are real, the curves intersect at real points; if the values of the coordinates are imaginary, the curves do not intersect at real points.

EXAMPLE 2-11: Plot the curves $x^2 + y^2 = 25$ and $3y^2 = 16x$, and find their points of intersection.

Solution: Solve the two equations simultaneously

$$\begin{array}{r} 3x^2 \qquad + 3y^2 - 75 = 0 \\ 16x - 3y^2 \qquad = 0 \\ \hline 3x^2 + 16x \qquad - 75 = 0 \\ (3x+25)(x-3) = 0 \end{array}$$

which gives you two values of x: $x = 3$ and $x = -25/3$. Substitute these x values into the equation $3y^2 = 16x$ to find the values of y:

$$y = \sqrt{\frac{16(3)}{3}} = \pm 4 \qquad (x = 3)$$

$$y = \sqrt{\left(\frac{16}{3}\right)\left(-\frac{25}{3}\right)} = \sqrt{-\frac{400}{9}} = \pm\frac{20i}{3} \qquad \left(x = -\frac{25}{3}\right)$$

So the solutions are $x = 3$, $y = \pm 4$, and $x = -25/3$, $y = \pm 20i/3$. This means you have found two real points of intersection: $(3, 4)$ and $(3, -4)$. The two curves are plotted on the same axes, as shown in Figure 2-9.

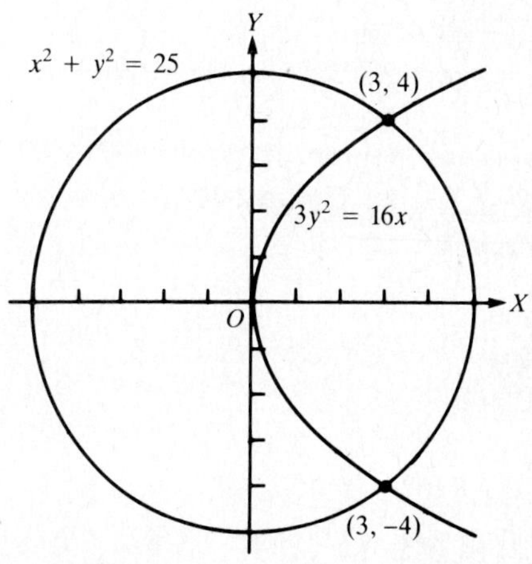

Figure 2-9. Intersection of curves: $x^2 + y^2 = 25$ and $3y^2 = 16x$.

2-4. Equation of a Locus

- The **equation of a locus** is an equation that satisfies the geometric properties under which a point $P(x, y)$ moves in tracing a locus; i.e., an equation that satisfies, in terms of x and y, all the coordinates of all the points (and no others) on a given curve.

Simple .... But the 'plot' thickens: There are no specific rules for finding such equations. You just have to think analytically—and while you're thinking, try the following steps:

(1) If the coordinate axes are not determined by the statement of a given problem, you may choose your own axes in such a way that the resulting equation will have a simple form. For example, curves that are symmetric with respect to at least one coordinate axis, or with the origin, can often be expressed more simply than curves without symmetry; so it's useful to choose axes with which the curves will be symmetric in one way or another. (You can make your own choice of axes because a locus is independent of its system of reference—the axes to which it is referred.)
(2) After choosing and constructing the axes, place the point $P(x, y)$ whose locus you wish to determine in a representative position, i.e., in a position that meets the geometric condition stated in the problem.
(3) Express the geometric condition that the tracing point P must satisfy in terms of (x, y) coordinates and any other constants involved in the definition of the locus. The expression thus obtained (or its simplified form) is the equation of the locus if it contains no variables except x and y and if it is satisfied by all the coordinates of all points on the locus and by no others.
(4) Study the equation you've obtained to determine the properties of the locus.

EXAMPLE 2-12: Find the locus of a point that is always equidistant from the end points of the line segment AB joining the points $(-1, 4)$ and $(2, 2)$.

Solution: Here, the coordinate axes are given, since points A and B are already located with reference to the (x, y) coordinate system: $A(-1, 4)$ and $B(2, 2)$. Call the tracing point $P(x, y)$ and place it in its representative position, i.e., the point at which $PA = PB$ (see Figure 2-10). Now, to express the geometric condition $PA = PB$ in terms of coordinates, use the formula for the distance between two points (eq. 1-2)

$$\sqrt{(x + 1)^2 + (y - 4)^2} = \sqrt{(x - 2)^2 + (y - 2)^2}$$

and simplify to get the equation of the locus:

$$6x - 4y + 9 = 0$$

Finally, when you sketch the graph of the equation, you find the locus to be a straight line that is the perpendicular bisector of the given segment, as shown in Figure 2-10.

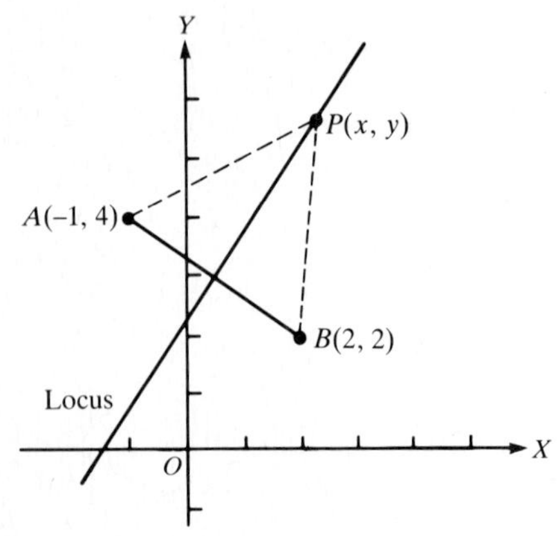

Figure 2-10

EXAMPLE 2-13: A point moves so that the sum of its distances from the points $(4, 0)$ and $(-4, 0)$ is 10 units. Find the equation of the locus.

Solution: Let $P(x, y)$ be the tracing point and let F and F' represent the given points $(4, 0)$ and $(-4, 0)$, respectively. Then the geometric condition on the point P is that $PF' + PF = 10$, so by eq. (1-2)

$$PF' = \sqrt{(x + 4)^2 + y^2} \quad \text{and} \quad PF = \sqrt{(x - 4)^2 + y^2}$$

and

$$PF' + PF = \sqrt{(x + 4)^2 + y^2} + \sqrt{(x - 4)^2 + y^2} = 10$$

Transpose the second radical to the right side, square both sides, and expand the squared terms to get

$$x^2 + 8x + 16 + y^2 = 100 - 20\sqrt{(x-4)^2 + y^2} + x^2 - 8x + 16 + y^2$$

which reduces to

$$4x - 25 = -5\sqrt{(x-4)^2 + y^2}$$

Squaring again and reducing, you have

$$9x^2 + 25y^2 = 225$$

which is the equation of the locus. From Figure 2-11 you can see that the equation is an ellipse.

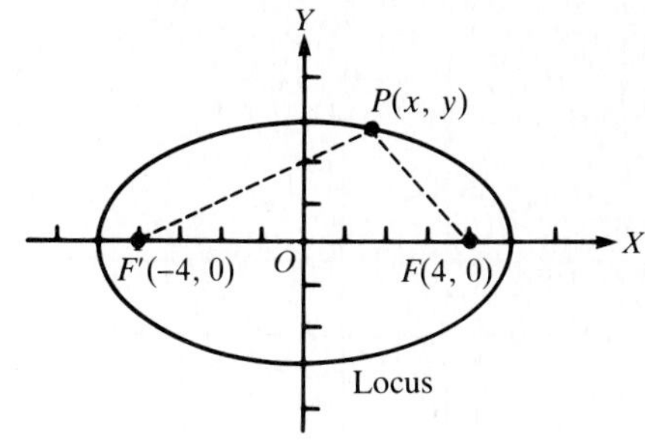

Figure 2-11

A. Translation of axes

In finding the equation of a curve, it is necessary to refer the coordinates of the tracing point to a set of coordinate axes. But the set of axes can be *moved*, thereby changing the coordinates of any fixed point and the form of the equation of any fixed curve, which must now be referred to the new axes. (You may, for instance, change the axes to which a curve is referred in order to simplify the equation of the curve.) When such a change is made and the new axes are drawn *parallel* to the old, the transformation on the coordinates is termed a **translation**.

There is obviously a relationship that exists between the coordinates of a point referred to one set of axes and the coordinates of the same point referred to a second set of axes parallel to the original set, and that relationship can be obtained as follows.

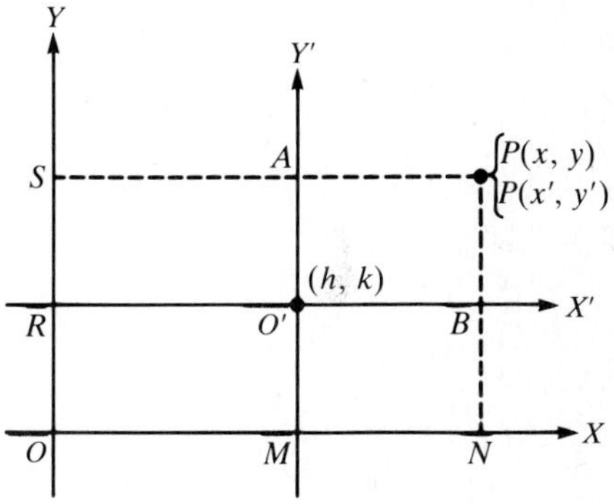

Figure 2-12. Translation of axes.

(1) Let OX and OY be a set of coordinate axes, and $O'X'$ and $O'Y'$ be a second set parallel to the first, as in Figure 2-12. Then each point in the plane will have two sets of coordinates: (x, y) with reference to the original axes OX and OY, and (x', y') with reference to the new axes $O'X'$ and $O'Y'$.

(2) Let (h, k) be the coordinates of the new origin with respect to the old axes, and let P be any point in the plane. Then from Figure 2-12, $x = SP$, $x' = AP$, $h = SA$, $y = NP$, $y' = BP$, and $k = NB$. But $SP = SA + AP$ and $NP = NB + BP$, which can be expressed in coordinate terms as

TRANSLATION FORMULAS $\quad x = x' + h \quad$ and $\quad y = y' + k \qquad$ **(2-1)**

note: These translation formulas are true for any position of the point P, or of the axes, as long as the two sets of axes are parallel to each other.

EXAMPLE 2-14: Transform the equation $3x - 2y + 6 = 0$ by translating the origin to the point $(2, 6)$.

Solution: Use the formulas of translation (2-1), where $(h, k) = (2, 6)$:

$$x = x' + 2 \quad \text{and} \quad y = y' + 6$$

Substitute these values into the equation of the given line:

$$3(x' + 2) - 2(y' + 6) + 6 = 0$$

so

$$3x' - 2y' = 0$$

is the form of the equation of the line referred to the $O'X'$ and $O'Y'$ axes. This transformation leaves the line itself unaltered, but changes the form of the equation of the line by moving the frame of reference (see Figure 2-13).

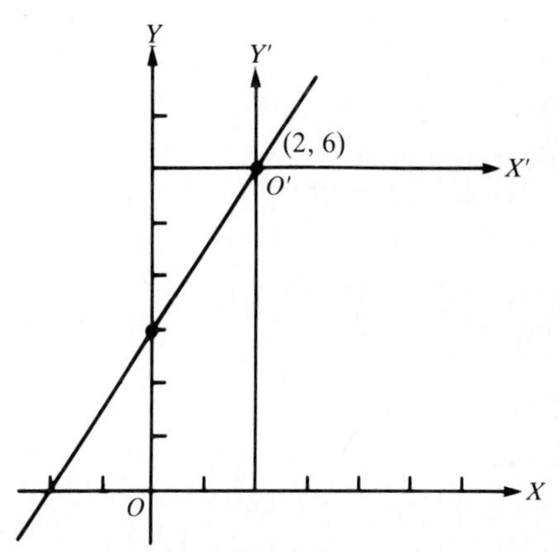

Figure 2-13

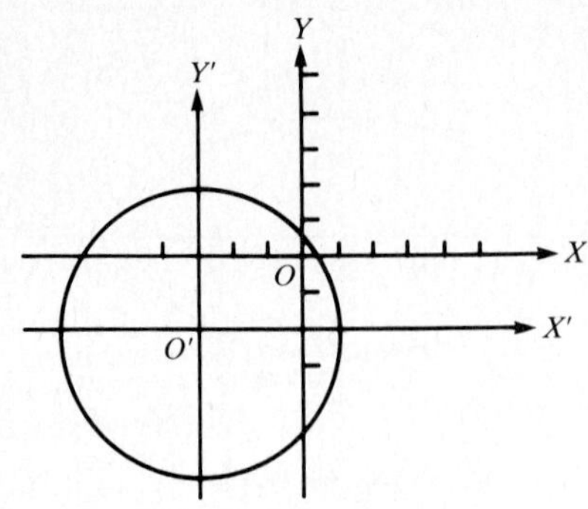

Figure 2-14

EXAMPLE 2-15: Transform the equation $x^2 + y^2 + 6x + 4y - 3 = 0$ by translating the axes to the new origin $(-3, -2)$.

Solution: The translation formulas (2-1) become $x = x' - 3$ and $y = y' - 2$. Substituting these values into the equation gives

$$(x' - 3)^2 + (y' - 2)^2 + 6(x' - 3) + 4(y' - 2) - 3 = 0$$

$$(x')^2 + (y')^2 = 16$$

The transformation changes the form of the equation but does not affect the locus. As Figure 2-14 shows, both forms of the equation represent a circle of radius 4: one having a center $(0, 0)$ with reference to the new axes, and the other having a center $(-3, -2)$ with reference to the original axes.

B. Simplification of equations by translation of axes

An important use of the translation formulas is to simplify the equation of a given curve by some suitable choice of axes.

EXAMPLE 2-16: Simplify the equation $x^2 + y^2 - 10x + 4y - 7 = 0$ by removing the first-degree terms.

Solution:

FIRST METHOD: Substitute the translation formulas $x = x' + h$ and $y = y' + k$ into the equation, expand the resulting equation (square the binomials and perform the indicated multiplications), and collect like terms. Thus

$$(x' + h)^2 + (y' + k)^2 - 10(x' + h) + 4(y' + k) - 7 = 0$$

$$(x')^2 + 2x'h + h^2 + (y')^2 + 2y'k + k^2 - 10x' - 10h + 4y' + 4k - 7 = 0$$

Remove the x' and y' terms and set their coefficients equal to zero to find values for h and k:

$$2h - 10 = 0 \quad \text{and} \quad 2k + 4 = 0$$

$$h = 5 \qquad\qquad k = -2$$

Substituting these values in the equation gives the equation of the locus with reference to the new axes

$$(x')^2 + (y')^2 = 36$$

in which the first-degree terms have been removed. Then the new origin is the point $(5, -2)$ in the XY-system.

SECOND METHOD: Another procedure that is often used involves *completing the square*. To complete the square of $x^2 - 10x$, you need to add 25; and to complete the square of $y^2 + 4y$, you need to add 4. However, if you add these values to the left member of the equation, you must also add them to the right member (to preserve the equality). Making these additions and moving -7 to the right side, you get

$$(x - 5)^2 + (y + 2)^2 = 7 + 25 + 4 = 36$$

Then if you let $x - 5 = x'$ and $y + 2 = y'$, the equation becomes simply $(x')^2 + (y')^2 = 36$, where again the coordinates of the new origin (h, k) are $(5, -2)$.

Both of these methods for determining the new origin give the same results; however, in the present case the second method would be preferable.

note: The second method should *not* be used with an equation that contains an xy-term.

SUMMARY

1. There are two fundamental problems in analytic geometry:
   - Given an equation, find the corresponding locus and its properties.
   - Given a geometrically defined locus, find the corresponding equation.
2. The locus or graph of an equation in two variables is the curve that contains all of the points, and no others, whose coordinates satisfy the given equation.
3. The intercepts of a curve are the directed distances from the origin to the points where the curve crosses the coordinate axes.
4. Two points are symmetric with respect to a line, called the axis of symmetry, if that line is the perpendicular bisector of the segment joining the two points.
5. If certain values of one variable cause the other variable to become imaginary in an equation of two variables, such values must be excluded.
6. If one of the variables of an equation becomes infinite for a finite value of the other variable, the tracing point of the curve recedes into infinity, and there are generally two or more branches of the curve.
7. To find the infinite extent of a curve, solve the equation for x; if the result is a fraction, set the denominator equal to zero and solve for y. Then solve the equation for y; if the result is a fraction, set the denominator equal to zero and solve for x. In general, the values found for x and y will represent lines along which the curve recedes into infinity.
8. To find the equation of a locus
   - Choose the coordinate axes that simplify the form of the resulting equation.
   - After constructing the axes, place the point $P(x, y)$ whose locus you wish to determine in a representative position.
   - Express the condition that P must satisfy in terms of (x, y) coordinates and any other constants involved in the definition of the locus. The resulting equation (in simplified form) is the equation of the locus if it contains no variables except x and y and is satisfied by the coordinates of all points on the locus, and by those of no other points.
9. In a translation, the axes to which an equation of a locus is referred are moved so that the new set of axes is parallel to the original set, all the coordinates are changed, and the equation is transformed.
10. The translation formulas are

$$x = x' + h \qquad \text{and} \qquad y = y' + k$$

where x' and y' are the coordinates with reference to the new axes and h and k are the coordinates of the new origin with respect to the old axes.

RAISE YOUR GRADES

Can you . . .?

☑ prepare a table of coordinate values and plot the locus of a equation
☑ find the intercepts of a curve
☑ test an equation for symmetry
☑ test an equation for excluded values
☑ find the infinite extent of a curve
☑ plot and find the points of intersection of two curves
☑ find the equation of a locus defined by means of a geometric property common to all points on the locus
☑ transform an equation by translating the origin of its coordinate axes to a new set of axes parallel to the original axes
☑ simplify an equation by translation of axes

SOLVED PROBLEMS

Locus of an Equation

PROBLEM 2-1 Draw the loci of the following equations by plotting points: (**a**) $y = x - 2$; (**b**) $2y = x - 6$; (**c**) $2x - 3y = 6$; (**d**) $x^2 = 4y - 12$; (**e**) $y^2 + 2x - 4 = 0$.

Solution: Solve each question for y, compute a table of values for x and y, and plot: (**a**) $y = x - 2$ (see Figure 2-15); (**b**) $y = (x - 6)/2$ (see Figure 2-16); (**c**) $y = (2x - 6)/3$ (see Figure 2-17); (**d**) $y = (x^2 + 12)/4$ (see Figure 2-18); (**e**) $y = \pm\sqrt{4 - 2x}$ (see Figure 2-19).

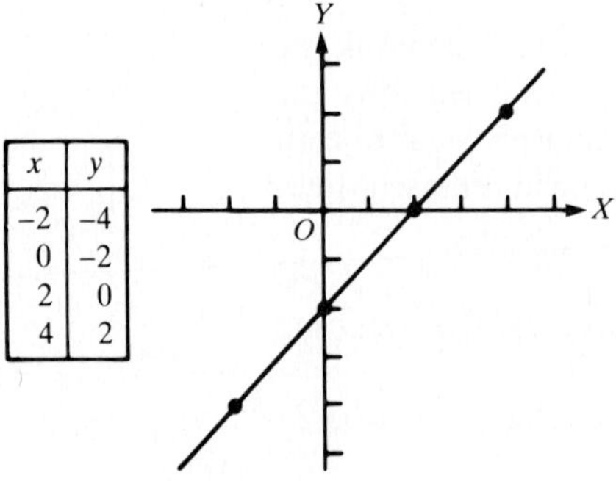

x	y
-2	-4
0	-2
2	0
4	2

Figure 2-15. (**a**) $y = x - 2$.

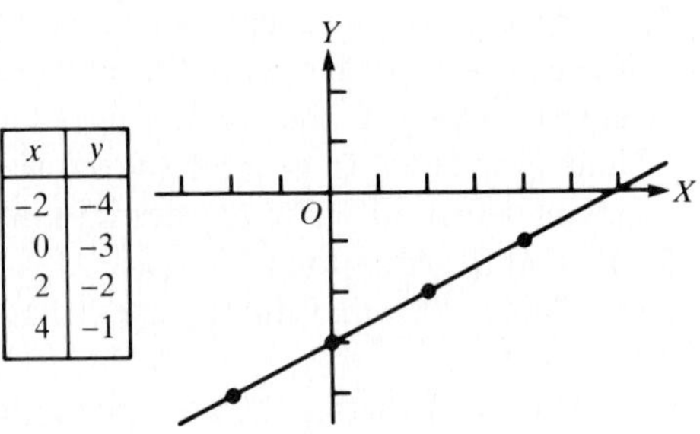

x	y
-2	-4
0	-3
2	-2
4	-1

Figure 2-16. (**b**) $2y = x - 6$.

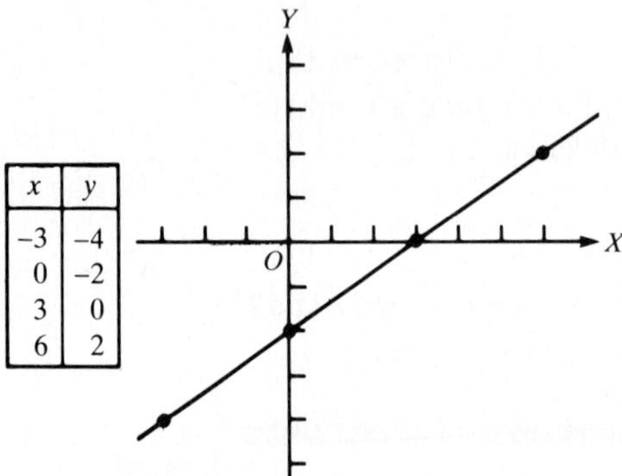

x	y
-3	-4
0	-2
3	0
6	2

Figure 2-17. (**c**) $2x - 3y = 6$.

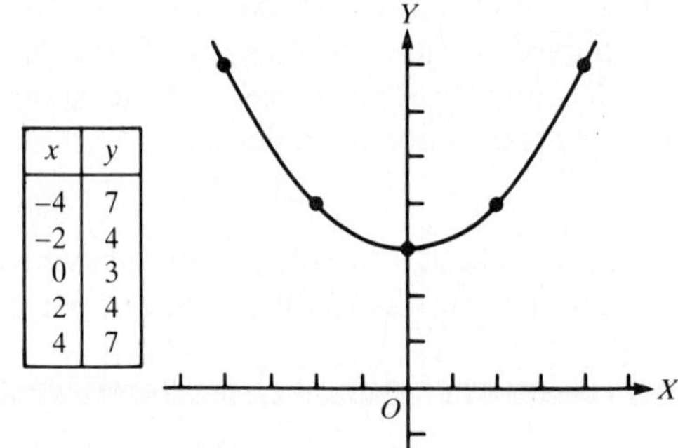

x	y
-4	7
-2	4
0	3
2	4
4	7

Figure 2-18. (**d**) $x^2 = 4y - 12$.

x	y
2	0
0	±2
-3	±3.16
-6	±4

Figure 2-19. (**e**) $y^2 + 2x - 4 = 0$.

Using Properties of Equations to Specify Points on Curves

PROBLEM 2-2 Find the X- and Y-intercepts of the equation $y = x^2 - 3x + 2$.

Solution: Set $y = 0$ and solve for x:

$$x^2 - 3x + 2 = 0$$
$$(x - 2)(x - 1) = 0$$

So the roots are $x = 1$ and $x = 2$, which means that the X-intercepts are $(1, 0)$ and $(2, 0)$.
Similarly, setting $x = 0$, you get $y = 2$; so the one Y-intercept is $(0, 2)$.

PROBLEM 2-3 Find all the intercepts of the equation $y^2 + 2x = 16$.

Solution: When you set $y = 0$, you get $x = 8$; and when $x = 0$, you get two roots, $y = \pm 4$. Therefore, the X-intercept of the curve is $(8, 0)$, and the Y-intercepts are $(0, \pm 4)$.

PROBLEM 2-4 Examine the curve $x^2 - x + y^4 - 2y^2 - 6 = 0$ for symmetry.

Solution: Since y appears in even powers only, changing y into $-y$ will not affect the function. Therefore the curve is symmetric with respect to the X-axis. But if $-x$ is substituted for x, the equation is changed to $x^2 + x + y^4 - 2y^2 - 6 = 0$. Therefore the curve is not symmetric with respect to the Y-axis. And since you can't change both x and y to their negatives without affecting the equation, the curve is not symmetric with respect to the origin.

PROBLEM 2-5 Examine $y^2 = x(x - 1)(x + 3)$ for symmetry.

Solution: Expanding the equation, you get $y^2 = x^3 + 2x^2 - 3x$. Therefore the curve is symmetric with the respect to the X-axis, since y appears only to an even power. There is no other symmetry, because a substitution of $-x$ for x will affect the equation (which you can see at a glance because x appears as an odd power).

PROBLEM 2-6 Discuss the extent of the graph of $y = x^2 - 3x + 2$.

Solution: The independent variable x may range from $-\infty$ to $+\infty$. To find out whether y is bounded, solve the equation for x as a function of y:

$$x^2 - 3x + (2 - y) = 0$$
$$x^2 - 3x + \tfrac{9}{4} = y - 2 + \tfrac{9}{4}$$
$$(x - \tfrac{3}{2})^2 = y + \tfrac{1}{4}$$
$$x - \tfrac{3}{2} = \pm\sqrt{y + \tfrac{1}{4}}$$
$$x = \tfrac{3}{2} \pm \sqrt{y + \tfrac{1}{4}}$$

You can see that y is restricted to values equal to or greater than $-\frac{1}{4}$. That is, values of $y < -\frac{1}{4}$ must be excluded because they would make the value under the radical negative, and the value of x would be complex (imaginary). So the whole graph lies in the upper half-plane determined by the line through $(\frac{3}{2}, -\frac{1}{4})$ parallel to the X-axis. The point $(\frac{3}{2}, -\frac{1}{4})$ is the *minimum point* of the curve.

PROBLEM 2-7 Discuss and plot the locus of the equation $9x^2 + 16y^2 = 144$.

Solution: First find the X- and Y-intercepts. When $y = 0$, $x = \pm 4$; when $x = 0$, $y = \pm 3$. Hence the X-intercepts are $(\pm 4, 0)$ and the Y-intercepts are $(0, \pm 3)$.

Next examine the equation for symmetry. Since the equation contains only even powers of x and y, the curve is symmetric about both axes and about the origin. Now you know that you only have to plot the points on the part of the curve that lies in the first quadrant—because you can determine the rest of the curve by symmetry.

Then check for excluded values. Solving for y and x, you get

$$y = \pm\tfrac{3}{4}\sqrt{16 - x^2} \qquad \text{and} \qquad x = \pm\tfrac{4}{3}\sqrt{9 - y^2}$$

If $|x|$ is greater than 4, then $16 - x^2$ is negative and y is imaginary. Therefore x can have no value greater than 4 or less than -4. Similarly, $|y|$ can have no value greater than 3 or less than -3.

Finally, compute a table of values and draw the graph, as shown in Figure 2-20.

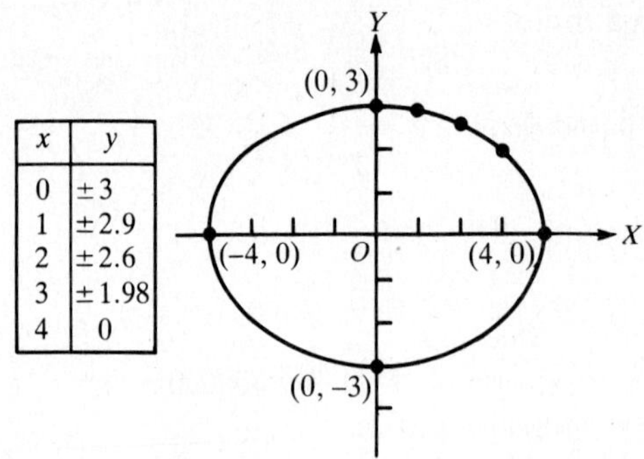

x	y
0	± 3
1	± 2.9
2	± 2.6
3	± 1.98
4	0

Figure 2-20. $9x^2 + 16y^2 = 144$.

PROBLEM 2-8 Find the lines of infinite extent and plot the graph of the equation $xy - 2y = 8$.

Solution: Solve for x and y:

$$x = \frac{2y + 8}{y} \qquad \text{and} \qquad y = \frac{8}{x - 2}$$

Both results are fractions, so you find the values of y and x that make the denominators zero:

$$y = 0 \qquad \text{and} \qquad x - 2 = 0$$
$$x = 2$$

Draw these values as straight lines: $y = 0$ is the same as the X-axis, and $x = 2$ is parallel to the Y-axis. Now you've got the bounds of the curve—the lines of infinite extent—so you can compute a table of values and plot the curve, as shown in Figure 2-21. (Note that the curve has two branches.)

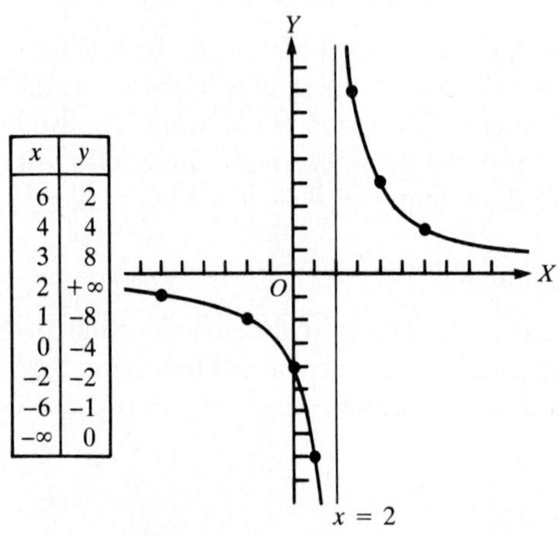

x	y
6	2
4	4
3	8
2	$+\infty$
1	-8
0	-4
-2	-2
-6	-1
$-\infty$	0

Figure 2-21. $xy - 2y = 8$.

Intersections of Curves

PROBLEM 2-9 Find the points of intersection of the curves $y = x^2$ and $x - y + 2 = 0$.

Solution: Solve these two equations simultaneously: Simply substitute the value of y from either equation into the other and then solve the resulting quadratic equation in x. Thus $x - x^2 + 2 = 0$, so that $x = -1$ or 2; therefore $y = 1$ or 4. Both these solutions are real, so the points of intersection $(-1, 1)$ and $(2, 4)$ are real. Now plot the two curves: The graph of $y = x^2$ is a symmetric curvilinear line (a *parabola*) and the graph of $x - y + 2 = 0$ is a straight line, as Figure 2-22 shows.

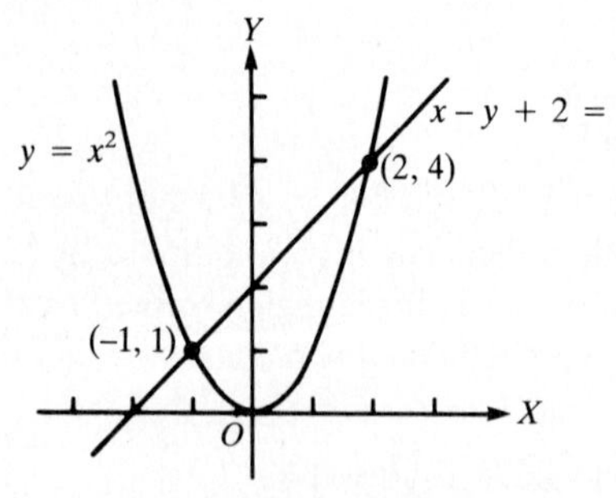

Figure 2-22

PROBLEM 2-10 Plot the curves $x + y = 7$ and $xy = 6$ and find their points of intersection.

Solution: Solving the first equation for x, you get $x = 7 - y$. Insert this value of x into the second equation:

$$(7 - y)y = 6$$
$$y^2 - 7y + 6 = (y - 1)(y - 6) = 0$$

so $y = 6$ or $y = 1$. Substituting these values into the first equation, you get $x = 1$ or $x = 6$. So the coordinates of the two points of intersection are (1,6) and (6,1). Establishing a table of (x, y) values for each of the equations and plotting, you can draw the curves shown in Figure 2-23. The first equation is a straight line and the second is the upper branch of a *hyperbola*.

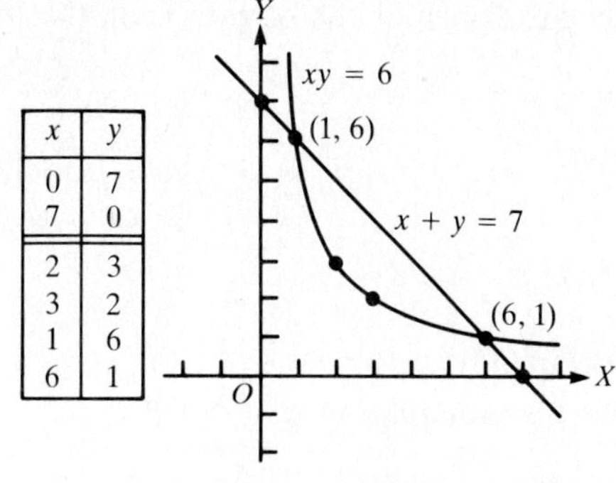

x	y
0	7
7	0
2	3
3	2
1	6
6	1

Figure 2-23

Equation of a Locus

PROBLEM 2-11 A point P moves so that it is always 3 units distant from the point $C(-2, 3)$. Find the equation of its locus and sketch the figure.

Solution: Use the procedure for finding an equation of a locus.

(1) Since the problem states that the point C is on the coordinates $(-2, 3)$, you're stuck with the standard X,Y-axes. Construct them as in Figure 2-24.

(2) Place the point $P(x, y)$ where the problem says it will be, 3 units away from $C(-2, 3)$— anywhere will do.

(3) Express the geometric condition of the problem in coordinate form. Here, you have a distance, so (naturally enough) you use the distance formula (1-2), into which you substitute what you know:

$$d = \sqrt{(x_2 - x_1)^2 + (y_2 - y_1)^2}$$

$$PC = \sqrt{(x + 2)^2 + (y - 3)^2} = 3$$

$$(x + 2)^2 + (y - 3)^2 = 9$$

$$x^2 + y^2 + 4x - 6y + 4 = 0$$

The locus is the equation for a circle with radius 3, centered at $(-2, 3)$, as shown in Figure 2-24.

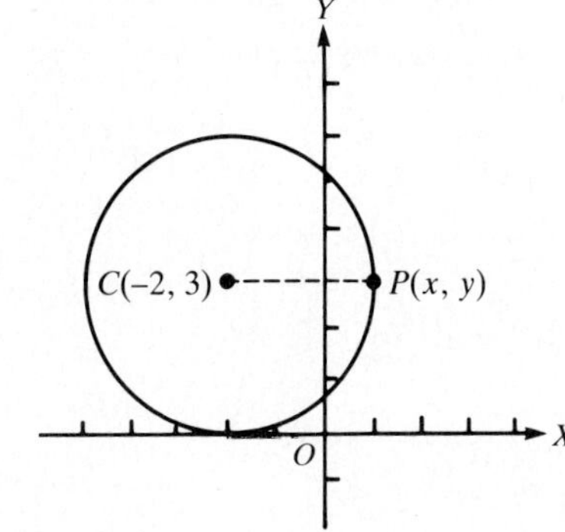

Figure 2-24

PROBLEM 2-12 Find the equation of the locus of a point that moves so that it always is equidistant from the line $x = -2$ and the point $(2, 0)$.

Solution: Sketch the situation using the standard X,Y-axes. Identify one known point as $F(2, 0)$, the other known point (on the line $x = -2$) as $M(-2, y)$, and the unknown point as $P(x, y)$, as shown in Figure 2-25.

Now notice that you've got two distances that you can express in coordinate form by the distance formula:

$$PM = \sqrt{(x + 2)^2 + (y - y)^2}$$

and

$$PF = \sqrt{(x - 2)^2 + (y - 0)^2}$$

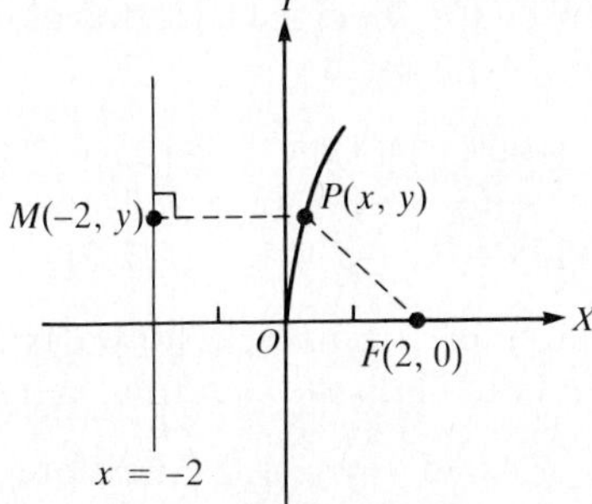

Figure 2-25

So you can find the equation of the locus by expressing $PM = PF$:

$$\sqrt{(x+2)^2} = \sqrt{(x-2)^2 + y^2}$$
$$(x+2)^2 = (x-2)^2 + y^2$$
$$x^2 + 4x + 4 = x^2 - 4x + 4 + y^2$$
$$8x = y^2$$

PROBLEM 2-13 If a point moves so that its distance from $(2, 0)$ is twice its distance from $(-2, 0)$, what is the equation of its locus?

Solution: Letting $P(x, y)$ be the moving point, F_1 be the fixed point $(2, 0)$, and F_2 be the fixed point $(-2, 0)$, you can define the distances as

$$PF_1 = \sqrt{(x-2)^2 + y^2} \quad \text{and} \quad PF_2 = \sqrt{(x+2)^2 + y^2}$$

Since $PF_1 = 2(PF_2)$,

$$\sqrt{(x-2)^2 + y^2} = 2\sqrt{(x+2)^2 + y^2}$$
$$x^2 - 4x + 4 + y^2 = 4(x^2 + 4x + 4 + y^2)$$
$$3x^2 + 3y^2 + 20x + 12 = 0$$

PROBLEM 2-14 Find the new coordinates of the points $(2, 4)$, $(-2, 2)$, and $(-2, 0)$ if the axes are translated to a new origin at: **(a)** $(4, 4)$; **(b)** $(2, 2)$; **(c)** $(0, -4)$.

Solution: Using the translation formulas (2-1), $x = x' + h$ and $y = y' + k$, where (h, k) are the coordinates of the new origin:

(a) Let $(h, k) = (4, 4)$. Then if $(x, y) = (2, 4)$,

$$x = x' + h \qquad y = y' + k$$
$$2 = x' + 4 \qquad 4 = y' + 4$$
$$x' = -2 \qquad y' = 0$$

and if $(x, y) = (-2, 2)$,

$$-2 = x' + 4 \qquad 2 = y' + 4$$
$$x' = -6 \qquad y' = -2$$

and if $(x, y) = (-2, 0)$,

$$-2 = x' + 4 \qquad 0 = y' + 4$$
$$x' = -6 \qquad y' = -4$$

So the coordinates with the origin at $(4, 4)$ are $(-2, 0)$, $(-6, -2)$, and $(-6, -4)$.

(b) Let $(h, k) = (2, 2)$. Then if $(x, y) = (2, 4)$, you have $x' = 0$ and $y' = 2$; if $(x, y) = (-2, 2)$, you have $x' = -4$ and $y' = 0$; and if $(x, y) = (-2, 0)$, you have $x' = -4$ and $y' = -2$. So the coordinates with the origin at $(2, 2)$ are $(0, 2)$, $(-4, 0)$, and $(-4, -2)$.

(c) The coordinates with the origin at $(0, -4)$ are $(2, 8)$, $(-2, 6)$, and $(-2, 4)$.

PROBLEM 2-15 Find the equation of each of the following curves if the axes are translated to the new origin indicated:

(a) $2x - 3y = 6$; $(4, 1)$
(b) $x^2 + y^2 - 6x + 4y - 12 = 0$; $(3, -2)$
(c) $3y^2 - 12y - 7x - 2 = 0$; $(-2, 2)$

Solution: Use the translation formulas (2-1) to find the new coordinates, substitute the new coordinate values into the equation, and simplify.

(a) $x = x' + 4$ and $y = y' + 1$. Therefore

$$2(x' + 4) - 3(y' + 1) = 6$$
$$2x' - 3y' - 1 = 0$$

(b) $$(x')^2 + (y')^2 = 25$$

(c) $$3(y')^2 - 7x' = 0$$

PROBLEM 2-16 Remove the first-degree terms from the following equations by translating the axes:

(a) $4x^2 + 4y^2 + 12x - 4y - 6 = 0$
(b) $x^2 + y^2 + 10x - y + 3 = 0$
(c) $x^2 + y^2 + 5x + 3y - 4 = 0$
(d) $y^2 - 8x^2 - 8y + 40 = 0$

Solution: Use the first method shown in Example 2-16 for **(a)** and **(b)**.

(a) $$4x^2 + 4y^2 + 12x - 4y = 6$$

Divide by 4:

$$x^2 + y^2 + 3x - y = \tfrac{6}{4}$$

Let $x = x' + h$ and $y = y' + k$, where (h, k) are the coordinates of the new origin; then substitute:

$$(x' + h)^2 + (y' + k)^2 + 3(x' + h) - (y' + k) = \tfrac{6}{4}$$

Expand and collect like terms:

$$(x')^2 + 2x'h + h^2 + (y')^2 + 2y'k + k^2 + 3x' + 3h - y' - k = \tfrac{6}{4}$$
$$(x')^2 + (y')^2 + (2h + 3)x' + (2k - 1)y' + h^2 + k^2 + 3h - k = \tfrac{6}{4}$$

Set the coefficients of the x' and y' terms equal to zero to find values for h and k:

$$2h + 3 = 0 \qquad 2k - 1 = 0$$
$$h = -\tfrac{3}{2} \qquad k = \tfrac{1}{2}$$

and substitute these values into the expanded equation:

$$(x')^2 + (y')^2 + [2(-\tfrac{3}{2}) + 3]x' + [2(\tfrac{1}{2}) - 1]y' + \tfrac{9}{4} + \tfrac{1}{4} - \tfrac{9}{2} - \tfrac{1}{2} = \tfrac{6}{4}$$
$$(x')^2 + (y')^2 = 4$$

(b) $$4(x')^2 + 4(y')^2 = 89$$

Use the second method shown in Example 2-16 for **(c)** and **(d)**.

(c) $$x^2 + y^2 + 5x + 3y - 4 = 0$$

Complete the square:

$$(x^2 + 5x + \tfrac{25}{4}) + (y^2 + 3y + \tfrac{9}{4}) = 4 + \tfrac{25}{4} + \tfrac{9}{4}$$
$$(x + \tfrac{5}{2})^2 + (y + \tfrac{3}{2})^2 = \tfrac{25}{2}$$

Let $x + \tfrac{5}{2} = x'$ and $y + \tfrac{3}{2} = y'$; then

$$2(x')^2 + 2(y')^2 = 25$$

(d) $$8(x')^2 - (y')^2 = 24$$

Supplementary Exercises

PROBLEM 2-17 Draw the loci of the following equations: **(a)** $y = 3x + 2$; **(b)** $y = x^2 - 2x - 1$; **(c)** $x^2 + y^2 = 16$.

PROBLEM 2-18 Examine the curve $x^2 - y^2 - 3 = 0$ for symmetry.

PROBLEM 2-19 Examine the curve $xy - 1 = 0$ for symmetry.

PROBLEM 2-20 Find the intercepts and discuss the symmetry and extent of $y = \dfrac{x(x-1)}{x+2}$.

PROBLEM 2-21 Analyze the curve $y = \dfrac{(x+1)(x-3)}{x^2-4}$ for intercepts and symmetry.

PROBLEM 2-22 Find the lines of infinite extent and plot the graphs of the following equations: **(a)** $4y - xy = 16$; **(b)** $(x^2 - 2x)y = 4$; **(c)** $xy^2 - 4x = 6y^2$; **(d)** $3xy - 4y = 2x + 3$.

PROBLEM 2-23 Find the points of intersection of the following curves:

(a) $x^2 - y^2 = 9$
$x^2 + y^2 = 25$
(b) $x^2 + y^2 = 9$
$x^2 - y^2 = 4$
(c) $x^2 + y^2 = 16$
$9x^2 + 25y^2 = 225$
(d) $2x^2 + y^2 = 7$
$x^2 - 2y^2 = -4$
(e) $x^2 + xy = 40$
$2x - 3y = 1$

PROBLEM 2-24 Find the equation of the locus of the point $P(x, y)$ in each of the following situations:

(a) P is on a line drawn through the origin and the point $(3, -7)$.
(b) P is on a line drawn through the points $(-3, 4)$ and $(5, -3)$.
(c) P is on a line drawn parallel to the Y-axis and 6 units to the right of it.
(d) P is on a line parallel to the X-axis and 5 units above it.
(e) P is twice as far from $(0, 0)$ as from $(6, 0)$.

PROBLEM 2-25 Find the new coordinates of the following points if the origin is moved to the point $(-3, 5)$: **(a)** $(3, 2)$; **(b)** $(-5, 1)$; **(c)** $(-3, -1)$; **(d)** $(4, -6)$; **(e)** $(7, 5)$.

PROBLEM 2-26 Find the transformed equation of the curve in each of the following problems if the origin is moved to the point indicated:

(a) $2xy + 4x - 6y - 15 = 0$; $(3, -2)$
(b) $3xy - 3x - 13y + 13 = 0$; $(4, 1)$
(c) $x^2 - 2xy + 8x - 6y + 15 = 0$; $(-3, 1)$
(d) $x^2 + 2xy + y^2 + 2x + 2y + 1 = 0$; $(2, -3)$
(e) $3x^2 - xy + y^2 - 9x - 4y + 14 = 0$; $(2, 3)$

PROBLEM 2-27 Simplify the following equations by translating the axes to remove the first-degree terms. In each case state the values used for h and k.

(a) $xy - 3x + 2y - 4 = 0$
(b) $x^2 + 3xy + 6x - 9y + 11 = 0$
(c) $xy + 2y^2 - 3x - 6y - 5 = 0$
(d) $3x^2 + 2xy + y^2 - 2x + 2y - 4 = 0$
(e) $2x^2 + 4xy + y^2 + 8x + 6y - 3 = 0$

Answers to Supplementary Exercises

2-17:

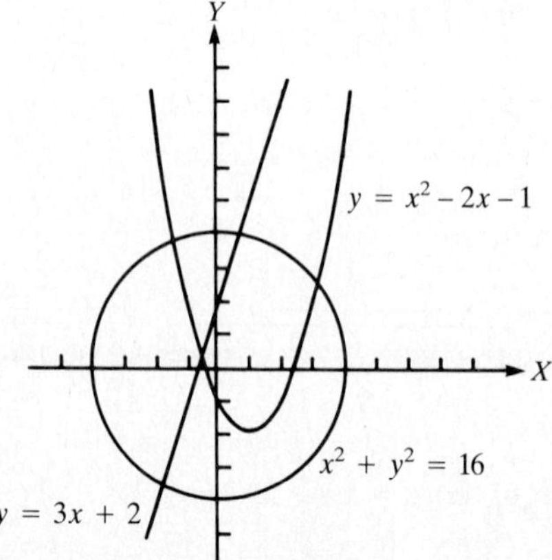

Figure 2-26

2-18: There is symmetry with respect to both axes and to the origin.

2-19: There is symmetry with respect to the origin.

2-20: The X-intercepts are $(0, 0)$ and $(1, 0)$. There is no Y-intercept except $(0, 0)$. The graph is not confined to a finite portion of the plane, since both x and y can range from $-\infty$ to $+\infty$. There is no symmetry with respect to either axis or to the origin.

2-21: The X-intercepts are $(-1, 0)$ and $(3, 0)$; the Y-intercept is $(0, \frac{3}{4})$. The curve is not symmetric with respect to either of the axes or to the origin.

2-22: (a) $x - 4 = 0; y = 0$
(b) $x = 0; x - 2 = 0; y = 0$
(c) $x - 6 = 0; y \pm 2 = 0$
(d) $3x - 4 = 0; 3y - 2 = 0$

2-23: (a) $(\sqrt{17}, \pm 2\sqrt{2}); (-\sqrt{17}, \pm 2\sqrt{2})$
(b) $(\frac{1}{2}\sqrt{26}, \pm\frac{1}{2}\sqrt{10}); (-\frac{1}{2}\sqrt{26}, \pm\frac{1}{2}\sqrt{10})$
(c) $(\pm\frac{5}{4}\sqrt{7}, \pm\frac{9}{4})$
(d) $(\pm\sqrt{2}, \pm\sqrt{3})$
(e) $(5, 3); (-\frac{24}{5}, -\frac{53}{15})$

2-24: (a) $7x + 3y = 0$
(b) $7x + 8y = 11$
(c) $x = 6$
(d) $y = 5$
(e) $x^2 + y^2 - 16x + 48 = 0$

2-25: (a) $(6, -3)$
(b) $(-2, -4)$
(c) $(0, -6)$
(d) $(7, -11)$
(e) $(10, 0)$

2-26: (a) $2x'y' = 3$
(b) $3x'y' - y' = 0$
(c) $(x')^2 - 2x'y' = 0$
(d) $(x')^2 + 2x'y' + (y')^2 = 0$
(e) $3(x')^2 - x'y' + (y')^2 = 1$

2-27: (a) $x'y' = -2; h = -2, k = 3$
(b) $(x')^2 + 3x'y' = -38; h = 3, k = -4$
(c) $x'y' + 2(y')^2 = 5; h = -6, k = 3$
(d) $3(x')^2 + 2x'y' + (y')^2 = 7; h = 1, k = -2$
(e) $2(x')^2 + 4x'y' + (y')^2 = 10; h = -1, k = -1$

3 THE STRAIGHT LINE

THIS CHAPTER IS ABOUT

☑ Standard Forms of the Equation of a Line
☑ General and Normal Forms of the Equation of a Line
☑ Distance from a Line to a Point
☑ Equations of Angle Bisectors
☑ Area of a Triangle
☑ Systems of Lines

3-1. Standard Forms of the Equation of a Line

The equation of a straight line in x and y is first-degree in the x and y terms, and is satisfied by the coordinates of every point on the line and by the coordinates of no other points. Linear equations may be expressed in several standard forms, depending on the information used to determine the line.

A. Point-slope form

The equation of a line L that passes through a fixed point $P_1(x_1, y_1)$ and has a given slope m can be written in point-slope form (see Figure 3-1). Taking $P(x, y)$ as any other point on the line, we write the slope m of the line as

$$m = \frac{y - y_1}{x - x_1}$$

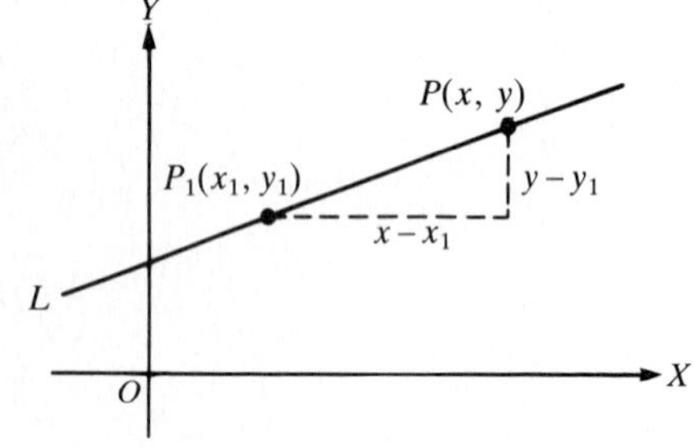

Figure 3-1. Point-slope form: $y - y_1 = m(x - x_1)$.

because (x_1, y_1) and (x, y) are on the same line. Clearing fractions, we get the **point-slope form**:

POINT-SLOPE FORM $\qquad y - y_1 = m(x - x_1) \qquad$ **(3-1)**

This equation is true for any position of the point P on the line. So we can consider P a *tracing point*: As P moves, its coordinates will vary, but will always satisfy the equation.

- The point-slope form of the equation of a line should be used to write the equation of any straight line that passes through a fixed point and has a given slope.

If the coordinates of the given point P_1 are $(0, 0)$, the point-slope form (3-1) becomes $y = mx$, which represents a line that passes through the origin and has slope m.

EXAMPLE 3-1: Find the equation of the line that passes through the point $(2, -\frac{5}{2})$ and has slope $-\frac{3}{4}$.

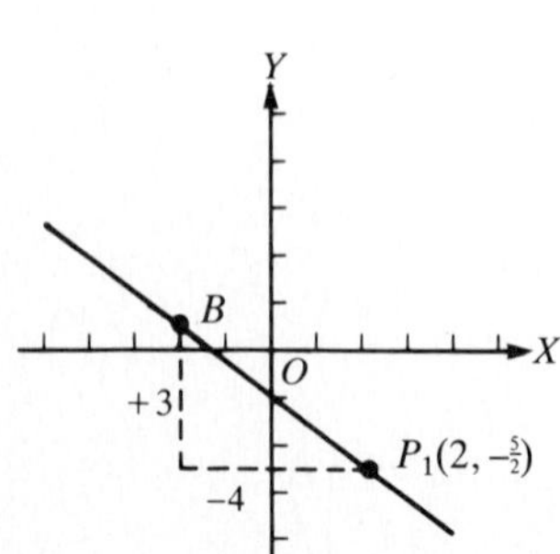

Figure 3-2

Solution: To draw the figure, plot the given point $P_1(2, -\frac{5}{2})$. Then use the slope to obtain a second point B by measuring four units to the left of P_1 and three units up (Figure 3-2). Now write the equation of the line through B and P_1 in point-slope form:

$$y - y_1 = m(x - x_1)$$
$$y + \tfrac{5}{2} = -\tfrac{3}{4}(x - 2)$$
$$3x + 4y + 4 = 0$$

note: You can check this equation by plotting its graph from a table of values, thereby showing that the line satisfies the given conditions.

EXAMPLE 3-2: Write the equations of the lines that pass through the following points and have the indicated slopes: **(a)** $(-3, 2)$, $m = \frac{2}{3}$; **(b)** $(2, 4)$, $m = 3$; **(c)** $(-4, -6)$, $m = \frac{5}{7}$.

Solution:
(a) $y - 2 = \frac{2}{3}(x + 3)$ or $2x - 3y + 12 = 0$
(b) $y - 4 = 3(x - 2)$ or $3x - y - 2 = 0$
(c) $y + 6 = \frac{5}{7}(x + 4)$ or $5x - 7y - 22 = 0$

B. Slope-intercept form

If the *Y*-intercept of a line is b, the coordinates of the point of intersection of the line and the *Y*-axis are $(0, b)$ (Figure 3-3). To express the equation of a line in terms of its *Y*-intercept b and slope m, we begin by writing the equation of the line through the point $(0, b)$ with the slope m in point-slope form:

$$y - y_1 = m(x - x_1)$$
$$y - b = m(x - 0)$$

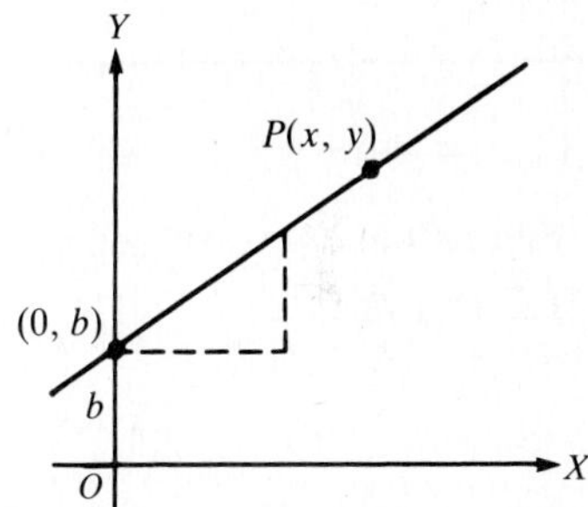

Figure 3-3. Slope-intercept form: $y = mx + b$.

Then the point-slope form reduces to the **slope-intercept form**:

SLOPE-INTERCEPT FORM $\qquad y = mx + b \qquad$ **(3-2)**

- The slope-intercept form of the equation of a line should be used to write the equation of any straight line whose *Y*-intercept and slope are known.

This form enables us to find the slope and the *Y*-intercept of any line whose equation is given.

EXAMPLE 3-3: Find the slope and *Y*-intercept of the line whose equation is $2x + 3y - 12 = 0$. Draw its graph.

Solution: Solve the equation for y:

$$2x + 3y - 12 = 0$$
$$y = -\tfrac{2}{3}x + 4$$

Now notice that this solution has changed the equation to its slope-intercept form (3-2), $y = mx + b$. So all you have to do is to identify the slope and the *Y*-intercept:

$$\text{slope} = m = -\tfrac{2}{3} \qquad Y\text{-intercept} = b = 4$$

Having found these two characteristics, you can easily draw the line. Locate the *Y*-intercept $(0, 4)$ and then construct an angle α whose tangent is $-\frac{2}{3}$, as shown in Figure 3-4. The terminal side of the angle α is the graph of the line.

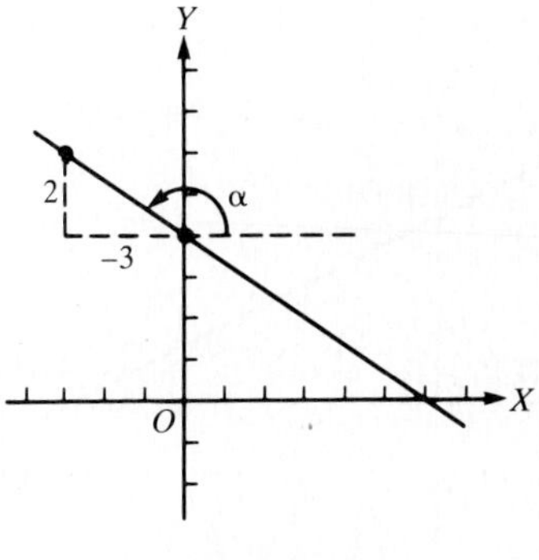

Figure 3-4

EXAMPLE 3-4: Find the slopes m and *Y*-intercepts b of the following lines: **(a)** $3x - 5y - 10 = 0$; **(b)** $4x + 3y - 18 = 0$; **(c)** $3x + y = 7$.

Solution:

(a) $3x - 5y - 10 = 0$
$y = \frac{3}{5}x - 2$
$m = \frac{3}{5}, \quad b = -2$

(b) $4x + 3y - 18 = 0$
$y = -\frac{4}{3}x + 6$
$m = -\frac{4}{3}, \quad b = 6$

(c) $3x + y = 7$
$y = -3x + 7$
$m = -3, \quad b = 7$

C. Two-point form

To find the equation of a line determined by two points, we begin by finding the slope of the line that passes through the two points. Then we substitute this slope and one of the points in the point-slope form to get the **two-point form** of the equation. Thus, if $P_1(x_1, y_1)$ and $P_2(x_2, y_2)$ are the given points (Figure 3-5), the slope of the line is

$$m = \frac{y_1 - y_2}{x_1 - x_2}$$

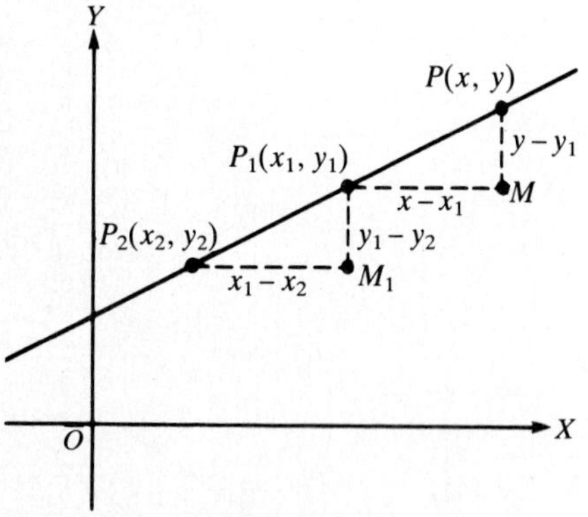

Using this slope and point (x_1, y_1) in the point-slope form (3-1), we get

$$y - y_1 = \left(\frac{y_1 - y_2}{x_1 - x_2}\right)(x - x_1)$$

which can be written as the two-point form:

TWO-POINT FORM $$\frac{y - y_1}{x - x_1} = \frac{y_1 - y_2}{x_1 - x_2} \qquad \textbf{(3-3)}$$

Figure 3-5. Two-point form: $\dfrac{y - y_1}{x - x_1} = \dfrac{y_1 - y_2}{x_1 - x_2}$

We can also derive formula (3-3) by similar triangles (see Figure 3-5). Taking $P(x, y)$ as any point on the line, we can write

$$\frac{MP}{P_1M} = \frac{M_1P_1}{P_2M_1} \quad \text{or} \quad \frac{y - y_1}{x - x_1} = \frac{y_1 - y_2}{x_1 - x_2}$$

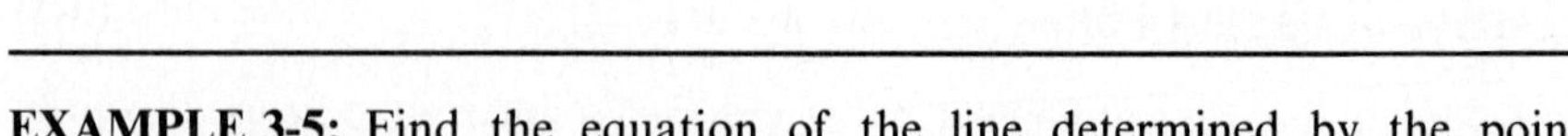

EXAMPLE 3-5: Find the equation of the line determined by the points $(-2, -2)$ and $(5, 2)$ shown in Figure 3-6.

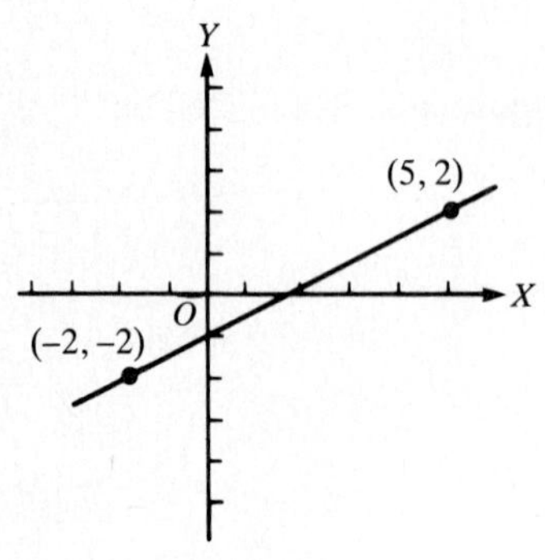

Figure 3-6

Solution: From the two-point form (3-3)

$$\frac{y - y_1}{x - x_1} = \frac{y_1 - y_2}{x_1 - x_2}$$

$$\frac{y + 2}{x + 2} = \frac{-2 - 2}{-2 - 5}$$

$$-4(x + 2) = -7(y + 2)$$

$$-4x - 8 = -7y - 14$$

$$4x - 7y = 6$$

Again, it's a good idea to test the accuracy of your work by substituting the coordinates of the given points in the final equation of the line.

D. Two-intercept form

If the X- and Y-intercepts of a line are a and b, respectively, so that the coordinates of the points of intersection of the line and the axes are $(a, 0)$ and $(0, b)$ (see Figure 3-7), the equation of the line through these two points can be found from the two-point form (3-3):

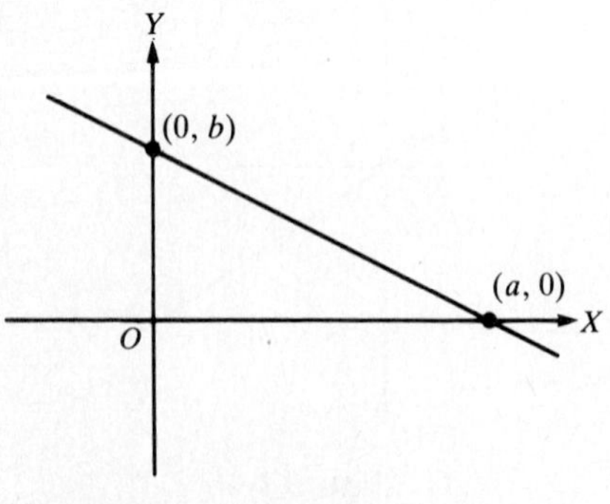

Figure 3-7. Two-intercept form: $\dfrac{x}{a} + \dfrac{y}{b} = 1$

$$\frac{y - y_1}{x - x_1} = \frac{y_1 - y_2}{x_1 - x_2} \quad \text{or} \quad \frac{y - b}{x - 0} = \frac{b - 0}{0 - a} \quad \text{or} \quad \frac{y - b}{x} = -\frac{b}{a}$$

Reducing this last equation to $bx + ay = ab$ and dividing both sides of the equation by ab, we get

TWO-INTERCEPT FORM
$$\frac{x}{a} + \frac{y}{b} = 1 \tag{3-4}$$

which is called the **two-intercept form.**

EXAMPLE 3-6: Change the equation $4x - 5y - 8 = 0$ to the two-intercept form.

Solution: Transpose the constant term to the right side and divide the equation by the constant term:

$$4x - 5y = 8$$

$$\frac{x}{2} - \frac{5y}{8} = 1$$

Express this result in the two-intercept form:

$$\frac{x}{a} + \frac{y}{b} = 1$$

$$\frac{x}{2} + \frac{y}{-8/5} = 1$$

Or, you can find the intercepts directly from the equation and then substitute them in the intercept form. Thus, setting first x and then y equal to zero in the equation $4x - 5y - 8 = 0$, you get $a = 2$ for the X-intercept and $b = -\frac{8}{5}$ for the Y-intercept. Substituting these values in the two-intercept form (3-4) gives the same result.

3-2. General and Normal Forms of the Equation of a Line

A. General form

The most general form of a first-degree equation in the variables x and y is

GENERAL EQUATION OF A LINE
$$Ax + By + C = 0 \tag{3-5}$$

where A, B, and C are any constants, including zero—except that A and B cannot be zero at the same time.

The equation of a straight line may be written in any of the several forms discussed in Section 3-1, each of which has unique advantages. But when these forms of the equation are cleared of fractions and simplified, they take the general form (3-5). Thus we have a theorem (which we won't attempt to prove here):

- Every equation of the first degree in x and y is the equation of a straight line (and conversely).

Given the general equation $Ax + By + C = 0$, we can make the following observations:

(1) If $C = 0$, the line passes through the origin.
(2) If $B = 0$, the line is vertical; if $B \neq 0$, the line has slope $m = -A/B$ and Y-intercept $b = -C/B$.
(3) If $A = 0$, the line is horizontal.

EXAMPLE 3-7: Describe the lines defined by the following equations: (**a**) $4x + 3y = 0$; (**b**) $4x - 12 = 0$; (**c**) $3y = 0$; (**d**) $4x + 3y - 12 = 0$.

Solution:

(**a**) Since $C = 0$, the line passes through the origin; and since $B \neq 0$, $m = -A/B = -4/3$.

(**b**) Since $B = 0$, the line is vertical.

(**c**) Since $A = 0$, the line is horizontal.

(**d**) Since the constants A, B, and C are all present—and therefore not zero—the line has the slope $m = -A/B = -4/3$ and Y-intercept $b = -C/B = 4$.

B. Normal form

We can also develop the equation of a line from trigonometric information.

- A straight line is determined by two quantities: (1) the perpendicular distance from the origin to the line and (2) the angle this perpendicular makes with the positive X-axis.

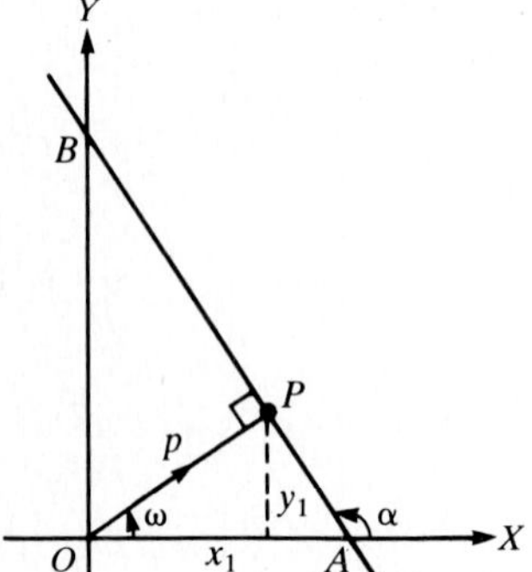

Figure 3-8. Normal form: $x \cos \omega + y \sin \omega = p$.

The equation of a line expressed in terms of these quantities is called the **normal form** of the equation of a line.

Let AB be any straight line. Then let $OP = p$ be the perpendicular drawn from the origin to line AB and ω be the angle that OP makes with the positive X-axis (Figure 3-8). The direction from O to P is assumed positive. So the coordinates of the point P lying on AB are

$$x_1 = p \cos \omega \qquad \text{and} \qquad y_1 = p \sin \omega$$

Now if α represents the inclination of AB, then the slope of AB is $m = \tan \alpha = -\cot \omega$, since $\alpha = 90° + \omega$. Thus by the point-slope form, the equation of the line AB is

$$y - p \sin \omega = -\cot \omega(x - p \cos \omega)$$

By the identities $\cot \omega = \dfrac{\cos \omega}{\sin \omega}$ and $\sin^2\omega + \cos^2\omega = 1$, this equation reduces to the normal form:

NORMAL FORM $$x \cos \omega + y \sin \omega = p \qquad \textbf{(3-6)}$$

C. Reduction to normal form

In order for the general form $Ax + By + C = 0$ and the normal form $x \cos \omega + y \sin \omega - p = 0$ of an equation to represent the same line, the coefficients of the equation forms must be proportional. Therefore

$$\frac{\cos \omega}{A} = \frac{\sin \omega}{B} = \frac{-p}{C} = r$$

where r is the common ratio. This gives us $\cos \omega = rA$, $\sin \omega = rB$, and $p = -rC$. We know from trigonometry that $\cos^2\omega + \sin^2\omega = 1$, so

$$r^2A^2 + r^2B^2 = 1$$

Solving for r

$$r^2(A^2 + B^2) = 1$$

$$r = \frac{1}{\pm\sqrt{A^2 + B^2}}$$

and substituting, we get

$$\cos\omega = rA = \frac{A}{\pm\sqrt{A^2 + B^2}}, \qquad \sin\omega = rB = \frac{B}{\pm\sqrt{A^2 + B^2}},$$

$$p = -rC = \frac{-C}{\pm\sqrt{A^2 + B^2}}$$

The normal form $x\cos\omega + y\sin\omega - p = 0$ may now be written

$$\frac{Ax}{\pm\sqrt{A^2 + B^2}} + \frac{By}{\pm\sqrt{A^2 + B^2}} + \frac{C}{\pm\sqrt{A^2 + B^2}} = 0$$

or, more compactly,

CONVERSION FORMULA: GENERAL TO NORMAL FORM

$$\frac{Ax + By + C}{\pm\sqrt{A^2 + B^2}} = 0 \tag{3-7}$$

note: The sign before the radical is the same as that of B when $B \neq 0$, or the same as that of A when $B = 0$.

EXAMPLE 3-8: Change the following equations to normal form: **(a)** $3x + 4y + 5 = 0$; **(b)** $5x - 12y - 10 = 0$; **(c)** $-5y + 7 = 0$; **(d)** $-3x - 2 = 0$.

Solution:

(a) Since $A = 3$ and $B = 4$, by the conversion formula (3-7) you can write

$$\frac{Ax + By + C}{\pm\sqrt{A^2 + B^2}} = \frac{3x + 4y + 5}{\sqrt{3^2 + 4^2}} = \frac{3x + 4y + 5}{5} = 0$$

(b)
$$\frac{5x - 12y - 10}{-\sqrt{25 + 144}} = \frac{5x - 12y - 10}{-13} = 0$$

(c)
$$\frac{-5y + 7}{-\sqrt{25}} = y - \frac{7}{5} = 0$$

(d)
$$\frac{-3x - 2}{-\sqrt{9}} = x + \frac{2}{3} = 0$$

3-3. Distance from a Line to a Point

Probably the most important use of the normal form is in finding the perpendicular distance from a line to a point. To find a formula for this distance, we let L represent any line in the plane, so that the equation of L is $x\cos\omega + y\sin\omega - p = 0$, and we let P_1 be any point with coordinates (x_1, y_1), as shown in Figure 3-9. Then we draw line L_1 through P_1 such that L_1 is parallel to L and the equation of L_1 is

$$x\cos\omega + y\sin\omega - p_1 = 0$$

where $OQ = p_1$. Since the point (x_1, y_1) lies on L_1, it must satisfy the equation of L_1, so we can write

$$x_1\cos\omega + y_1\sin\omega - p_1 = 0$$

From Figure 3-9 we see that $OQ = p_1 = p + d$, so we substitute this value to get

$$x_1\cos\omega + y_1\sin\omega - p - d = 0$$

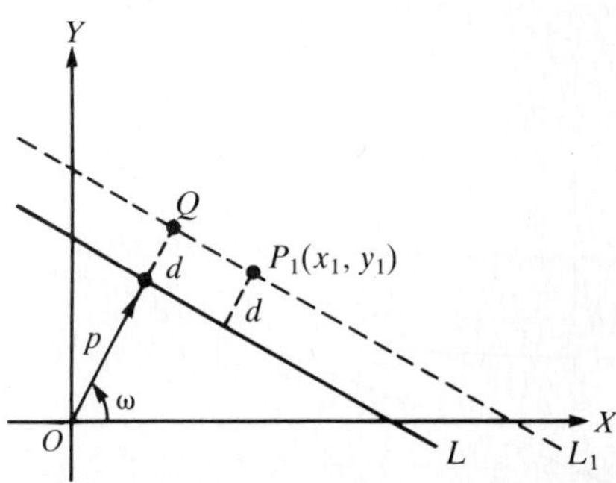

Figure 3-9. Distance from a line to a point:

$$d = x_1\cos\omega + y_1\sin\omega - p = \frac{Ax_1 + By_1 + C}{\pm\sqrt{A^2 + B^2}}$$

Solving for d and using the conversion formula (3-7), we can write

LINE-TO-POINT DISTANCE FORMULA

$$d = x_1 \cos \omega + y_1 \sin \omega - p = \frac{Ax_1 + By_1 + C}{\pm\sqrt{A^2 + B^2}} \tag{3-8}$$

From (3-8), we can derive a general procedure: To find the distance from the line $Ax + By + C = 0$ to the point (x_1, y_1)

(1) Change the equation of the line to the normal form by dividing through by $\pm\sqrt{A^2 + B^2}$.
(2) Choose the sign of the radical so it is the same as the sign of B when $B \neq 0$, or the same as the sign of A when $B = 0$.
(3) Substitute the coordinates (x_1, y_1) of the given point into the normal equation.

The result will be the numerical distance from the line to the point. When P_1 is below the line (or to the left of it, in case the line is vertical), d is negative; otherwise, d is positive.

EXAMPLE 3-9: Find the distance from the line $3x - 4y - 8 = 0$ to the points $(2, 3)$ and $(1, -4)$; give the position of the points with respect to the line.

Solution: Use the conversion formula (3-7) to change $3x - 4y - 8 = 0$ to the normal form:

$$\frac{Ax + By + C}{\pm\sqrt{A^2 + B^2}} = 0$$

$$\frac{3x - 4y - 8}{-\sqrt{9 + 16}} = 0$$

$$\frac{3x - 4y - 8}{-5} = 0$$

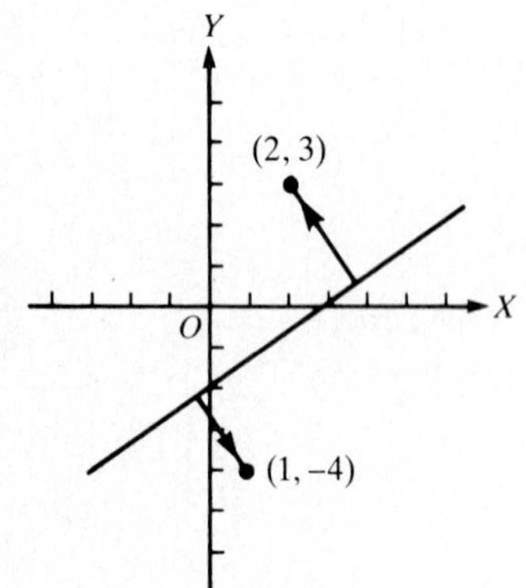

Figure 3-10

Substitute $x = 2$ and $y = 3$ to obtain the distance from $(2, 3)$:

$$d = \frac{3(2) - 4(3) - 8}{-5} = \frac{14}{5}$$

The positive sign of d indicates that the point $(2, 3)$ is above the line, as in Figure 3-10.

Substitute $x = 1$ and $y = -4$ to obtain the distance from $(1, -4)$:

$$d = \frac{3(1) - 4(-4) - 8}{-5} = -\frac{11}{5}$$

The negative sign indicates that the point is below the line, as Figure 3-10 shows.

3-4. Equations of Angle Bisectors

It's often necessary or convenient to find the equations of the lines that bisect the angles made by two intersecting lines, i.e., the locus of points equidistant from the two lines. To do this, we let the equations of two intersecting lines L_1 and L_2 be

$$L_1 = A_1x + B_1y + C_1 = 0$$

$$L_2 = A_2x + B_2y + C_2 = 0$$

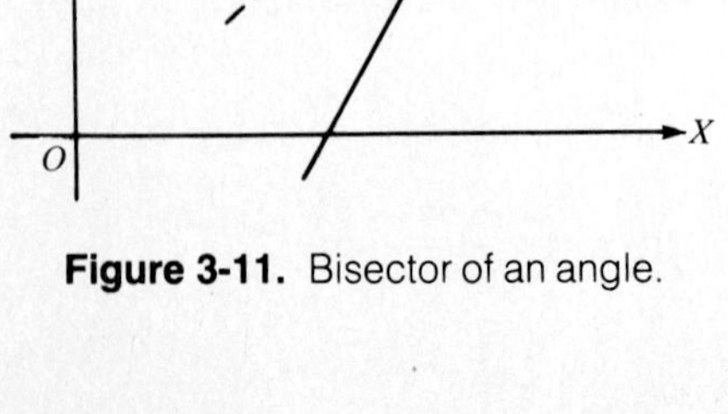

Figure 3-11. Bisector of an angle.

Then we let P_1 be a point on the desired bisector such that d_1 and d_2 are the respective perpendicular distances from L_1 and L_2 to P_1 (see Figure 3-11). Now we can use the distance formula (3-8):

$$d_1 = \frac{A_1x + B_1y + C_1}{\pm\sqrt{A_1^2 + B_1^2}} \quad \text{and} \quad d_2 = \frac{A_2x + B_2y + C_2}{\pm\sqrt{A_2^2 + B_2^2}}$$

Then, since $d_1 = \pm d_2$, we have

ANGLE BISECTORS

$$\frac{A_1x + B_1y + C_1}{\pm\sqrt{A_1^2 + B_1^2}} = \pm\frac{A_2x + B_2y + C_2}{\pm\sqrt{A_2^2 + B_2^2}} \qquad \textbf{(3-9)}$$

Equation (3-9) gives the equations of *both* angle bisectors; but getting a *particular* bisector in a numerical problem is easy: We can determine the signs of the perpendicular distances by sketching the figure to give the desired bisector, or we can compute both bisectors and select the desired one by comparing slopes or intercepts.

EXAMPLE 3-10: Find the equation of the bisector of the acute angle formed by $L_1 = 5x - 12y + 10 = 0$ and $L_2 = 12x - 5y + 15 = 0$.

Solution: Let $P(x, y)$ be on the bisector of the acute angle formed by lines L_1 and L_2 as in Figure 3-12. Then convert to normal form and find the perpendicular distances by eq. (3-8):

$$d_1 = \frac{5x - 12y + 10}{-13} \quad \text{and} \quad d_2 = \frac{12x - 5y + 15}{-13}$$

You know that $d_1 = \pm d_2$, so you can write the equations for *both* bisectors by eq. (3-9):

$$\frac{5x - 12y + 10}{-13} = \pm\frac{12x - 5y + 15}{-13}$$

$$5x - 12y + 10 = \pm(12x - 5y + 15)$$

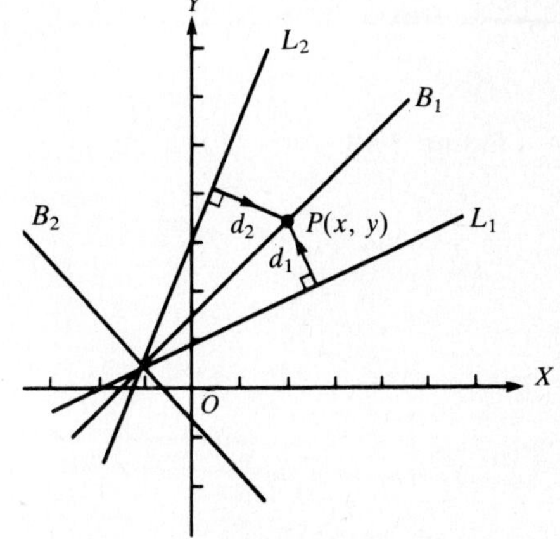

Figure 3-12

which gives you two possible equations, one taking the positive sign and one taking the negative sign:

$$7x + 7y + 5 = 0 \quad \text{and} \quad 17x - 17y + 25 = 0$$

To obtain the bisector of the acute angle, you need to know the signs of d_1 and d_2, which can be found from the figure. Figure 3-12 shows that d_1 is positive (because P lies above L_1) and d_2 is negative (because P lies below L_2), so $d_1 = -d_2$. Thus the equation of the bisector of the acute angle, B_1, takes the negative sign and can be written as

$$d_1 = -d_2$$

$$5x - 12y + 10 = -(12x - 5y + 15)$$

$$17x - 17y + 25 = 0$$

Alternative Solution: You can also distinguish one bisector from the other by comparing their intercepts or slopes with those of the lines. In this case, you can compute the Y-intercepts of L_1 and L_2 and compare them with the Y-intercepts of the two bisectors:

L_1:	$5x - 12y + 10 = 0;$	$y = \frac{5}{6}$
L_2:	$12x - 5y + 15 = 0;$	$y = 3$
B (positive sign):	$7x + 7y + 5 = 0;$	$y = -\frac{5}{7}$
B (negative sign):	$17x - 17y + 25 = 0;$	$y = \frac{25}{17}$

The Y-intercept of the bisector of the acute angle between L_1 and L_2 must fall between the Y-intercepts of L_1 and L_2, so $17x - 17y + 25 = 0$ is the equation of the acute bisector B_1 because $\frac{5}{6} < \frac{25}{17} < 3$.

3-5. Area of a Triangle

Now we can find the area of a triangle located anywhere in the plane. Let any triangle have vertices $A(x_1, y_1)$, $B(x_2, y_2)$, and $C(x_3, y_3)$, as shown in Figure 3-13. We can find the length b of the base AB by the distance formula (1-2):

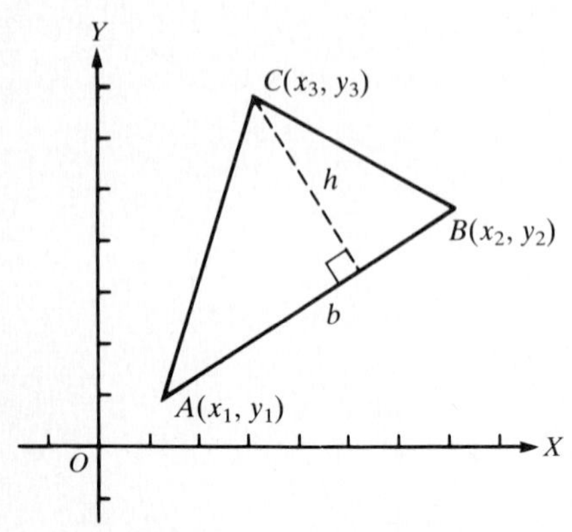

Figure 3-13. Area of a triangle.

$$b = d = \sqrt{(x_2 - x_1)^2 + (y_2 - y_1)^2}$$

Then we need a formula for the altitude h, so we write the equation of the straight line AB in two-point form (3-3):

$$\frac{y - y_1}{x - x_1} = \frac{y_2 - y_1}{x_2 - x_1}$$

which may be rewritten as

$$-(y_2 - y_1)x + (x_2 - x_1)y + (x_1y_2 - x_2y_1) = 0$$

Then by the formula for the distance between a line and a point (3-8), we can find the distance h from this line to the vertex C:

$$d = \frac{Ax_1 + By_1 + C}{\pm\sqrt{A^2 + B^2}}$$

$$= h = \frac{-(y_2 - y_1)x_3 + (x_2 - x_1)y_3 + (x_1y_2 - x_2y_1)}{\pm\sqrt{(x_2 - x_1)^2 + (y_2 - y_1)^2}}$$

We now have expressions for the length of the base b and the altitude h, so we can write the area of the triangle ABC as

$$\text{Area} = \tfrac{1}{2}bh$$

$$= \pm\tfrac{1}{2}[-(y_2 - y_1)x_3 + (x_2 - x_1)y_3 + (x_1y_2 - x_2y_1)]$$

Expanding this expression and rearranging its terms, we get

AREA OF A TRIANGLE

$$\text{Area} = \pm\tfrac{1}{2}[x_1(y_2 - y_3) - x_2(y_1 - y_3) + x_3(y_1 - y_2)] \quad \textbf{(3-10)}$$

which can also be conveniently expressed in determinant notation (see Appendix C-4):

$$\text{Area} = \pm\frac{1}{2}\begin{vmatrix} x_1 & y_1 & 1 \\ x_2 & y_2 & 1 \\ x_3 & y_3 & 1 \end{vmatrix}$$

The sign should be chosen to give a positive value to the area.

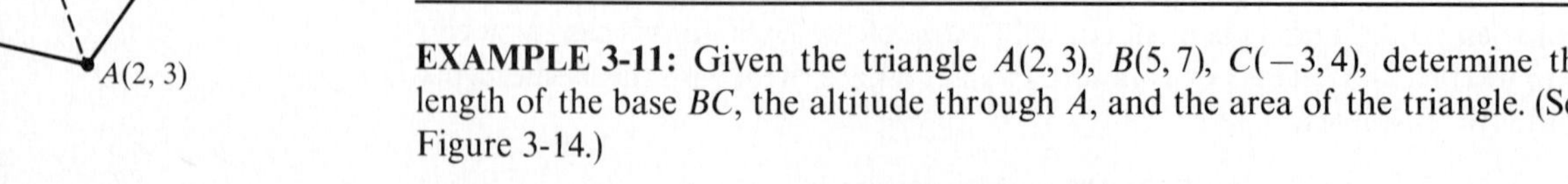

EXAMPLE 3-11: Given the triangle $A(2, 3)$, $B(5, 7)$, $C(-3, 4)$, determine the length of the base BC, the altitude through A, and the area of the triangle. (See Figure 3-14.)

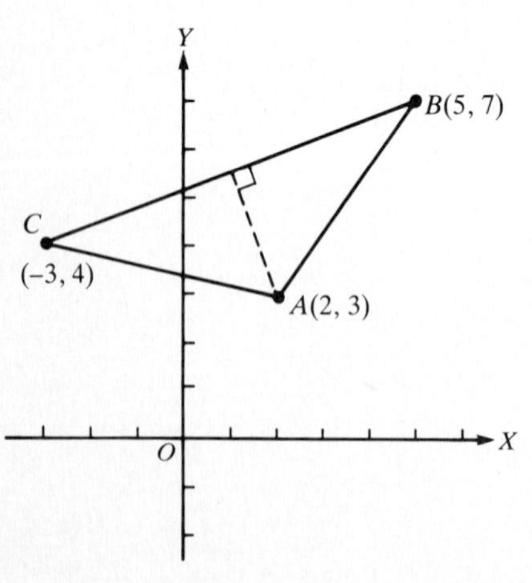

Figure 3-14

Solution: From eq. (1-2), the length b of base BC is

$$b = \sqrt{(x_2 - x_1)^2 + (y_2 - y_1)^2}$$

$$= \sqrt{(-3 - 5)^2 + (4 - 7)^2} = \sqrt{64 + 9}$$

$$= \sqrt{73}$$

From eq. (3-3), the equation of BC is

$$\frac{y - y_1}{x - x_1} = \frac{y_1 - y_2}{x_1 - x_2}$$

$$\frac{y - 7}{x - 5} = \frac{7 - 4}{5 + 3}$$

$$3x - 8y + 41 = 0$$

From eq. (3-8), the distance, or altitude h, from BC to A is

$$h = \frac{Ax_1 + By_1 + C_1}{\pm\sqrt{A^2 + B^2}} = \frac{3(2) - 8(3) + 41}{\sqrt{3^2 + 8^2}} = \frac{23}{\sqrt{73}}$$

Finding the area is easy now. You can use the simple geometric formula

$$\text{Area} = \frac{bh}{2} = \frac{1}{2}(\sqrt{73})\left(\frac{23}{\sqrt{73}}\right) = \frac{23}{2} \quad \text{square units}$$

Or, you can forget about the base and altitude and use eq. (3-10):

$$\begin{aligned} \text{Area} &= \tfrac{1}{2}[2(7 - 4) - 5(3 - 4) - 3(3 - 7)] \\ &= \tfrac{1}{2}(6 + 5 + 12) = \tfrac{1}{2}(23) \\ &= 23/2 \quad \text{square units} \end{aligned}$$

3-6. Systems of Lines

A. Definition of systems of lines

An equation of the first degree in x and y that contains an arbitrary constant (a constant to which any value may be assigned) represents an infinite number of straight lines. Because an infinite number of values may be given to the constant, each value will uniquely determine a line. So a first-degree equation in x and y that contains an arbitrary constant represents a **system of lines**, and the arbitrary constant is a *parameter*.

For example if we give different real values to k in the equation $y = \frac{1}{2}x + k$, we get a series of lines with slope $\frac{1}{2}$:

$$\begin{aligned} \text{If}\quad k &= -1, &\text{then}\quad y &= \tfrac{1}{2}x - 1 \\ k &= 0, & y &= \tfrac{1}{2}x \\ k &= 1, & y &= \tfrac{1}{2}x + 1 \\ k &= 2, & y &= \tfrac{1}{2}x + 2 \end{aligned}$$

etc.

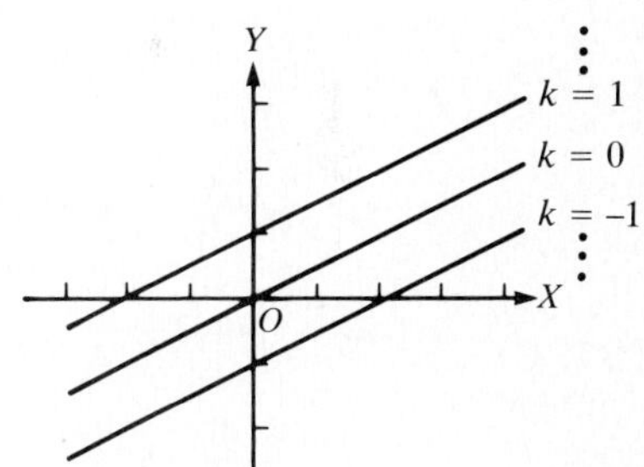

Figure 3-15. Systems of lines: $y = \frac{1}{2}x + k$.

Figure 3-15 shows a few members of this system (family) of lines, which is characterized by the fact that all members have the same slope.

Similarly, if the equation is $y - 2 = k(x - 2)$, we have the following equations as we vary the value of k:

$$\begin{aligned} k &= -1, & y - 2 &= -(x - 2) \\ k &= 0, & y - 2 &= 0 \\ k &= 1, & y - 2 &= x - 2 \end{aligned}$$

etc.

This represents a system of lines characterized by the fact that all of its members pass through the point (2, 2) (see Figure 3-16).

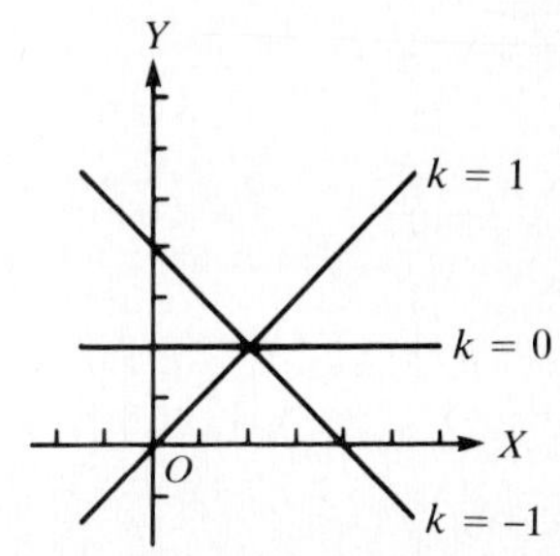

Figure 3-16. System of lines: $y - 2 = k(x - 2)$.

EXAMPLE 3-12: Find the equation of the system of lines having a Y-intercept of 2.

Solution: Here just one point of the line is given, so you know the slope will vary. The equation of any line that has a Y-intercept of 2 is $y = kx + 2$, where k = slope. In other words, for each value of the parameter k there is a line of different slope, but all the lines have the same Y-intercept.

EXAMPLE 3-13: Write the equation of the system of lines parallel to the line $2x - 3y + 6 = 0$. Determine the line of the system that passes through the point $(4, 3)$.

Solution: Any line parallel to the given line must have the same slope and may be written $2x - 3y = k$. Therefore, for each value of k this equation represents a line with unvarying slope $\frac{2}{3}$ (which you find by writing the equation in slope-intercept form). This gives you a system of lines parallel to the given line with k as the parameter.

To determine a line of the system that passes through the point (4, 3), simply substitute these coordinates in the equation of the system to obtain a value for k:

$$2x - 3y = k$$

$$2(4) - 3(3) = k$$

$$k = -1$$

So $2x - 3y + 1 = 0$ is the required equation.

B. Lines through the intersection of two given lines

Consider the two lines

$$L_1\!: \; A_1x + B_1y + C_1 = 0 \qquad \text{and} \qquad L_2\!: \; A_2x + B_2y + C_2 = 0$$

Next, consider the equation $L_1 + kL_2 = 0$, which can be written

FAMILY OF LINES THROUGH TWO INTERSECTING LINES

$$A_1x + B_1y + C_1 + k(A_2x + B_2y + C_2) = 0 \quad \textbf{(3-11)}$$

This equation represents a straight line since it is first-degree in x and y. And since it contains an arbitrary constant, or parameter, k, it represents a system of lines.

If L_1 and L_2 intersect at point (x_1, y_1), then $L_1 = A_1x_1 + B_1y_1 + C_1 = 0$ and $L_2 = A_2x_1 + B_2y_1 + C_2 = 0$, since the point lies on both lines. Also, because this point satisfies $L_1 = 0$ and $L_2 = 0$ separately, it must satisfy the equation of the system of lines $L_1 + kL_2 = 0$. In other words, all of the lines determined by the equation $L_1 + kL_2 = 0$ pass through the point of intersection of $L_1 = 0$ and $L_2 = 0$.

Equation (3-11) allows us to solve many exercises involving intersecting lines without actually finding their points of intersection.

EXAMPLE 3-14: Find the equation of the line that passes through the intersection of the lines $x - 2y + 4 = 0$ and $2x + y + 6 = 0$ and through the point $(3, -2)$.

Solution: Write the equation of the system of lines through the intersection of the given lines from eq. (3-11):

$$(x - 2y + 4) + k(2x + y + 6) = 0$$

To select the line of the system that passes through the point $(3, -2)$, find k by substituting $x = 3$ and $y = -2$ into the equation

$$(3 + 4 + 4) + k(6 - 2 + 6) = 0$$

$$10k = -11 \qquad \text{or} \qquad k = -\frac{11}{10}$$

then substitute this value for k in the equation of the system to get the equation of the desired line:

$$(x - 2y + 4) - \frac{11}{10}(2x + y + 6) = 0$$

$$12x + 31y + 26 = 0$$

SUMMARY

1. The equation of a straight line is an equation in x and y that is satisfied by the coordinates of every point on the line and by the coordinates of no other points. There are several standard forms:

Point-slope:	$y - y_1 = m(x - x_1)$
Slope-intercept:	$y = mx + b$
Two-point:	$\dfrac{y - y_1}{x - x_1} = \dfrac{y_1 - y_2}{x_1 - x_2}$
Two-intercept:	$\dfrac{x}{a} + \dfrac{y}{b} = 1$
General form:	$Ax + By + C = 0$
Normal form:	$x \cos \omega + y \sin \omega = p$

2. The formula for reducing the general equation of a straight line to the normal form is

$$\frac{Ax + By + C}{\pm\sqrt{A^2 + B^2}} = 0$$

The sign before the radical is the same as that of B if $B \neq 0$, and the same as that of A if $B = 0$.

3. The formula for finding the distance from a line to a point is

$$d = x_1 \cos \omega + y_1 \sin \omega - p = \frac{Ax_1 + By_1 + C}{\pm\sqrt{A^2 + B^2}}$$

4. The expression for finding the equations of the lines that bisect the angles made by two intersecting lines is

$$\frac{A_1x + B_1y + C_1}{\pm\sqrt{A_1^2 + B_1^2}} = \pm\frac{A_2x + B_2y + C_2}{\pm\sqrt{A_2^2 + B_2^2}}$$

5. The area of a triangle is given by the expression

$$\text{Area} = \pm\tfrac{1}{2}[x_1(y_2 - y_3) - x_2(y_1 - y_3) + x_3(y_1 - y_2)]$$

6. A first-degree equation in x and y that contains an arbitrary constant represents a system of lines. The arbitrary constant is known as the parameter.

7. The equation for finding the family of lines through the intersection of two given lines is

$$(A_1x + B_1y + C_1) + k(A_2x + B_2y + C_2) = 0$$

RAISE YOUR GRADES

Can you...?

☑ write the equation of a line that passes through a given point and has a given slope
☑ find the slope and Y-intercept of a straight line, given its equation
☑ write the equation of a line, given two points
☑ convert a linear equation to its two-intercept form
☑ determine if a line passes through the origin, is vertical, or is horizontal, given its first-degree equation in x and y
☑ change a linear equation to its normal form
☑ find the distance from a line to a given point
☑ find the equation of the bisector of the angle formed by two given lines
☑ determine the length of the altitude and the area of a triangle, given the coordinates of its vertices
☑ find the equation of a system of lines, given the Y-intercept
☑ find the equation of a line that passes through the intersection of two given lines and a given point

SOLVED PROBLEMS

Standard Forms of the Equation of a Line

PROBLEM 3-1 Find the equation of the line that passes through the point $(3, -1)$ and has a slope of $\frac{2}{7}$.

Solution: Write the equation in point-slope form (3-1):

$$y - y_1 = m(x - x_1)$$
$$y + 1 = \tfrac{2}{7}(x - 3)$$
$$2x - 7y - 13 = 0$$

PROBLEM 3-2 Find the equation of the line that passes through point $(3, -4)$, making an angle of $60°$ with the X-axis.

Solution: From trigonometry you know that the tangent of a $60°$ angle is $\sqrt{3}$; so $m = \sqrt{3}$. Then from the point-slope form (3-1)

$$y + 4 = \sqrt{3}(x - 3)$$
$$y - \sqrt{3}x + 4 + 3\sqrt{3} = 0$$

Insert the coordinates of the point and check your result:

$$-4 - 3\sqrt{3} + 4 + 3\sqrt{3} = 0$$

$$0 = 0$$

PROBLEM 3-3 Find the slope and Y-intercept of the equation $2x - 3y - 5 = 0$.

Solution: Solving the equation for y, you get $y = \frac{2}{3}x - \frac{5}{3}$. Comparing this with the slope-intercept form (3-2) of the equation of a straight line, namely, $y = mx + b$, you find that the slope is $m = \frac{2}{3}$ and the Y-intercept (value of y when $x = 0$) is $b = -\frac{5}{3}$.

PROBLEM 3-4 Find the slope and the Y-intercept for the line $2y + 3x = 7$.

Solution:

$$y = -\tfrac{3}{2}x + \tfrac{7}{2}$$

$$m = -\tfrac{3}{2} \qquad \text{and} \qquad b = \tfrac{7}{2}$$

PROBLEM 3-5 Find the equation of the line that passes through the points $(5, -1)$ and $(-4, 3)$.

Solution: Substitute the coordinates of the given points into the coordinate expression of the slope:

$$m = \frac{y_2 - y_1}{x_2 - x_1} = \frac{3 - (-1)}{-4 - 5} = -\frac{4}{9}$$

Using the slope you just obtained, find the value of the Y-intercept b by substituting the coordinates of either given point into the slope-intercept form (3-2):

$$y = -\tfrac{4}{9}x + b$$

$$b = \tfrac{4}{9}x + y = \tfrac{4}{9}(5) + (-1) = \tfrac{11}{9}$$

Now you have the slope-intercept form $y = -\frac{4}{9}x + \frac{11}{9}$, from which you can write the equation of the line

$$4x + 9y - 11 = 0$$

note: Check your value of b by substituting the coordinates of the second point.

Alternative Solution: Now that you know where you're coming from, do it the easy way—write the equation in two-point form (3-3), substituting the given coordinates:

$$\frac{y - y_1}{x - x_1} = \frac{y_1 - y_2}{x_1 - x_2}$$

$$\frac{y + 1}{x - 5} = \frac{-1 - 3}{5 + 4} = -\frac{4}{9}$$

$$4x + 9y - 11 = 0$$

PROBLEM 3-6 Write the equation of the line that passes through the points $(2, 1)$ and $(-6, 5)$.

Solution: Write the equation in two-point form (3-3), substituting the given coordinates for (x_1, y_1) and (x_2, y_2):

$$\frac{y - y_1}{x - x_1} = \frac{y_1 - y_2}{x_1 - x_2}$$

$$\frac{y - 1}{x - 2} = \frac{1 - 5}{2 + 6}$$

$$x + 2y - 4 = 0$$

PROBLEM 3-7 Write the equation of the line whose X- and Y-intercepts are respectively $a = 2$ and $b = 7$.

Solution: Write the two-intercept form (3-4):

$$\frac{x}{a} + \frac{y}{b} = 1$$

$$\frac{x}{2} + \frac{y}{7} = 1$$

$$7x + 2y - 14 = 0$$

PROBLEM 3-8 Change the equation $3x + 4y = 12$ to the two-intercept form. Identify the X- and Y-intercepts.

Solution: Divide both sides of the equation by 12:

$$\frac{3x}{12} + \frac{4y}{12} = \frac{12}{12} \qquad \text{or} \qquad \frac{x}{4} + \frac{y}{3} = 1$$

So the X-intercept is 4 and the Y-intercept is 3.

General and Normal Forms of the Equation of a Line

PROBLEM 3-9 Change the following equations to normal form: **(a)** $3x + 2y = 12$; **(b)** $x - 2y = -6$; **(c)** $3x + 5y + 15 = 0$.

Solution: Use the conversion formula (3-7)

$$\frac{Ax + By + C}{\pm\sqrt{A^2 + B^2}} = 0$$

which changes the general form $Ax + By + C = 0$ (eq. 3-5) to the normal form. [*Hint*: Remember that the sign of the radical is the same as that of B when $B \neq 0$, and the same as that of A when $B = 0$.]

(a) Since $A = 3$, $B = 2$, and $C = -12$, the sign of the radical is positive, and

$$\frac{3x + 2y - 12}{\sqrt{3^2 + 2^2}} = \frac{3x + 2y - 12}{\sqrt{13}}$$

or

$$\frac{3x}{\sqrt{13}} + \frac{2y}{\sqrt{13}} - \frac{12}{\sqrt{13}} = 0$$

(b) Since $A = 1$, $B = -2$, and $C = 6$, the sign of the radical is negative, and

$$\frac{x - 2y + 6}{-\sqrt{1^2 + (-2)^2}} = \frac{x}{-\sqrt{5}} - \frac{2y}{-\sqrt{5}} + \frac{6}{-\sqrt{5}} = 0$$

(c) Since $A = 3$, $B = 5$, and $C = 15$, the sign of the radical is positive, and

$$\frac{3x + 5y + 15}{\sqrt{3^2 + 5^2}} = \frac{3x}{\sqrt{34}} + \frac{5y}{\sqrt{34}} + \frac{15}{\sqrt{34}} = 0$$

Distance from a Line to a Point

PROBLEM 3-10 Find the directed distance from the line $4x - 3y = 6$ to the origin.

Solution: Use the formula (3-8) for the distance from a line to a point, where the line is given by the equation in normal form and the point (x_1, y_1) is the origin (0, 0):

$$d = \frac{Ax_1 + By_1 + C}{\pm\sqrt{A^2 + B^2}} = \frac{4x_1 - 3y_1 - 6}{-\sqrt{4^2 + (-3)^2}} = \frac{4(0) - 3(0) - 6}{-5} = \frac{6}{5}$$

note: The positive sign shows that the origin is above the line.

PROBLEM 3-11 Find the equation of the line that is parallel to and below the line $4x - 5y = 6$ when the lines are 2 units apart.

Solution: Choose a sample point $P(x, y)$ on the required line and apply the condition that P is 2 units away from the given line, so you have a statement of distance that can be expressed by formula (3-8):

$$d = -2 = \frac{4x - 5y - 6}{-\sqrt{41}}$$

Then rearrange to get the equation of the required line: $4x - 5y - 6 = 2\sqrt{41}$.

Equations of Angle Bisectors

PROBLEM 3-12 Find the equation of the bisector of the acute angle formed by the lines (L_1) $2x - y = 8$ and (L_2) $4x + 2y = 9$.

Solution: Let $P(x, y)$ be a point on the bisector of the acute angle, as in Figure 3-17. Then use the distance formula (3-8) to find the distance d_1 from P to L_1 and the distance d_2 from P to L_2:

$$d_1 = \frac{2x - y - 8}{-\sqrt{5}} \quad \text{and} \quad d_2 = \frac{4x + 2y - 9}{2\sqrt{5}}$$

Since $d_1 = \pm d_2$, you use eq. (3-9) to obtain the bisectors:

$$4\sqrt{5}x - 2\sqrt{5}y - 16\sqrt{5} = \pm(-4\sqrt{5}x - 2\sqrt{5}y + 9\sqrt{5})$$

To find the bisector of the acute angle, you need to know the signs of d_1 and d_2. Since Figure 3-17 shows that both d_1 and d_2 are positive, you use the plus sign in reducing the equality:

$$8\sqrt{5}x = 25\sqrt{5}$$

so the equation of the bisector of the acute angle is

$$x = \frac{25}{8}$$

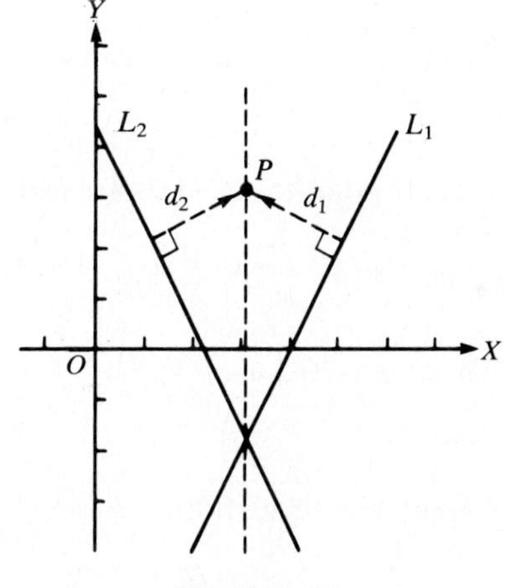

Figure 3-17

PROBLEM 3-13 Find and distinguish between the equations of the bisectors of the angles between the lines (L_1) $3x - 4y + 8 = 0$ and (L_2) $5x + 12y - 15 = 0$.

Solution: Let $P(x, y)$ be a point on the bisector of the acute angle, B_1, as shown in Figure 3-18. Then, from eq. (3-8)

$$d_1 = \frac{3x - 4y + 8}{-5} \quad \text{and} \quad d_2 = \frac{5x + 12y - 15}{13}$$

To obtain the two bisectors, use the relationship $d_1 = \pm d_2$; but since P lies below L_1 but above L_2, d_1 is negative and d_2 positive—so that $d_1 = -d_2$. Then the locus of P can be found by using the minus sign:

$$\frac{3x - 4y + 8}{-5} = -\frac{5x + 12y - 15}{13}$$

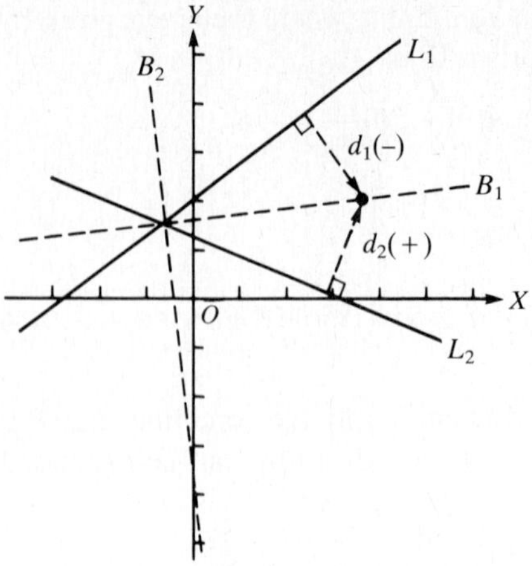

Figure 3-18

which gives you the equation of the bisector of the acute angle, B_1:

$$39x - 52y + 104 = -(-25x - 60y + 75)$$

$$14x - 112y + 179 = 0$$

Similarly, using the positive sign, the equation of the bisector of the obtuse angle, B_2:

$$\frac{3x - 4y + 8}{-5} = +\frac{5x + 12y - 15}{13}$$

$$39x - 52y + 104 = +(-25x - 60y + 75)$$

$$64x + 8y + 29 = 0$$

Area of a Triangle

PROBLEM 3-14 Given a triangle with vertices at $A(1, 1)$, $B(-1, 2)$, and $C(-2, -1)$, determine the altitude through B and the area of the triangle.

Solution: Use the distance formula to find the length of AC:

$$AC = \sqrt{(1 + 2)^2 + (1 + 1)^2} = \sqrt{13}$$

Now use eq. (3-3) to find the equation of AC:

$$\frac{y - 1}{x - 1} = \frac{1 - (-1)}{1 - (-2)} = \frac{2}{3}$$

$$2x - 2 = 3y - 3$$

$$2x - 3y + 1 = 0$$

Use the point-to-line distance formula to find altitude h, the distance from AC to B:

$$h = \frac{Ax_1 + By_1 + C}{\pm\sqrt{A^2 + B^2}} = \frac{2(-1) - 3(2) + 1}{-\sqrt{(2)^2 + (-3)^2}} = \frac{7}{\sqrt{13}}$$

The area is $\frac{1}{2}bh$, or

$$\text{Area} = \frac{1}{2}(\sqrt{13})\left(\frac{7}{\sqrt{13}}\right) = 3.5$$

Check: Use eq. (3-10):

$$\begin{aligned}\text{Area} &= \pm\tfrac{1}{2}[x_1(y_2 - y_3) - x_2(y_1 - y_3) + x_3(y_1 - y_2)] \\ &= \pm\tfrac{1}{2}[(2 + 1) - (-1)(1 + 1) + (-2)(1 - 2)] \\ &= \tfrac{1}{2}(7) = 3.5\end{aligned}$$

Systems of Lines

PROBLEM 3-15 Find the equation of the line that is perpendicular to $4x + 3y + 6 = 0$ and passes through the point $(-2, 3)$.

Solution: First, you need to find the equation of *all* lines perpendicular to the given line. Solve the equation of the given line for y:

$$4x + 3y + 6 = 0 \qquad \text{or} \qquad y = -\tfrac{4}{3}x - 2$$

So you know that its slope is $-4/3$. Then to find the equation for all lines perpendicular to the given line, use the negative reciprocal of the slope, which is $3/4$. Thus, $y = 3x/4 - k/4$, which gives you the desired equation of the family of perpendicular lines, i.e., $3x - 4y = k$, where the parameter k represents any assigned value.

Next, determine the one line in this system that passes through the point $(-2, 3)$ by substituting $(-2, 3)$ in the equation of the system. This gives you $3(-2) - 4(3) = k$, or $k = -18$. So the equation of the line is $3x - 4y + 18 = 0$.

PROBLEM 3-16 Find an equation for the family of lines for which the sum of the intercepts is 4.

Solution: Apply the condition $a + b = 4$ to the two-intercept form of the equation of a straight line (eq. 3-4), $x/a + y/b = 1$. Then $b = 4 - a$, and the required equation is

$$\frac{x}{a} + \frac{y}{4 - a} = 1$$

$$(4 - a)x + ay = a(4 - a)$$

Similarly, you can use $a = 4 - b$ and get $bx + (4 - b)y = b(4 - b)$.

PROBLEM 3-17 Find the equation of the line that has slope $\frac{4}{3}$ and passes through the point of intersection of the lines $4x - 5y - 5 = 0$ and $2x + 3y - 11 = 0$.

Solution: Applying eq. (3-11)—the system of lines through the intersection of given lines—you get

$$A_1x + B_1y + C_1 + k(A_2x + B_2y + C_2) = 0$$

$$4x - 5y - 5 + k(2x + 3y - 11) = 0$$

$$(4 + 2k)x + (3k - 5)y - 11k - 5 = 0$$

Solve for y to obtain the slope-intercept form $y = mx + b$:

$$y = \left(\frac{4 + 2k}{5 - 3k}\right)x + \frac{11k + 5}{3k - 5}$$

So the slope is $m = (4 + 2k)/(5 - 3k)$. This must equal $\frac{4}{3}$, so $(4 + 2k)/(5 - 3k) = \frac{4}{3}$ and $k = \frac{4}{9}$. Substitute this value of k and the equation becomes

$$(4x - 5y - 5) + \tfrac{4}{9}(2x + 3y - 11) = 0$$

$$44x - 33y - 89 = 0$$

PROBLEM 3-18 Find the equation of the line that passes through the intersection of the lines $3x - 4y = 5$ and $4x + 5y = -6$ and has a slope of -1.

Solution: Start with eq. (3-11):

$$A_1x + B_1y + C_1 + k(A_2x + B_2y + C_2) = 0$$

$$(3x - 4y - 5) + k(4x + 5y + 6) = 0$$

which is the equation of all lines meeting the first condition. Then rewrite it as

$$(3 + 4k)x + (-4 + 5k)y + (-5 + 6k) = 0$$

So the slope is $m = -(3 + 4k)/(-4 + 5k)$. And since the slope is to be $m = -1$, you let $(3 + 4k)/(-4 + 5k) = -1$, which gives you $k = 7$. Replacing k in the equation above and simplifying, you get

$$31x + 31y + 37 = 0$$

Supplementary Exercises

PROBLEM 3-19 Write the equations of the lines that pass through the following points and have the indicated slopes: **(a)** $(4, 2)$, 1; **(b)** $(0, 0)$, -2; **(c)** $(-1, 2)$, $\frac{1}{2}$; **(d)** $(5, 7)$, $-\frac{3}{2}$.

PROBLEM 3-20 Find the slope (m), X-intercept (a), and Y-intercept (b) of the following equations. Reduce each to slope-intercept form. **(a)** $x - 4y = 8$; **(b)** $x + y = 6$; **(c)** $9x + 4y = 36$; **(d)** $4x - 3y = 12$.

PROBLEM 3-21 Write the equations of the lines determined by the slope and Y-intercept given: **(a)** $m = 2, b = -3$; **(b)** $m = -4, b = 7$; **(c)** $m = -\frac{2}{3}, b = 2$; **(d)** $m = \frac{3}{2}, b = -4$.

PROBLEM 3-22 Write the following equations in two-intercept and slope-intercept form: **(a)** $x + 4y = 8$; **(b)** $3x + 2y = 6$; **(c)** $3x = 5y - 15$; **(d)** $4x - 3y = 6$.

PROBLEM 3-23 Find the equation of the line having X- and Y-intercepts $(1, 0)$ and $(0, -3)$, respectively.

PROBLEM 3-24 Find the equation of the line that passes through the following pairs of points: **(a)** $(2, 3), (8, 7)$; **(b)** $(-2, 1), (6, 5)$; **(c)** $(5, 7), (1, 1)$; **(d)** $(-1, 2), (3, 7)$.

PROBLEM 3-25 Write the equation $4x - 9y = -36$ in two-intercept form.

PROBLEM 3-26 Determine whether the following pairs of lines are parallel, perpendicular, or neither:

(a) $2x - 6y = 1$
$x - 3y = 3$

(b) $6x - 12y = 5$
$x + 2y = -3$

(c) $3x - 5y = 2$
$5x + 3y = 4$

(d) $3x - 5y = 1$
$6x - 10y = 3$

PROBLEM 3-27 Find the general form of the equation of the line determined by the data given in each of the following cases:

(a) The X-intercept is 5, and the line passes through $(3, -2)$.
(b) The Y-intercept is -3, and the line passes through $(-4, 3)$.

PROBLEM 3-28 Find the distance from the line to the indicated point in each of the following:

(a) $x - 4y + 4 = 0$, $(2, 1)$
(b) $2x - 3y - 2 = 0$, $(4, 0)$
(c) $3x - 5y = 0$, $(4, -2)$
(d) $3x - 8 = 0$, $(3, 5)$

PROBLEM 3-29 Find the distance between the parallel lines $15x + 8y + 68 = 0$ and $15x + 8y - 51 = 0$.

PROBLEM 3-30 Find the equations of the bisectors of the angles formed by the given lines in the following:

(a) $x - 3y + 6 = 0$ and $6x - 2y + 3 = 0$
(b) $4x - 3y + 17 = 0$ and $3x - 4y + 7 = 0$
(c) $7x - 6y + 84 = 0$ and $6x + 7y - 42 = 0$

PROBLEM 3-31 Find the area of the following triangles:

(a) $(0, 0), (-3, 4)$, and $(3, 5)$
(b) $(7, 5), (-11, 6)$, and $(3, -2)$

PROBLEM 3-32 Find the equation of the system of lines passing through the point $(-1, 3)$. Determine the particular line that passes through $(-2, 1)$.

PROBLEM 3-33 A system of lines has slope $-\frac{4}{3}$. What is the equation of the line of the system that makes a triangle of area 6 square units with the coordinate axes?

PROBLEM 3-34 Find the particular line of the system of lines passing through the intersection of $3x - 2y - 16 = 0$ and $x + 3y - 2 = 0$ that has the slope $\frac{2}{5}$.

Answers to Supplementary Exercises

3-19: **(a)** $x - y = 2$ **(b)** $2x + y = 0$ **(c)** $x - 2y = -5$ **(d)** $3x + 2y = 29$

3-20: **(a)** $m = \frac{1}{4}, a = 8, b = -2, y = \frac{1}{4}x - 2$
(b) $m = -1, a = 6, b = 6, y = -x + 6$
(c) $m = -\frac{9}{4}, a = 4, b = 9, y = -\frac{9}{4}x + 9$
(d) $m = \frac{4}{3}, a = 3, b = -4, y = \frac{4}{3}x - 4$

3-21: **(a)** $y = 2x - 3$ **(b)** $y = -4x + 7$ **(c)** $y = -\frac{2}{3}x + 2$ **(d)** $y = \frac{3}{2}x - 4$

3-22: (a) $\frac{x}{8}+\frac{y}{2}=1;\ y=\frac{-x}{4}+2$

(b) $\frac{x}{2}+\frac{y}{3}=1;\ y=\frac{-3x}{2}+3$

(c) $\frac{x}{-5}+\frac{y}{3}=1;\ y=\frac{3x}{5}+3$

(d) $\frac{x}{3/2}+\frac{y}{-2}=1;\ y=\frac{4x}{3}-2$

3-23: $3x-y-3=0$

3-24: (a) $2x-3y=-5$ (c) $3x-2y=1$
(b) $x-2y=-4$ (d) $5x-4y=-13$

3-25: $\frac{x}{-9}+\frac{y}{4}=1$

3-26: (a) parallel (c) perpendicular
(b) neither (d) parallel

3-27: (a) $x-y-5=0$
(b) $3x+2y+6=0$

3-28: (a) $-\frac{2\sqrt{17}}{17}$ (c) $-\frac{11\sqrt{34}}{17}$

(b) $-\frac{6\sqrt{13}}{13}$ (d) $\frac{1}{3}$

3-29: $d_1=\frac{15(0)+8(0)+68}{\sqrt{15^2+8^2}}=\frac{68}{17}=4$

$d_2=\frac{15(0)+8(0)-51}{17}=\frac{-51}{17}=-3$

$d_1-d_2=4-(-3)=7$ units apart

3-30: (a) $4x-4y+\frac{15}{2}=0$ and $2x+2y-\frac{9}{2}=0$
(b) $x+y+10=0$ and $7x-7y+24=0$
(c) $13x+y+42=0$ and
$x-13y+126=0$

3-31: (a) $13\frac{1}{2}$ (b) 65

3-32: $y-3=k(x+1),\ 2x-y+5=0$

3-33: $4x+3y\pm 12=0$

3-34: $2x-5y-14=0$

EXAM 1 (chapters 1–3)

1. Using graph paper, draw a pair of coordinate X,Y-axes, establish a scale, and plot the following points:
   (a) $P(-3, -5)$ (c) $R(-2, 5)$
   (b) $Q(2, -4)$ (d) $S(5, 1)$

2. Find the directed distance from
   (a) $(3, 2)$ to $(7, 2)$ (c) $(-6, 4)$ to $(-2, 4)$
   (b) $(7, 2)$ to $(3, 2)$ (d) $(-2, 3)$ to $(-6, 3)$

3. Find the distance between the points $(-2, 3)$ and $(4, -3)$.

4. Find the coordinates of the midpoint of the line segment joining $(-3, 4)$ and $(-5, 2)$.

5. Find the coordinates of the point that is two-thirds of the way from $(-5, -5)$ to $(7, 7)$.

6. Find the slope of the line joining $(-7, -3)$ and $(1, 5)$.

7. Show that the line through $(-1, -4)$ and $(4, 2)$ is parallel to the line through $(-3, -2)$ and $(2, 4)$.

8. Show that the line joining $(5, -2)$ and $(7, 4)$ is perpendicular to the line joining the points $(-3, 4)$ and $(9, 0)$.

9. Find the acute angle β that the line joining the points $(-4, -2)$ and $(2, 3)$ makes with the line joining $(-4, -1)$ and $(4, 1)$, to the nearest whole degree.

10. Draw the locus of the equation $4x + y - 8 = 0$.

11. Find the X- and Y-intercepts of the equation $x^2 + y - 9 = 0$.

12. Apply the three tests for symmetry to the equation $4x^2 + y^2 - 16 = 0$ and state your conclusions.

13. Examine the equation $x^2 + y - 9 = 0$ for extent. What conclusions can you draw?

14. Examine the curve $9x^2 - 4y^2 = 36$ for **(a)** intercepts, **(b)** symmetry, and **(c)** extent. State your conclusions.

15. Find the lines of infinite extent of the equation $xy + 3x = 6$.

16. Find the equation of the path traced by a point that moves in such a way that it remains equidistant from the points $(-2, 4)$ and $(4, -2)$.

17. Find the equation of the curve $y^2 = 4x$ when the axes are translated to the new origin $(1, 0)$.

18. Transform the equation $9x^2 + 4y^2 - 54x + 32y + 1 = 0$ by translating the axes to a new origin $(3, -4)$.

19. Remove the first-degree term from the equation $9x^2 - y^2 + 2y - 10 = 0$ by translating the axes. State the new origin.

20. Write the equation of the line that passes through $(7, -9)$ and has slope $m = 4$.

21. Find the slope m and Y-intercept b of the line whose equation is $2x + y = 8$.

22. Write the equation of the line determined by the pair of points $(0, 6)$ and $(-2, -3)$.

23. Change the equation $12x + 5y + 50 = 0$ to two-intercept form.

24. Determine the slope and Y-intercept of the equation $3x + 2y - 6 = 0$.

25. Change the equation $3x + 4y + 5 = 0$ to normal form.

26. Find the directed distance from the line $5x - 12y + 3 = 0$ to the point $(-2, 1)$.

27. Find the equation of the bisector of the pair of acute angles formed by the lines $x - 2y + 1 = 0$ and $x + 3y - 3 = 0$.

28. Find the area of the triangle whose vertices are $(1, -2)$, $(6, 1)$, and $(7, 8)$.

29. Find the equation for the family of lines perpendicular to the line $3x - 2y = 5$.

30. Find the equation of the line that passes through the intersection of lines $2x - y - 1 = 0$ and $3x + 2y - 12 = 0$, and through point $(-2, 1)$.

Answers to Exam 1

1.

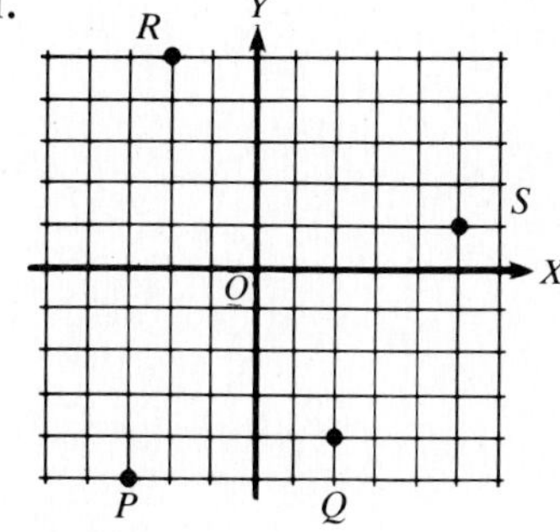

2. (a) 4 (c) 4
(b) 4 (d) 4

3. $6\sqrt{2}$

4. $(-4, 3)$

5. $(3, 3)$

6. $m = 1$

7. $m_1 = m_2 = \frac{6}{5}$
Since the slopes are equal, the lines are parallel.

8. $m_1 = 3$, $m_2 = -\frac{1}{3}$
Since $m_1 = -1/m_2$, the slopes of the lines are negative reciprocals of each other and the lines are perpendicular.

9. $\beta = 26°$

10.

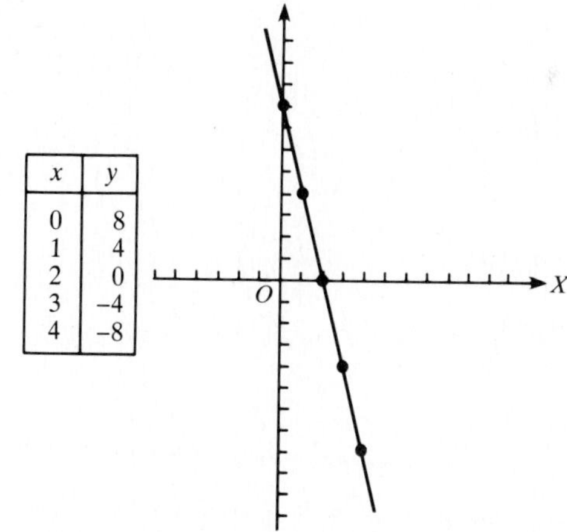

x	y
0	8
1	4
2	0
3	−4
4	−8

11. When $x = 0$, $y = 9$; when $y = 0$, $x = \pm 3$.

12. Since the equation remains unchanged when x is replaced by $-x$ and when y is replaced by $-y$, the curve is symmetric with respect to both axes and to the origin.

13. Solving for x gives $x = \pm\sqrt{9 - y}$, so values of $y > 9$ must be excluded because they make x imaginary.

14. (**a**) If $y = 0$, then $x = \pm 2$; if $x = 0$, then y becomes imaginary (i.e., the curve doesn't intersect the Y-axis).

(**b**) Since the equation remains unchanged when x and y are replaced simultaneously by their negatives, the curve is symmetric with respect to both axes and to the origin.

(**c**) Since $y = \pm\frac{3}{2}\sqrt{x^2 - 4}$, only values of $x \geq \pm 2$ yield real values of y. And since $x = \pm\frac{2}{3}\sqrt{y^2 + 9}$, the value of y can be any positive or negative number.

15. $x = 0$ and $y = -3$

16. $x - y = 0$

17. $(y')^2 = 4x' + 4$

18. $9(x')^2 + 4(y')^2 - 144 = 0$

19. $9(x')^2 - (y')^2 = 9$ with origin $(0, 1)$

20. $4x - y - 37 = 0$

21. $m = -2; b = 8$

22. $9x - 2y + 12 = 0$

23. $\dfrac{x}{-25/6} + \dfrac{y}{-10} = 1$

24. $m = -\frac{3}{2}, b = 3$

25. $\dfrac{3x + 4y + 5}{5} = 0$

26. $\frac{19}{13}$

27. $(1 - \sqrt{2})x + (3 + 2\sqrt{2})y = 3 + \sqrt{2}$

28. 16

29. $2x + 3y = k$

30. $x - 2y + 4 = 0$

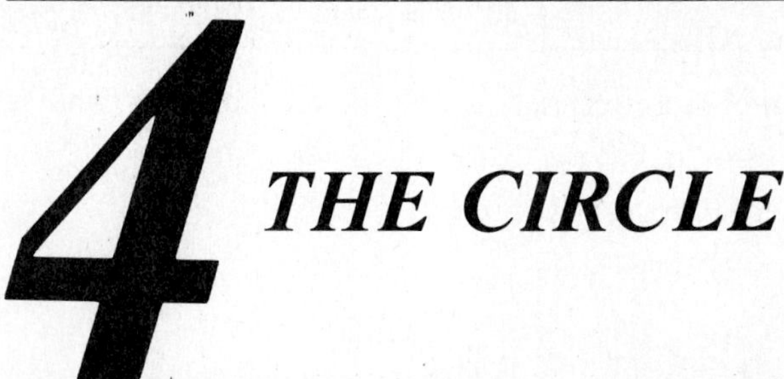

4 THE CIRCLE

THIS CHAPTER IS ABOUT

- ☑ Second-Degree Equations
- ☑ Standard Equation of a Circle
- ☑ General Equation of a Circle
- ☑ Conditions That Determine a Circle
- ☑ Families of Circles

4-1. Second-Degree Equations

The general form of a *second-degree equation*, which defines a **conic section**, is

SECOND-DEGREE EQUATION $$Ax^2 + Bxy + Cy^2 + Dx + Ey + F = 0$$

Second-degree equations can be approached from the viewpoint of finding the equation of a locus; that is, the law governing the motion of a point in a plane can be given as the definition of a curve. From this kind of definition we can find the algebraic expression that describes the path traced by the moving point. These points and lines all lie in a plane, so the curves are called **plane curves**, and include the *circle*, the *parabola*, the *ellipse*, and the *hyperbola*.

4-2. Standard Equation of a Circle

- A **circle** is the locus of a point that moves in such a way that its distance from a fixed point is always a constant.

The fixed point of a circle is called the *center*, and the constant distance is called the *radius* of the circle.

To determine the equation of a circle, we let $C(h, k)$ be the fixed point, $P(x, y)$ be the moving or tracing point, and $CP = r$ be the constant distance, as in Figure 4-1. Then we use the distance formula (1-2) to get the standard form of the equation of a circle:

$$\sqrt{(x - h)^2 + (y - k)^2} = r$$

EQUATION OF A CIRCLE (STANDARD FORM) $$(x - h)^2 + (y - k)^2 = r^2 \tag{4-1}$$

Since this equation is satisfied by all points on the circle, and by no other points, it is called the *standard form* of the equation of a circle with center (h, k) and radius r. It is sometimes also called the *center-radius* form of the equation of a circle because it exhibits the coordinates of the center and the length of the radius.

- If $r^2 > 0$, the circle is *real*. (If $r^2 < 0$, the circle is imaginary.)
- If $r^2 = 0$, the circle is a *point* circle.
- If the center of the circle is at the origin, then $(h, k) = (0, 0)$ and

$$x^2 + y^2 = r^2$$

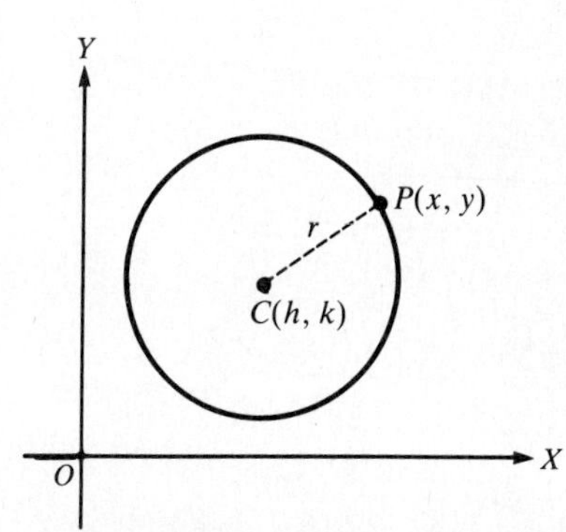

Figure 4-1. Circle as locus: $(x - h)^2 + (y - k)^2 = r^2$.

EXAMPLE 4-1: If the center of a circle is at $(3, -2)$ and the radius is 4, what is the equation of the circle?

Solution: From the standard form (4-1), you get

$$(x-h)^2 + (y-k)^2 = r^2$$

$$(x-3)^2 + (y+2)^2 = 16$$

or

$$x^2 + y^2 - 6x + 4y - 3 = 0$$

EXAMPLE 4-2: Find the equation of the circle with center $(2, -1)$ and radius 3.

Solution: Since $h = 2$, $k = -1$, and $r = 3$,

$$(x-h)^2 + (y-k)^2 = r^2$$

$$(x-2)^2 + (y+1)^2 = 3^2$$

or

$$x^2 + y^2 - 4x + 2y - 4 = 0$$

4-3. General Equation of a Circle

- *Every equation of the circle can be reduced to a general, second-degree form,* $x^2 + y^2 + Dx + Ey + F = 0$.

To develop a general equation for the circle, we return to eq. (4-1). Expanding the binomial, rearranging, and transposing r^2, we get

$$(x-h)^2 + (y-k)^2 = r^2$$

$$x^2 + y^2 - 2hx - 2ky + h^2 + k^2 - r^2 = 0$$

Then we set $D = -2h$, $E = -2k$, and $F = h^2 + k^2 - r^2$ (the constant term), which gives us the general form:

EQUATION OF A CIRCLE (GENERAL FORM)

$$x^2 + y^2 + Dx + Ey + F = 0 \qquad \textbf{(4-2)}$$

The converse is also true.

- *Every second-degree equation of the form* $x^2 + y^2 + Dx + Ey + F = 0$ *represents a circle.*

To prove this, first separate the x and y terms on the left-hand side and put the constant term on the right:

$$x^2 + Dx + y^2 + Ey = -F$$

Next, we complete the squares of the quadratic expressions: We add the square of half the coefficient of the first-degree term in x to the x terms and the square of half the coefficient of the first-degree term in y to the y terms; then we add the same amount on the right side. This gives

$$x^2 + Dx + \left(\frac{D}{2}\right)^2 + y^2 + Ey + \left(\frac{E}{2}\right)^2 = -F + \left(\frac{D}{2}\right)^2 + \left(\frac{E}{2}\right)^2$$

$$= \frac{D^2 + E^2 - 4F}{4}$$

The x terms and y terms are now perfect squares, so we can write

$$\left(x + \frac{D}{2}\right)^2 + \left(y + \frac{E}{2}\right)^2 = \frac{D^2 + E^2 - 4F}{4}$$

which is the algebraic expression of the condition that a tracing point (x, y) remains at a constant distance $\frac{1}{2}\sqrt{D^2 + E^2 - 4F}$ from a fixed point $(-D/2, -E/2)$. Hence it is the equation of a circle with center $(-D/2, -E/2)$ and radius $\frac{1}{2}\sqrt{D^2 + E^2 - 4F}$.

note: Since the radius is expressed as a radical, the equation represents a real circle, a point circle, or an imaginary circle when the radicand is positive, zero, or negative, respectively.

EXAMPLE 4-3: Change the equation $4x^2 + 4y^2 - 12x + 4y - 26 = 0$ to the standard form (4-1) and draw the graph.

Solution: First, divide through by 4:

$$4x^2 + 4y^2 - 12x + 4y - 26 = 0$$

$$x^2 + y^2 - 3x + y - \frac{26}{4} = 0$$

Next, leaving spaces for the terms to be added to complete the squares, move the constant term to the right-hand side:

$$x^2 - 3x \qquad + y^2 + y \qquad = \frac{26}{4}$$

The square of half the coefficient of the first-degree term in x goes in the first space and the square of half the coefficient of the first-degree term in y goes in the second space, so that

$$x^2 - 3x + \frac{9}{4} + y^2 + y + \frac{1}{4} = \frac{26}{4} + \frac{9}{4} + \frac{1}{4}$$

or

$$\left(x - \frac{3}{2}\right)^2 + \left(y + \frac{1}{2}\right)^2 = 3^2$$

This equation is the equation of a circle in the required form.

From the equation, you can tell that the center $(h, k) = (\frac{3}{2}, -\frac{1}{2})$ and that the radius $r = 3$, as shown in Figure 4-2.

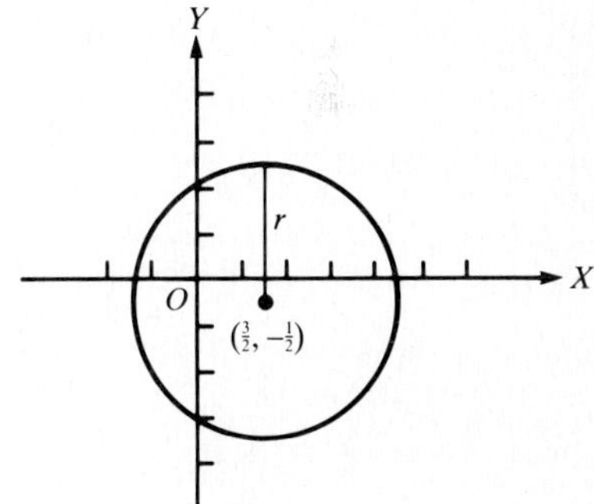

Figure 4-2

EXAMPLE 4-4: Find the general equation of the circle that has a center $(1, -3)$ and passes through the point $(4, 5)$.

Solution: First substitute $h = 1$ and $k = -3$ into the standard form (4-1):

$$(x - h)^2 + (y - k)^2 = r^2$$

$$(x - 1)^2 + (y + 3)^2 = r^2$$

which is the equation of the *family of circles* defined by the two parameters $(h, k) = (1, -3)$, the given center. Now, to find the particular circle, you need one more parameter, the radius r. To find r, you use the fact that the point $(4, 5)$ is on the circle and that its coordinates must satisfy the equation; so you can let $x = 4$ and $y = 5$:

$$r^2 = (4 - 1)^2 + (5 + 3)^2 = 9 + 64 = 73$$

$$r = \sqrt{73}$$

And if the radius of the circle is $\sqrt{73}$, the standard equation of the circle is

$$(x - 1)^2 + (y + 3)^2 = (\sqrt{73})^2 = 73$$

and the general form is

$$x^2 + y^2 - 2x + 6y - 63 = 0$$

EXAMPLE 4-5: Find the general equation of a circle in which the end points of its diameter are the points (2, 5) and (6, − 3).

Solution: The center of the circle must be the midpoint of the segment between the given points, or (4, 1); and the radius is the distance from $(h, k) = (4, 1)$ to either of the points. So, from the distance formula (1-2),

$$d = \sqrt{(x_2 - x_1)^2 + (y_2 - y_1)^2}$$

or

$$r = \sqrt{(4 - 2)^2 + (1 - 5)^2} = \sqrt{4 + 16} = \sqrt{20}$$

Hence if $h = 4$, $k = 1$, and $r = \sqrt{20}$, the standard equation is

$$(x - 4)^2 + (y - 1)^2 = (\sqrt{20})^2 = 20$$

so the general equation is

$$x^2 + y^2 - 8x - 2y - 3 = 0$$

EXAMPLE 4-6: Find the equation of a circle that passes through the points (2, − 1), (0, 2), and (1, 1).

Solution: You need to find the values of the constants *D*, *E*, and *F* in the general form of the circle (4-2). If the circle passes through the given point (2, − 1), the equation must be satisfied when $x = 2$ and $y = -1$. Making this substitution, you get

$$x^2 + y^2 + Dx + Ey + F = 0$$

$$4 + 1 + 2D - E + F = 0$$

showing one necessary relation between *D*, *E*, and *F*. Proceeding similarly, using the points (0, 2) and (1, 1), you get two more linear equations, $4 + 2E + F = 0$ and $2 + D + E + F = 0$, respectively; so you wind up with three linear equations:

$$5 + 2D - E + F = 0$$

$$4 + 2E + F = 0$$

$$2 + D + E + F = 0$$

Solving these three linear equations simultaneously (see Appendix C-5), you find that $D = 7$, $E = 5$, and $F = -14$. Thus the general equation of the circle becomes

$$x^2 + y^2 + 7x + 5y - 14 = 0$$

Check: The fact that the circle passes through the three given points can be checked by directly substituting the coordinate values of these points into the equation of the circle.

note: This problem COULD have been solved by substituting the coordinates of each of the given points into the standard form (4-1) and then solving the resulting three equations simultaneously for *h*, *k*, and *r*. But this algebraic computation is much more tedious than the method shown here.

4-4. Conditions That Determine a Circle

The standard and general forms of the equation of a circle $(x - h)^2 + (y - k)^2 = r^2$ (4-1) and $x^2 + y^2 + Dx + Ey + F = 0$ (4-2) each contain three arbitrary constants. Therefore, in order to obtain the equation of a particular circle, we have to be able to set up three independent equations from which the values of these constants—*h*, *k*, *r* or *D*, *E*, *F*—can be found. Because such equations are the analytical expressions of conditions that the circle must satisfy, we speak of a circle as being *determined* by three conditions. In practical terms, this means that when solving problems that specify the characteristics of a circle, we first decide which of the forms of the equation of a circle we need to use, and then we can set up three independent equations in the appropriate constants.

EXAMPLE 4-7: (a) Find the equation of the circle that passes through points (1, 2), (−2, 1), and (2, −3). **(b)** Find the center and radius of this circle.

Solution:

(a) Given only three sets of coordinates (and not a *hint* of the radius), select the general form $x^2 + y^2 + Dx + Ey + F = 0$ to represent the circle. Then think: *Since each point is on the circle (by definition), then the coordinates of the given points must satisfy the equation.* Therefore you can substitute the coordinates of the three known points into the general equation to obtain three linear equations:

$$1 + 4 + D + 2E + F = 0 \qquad (x = 1;\ y = 2)$$

$$4 + 1 - 2D + E + F = 0 \qquad (x = -2;\ y = 1)$$

$$4 + 9 + 2D - 3E + F = 0 \qquad (x = 2;\ y = -3)$$

Solving these equations simultaneously, you get $D = -\frac{1}{2}$, $E = \frac{3}{2}$, and $F = -\frac{15}{2}$. Now you can substitute these values into the general equation to get the equation of the circle:

$$x^2 + y^2 - \frac{x}{2} + \frac{3y}{2} - \frac{15}{2} = 0$$

or

$$2x^2 + 2y^2 - x + 3y - 15 = 0$$

(b) To find the center (h, k) and the radius r, you can change the general equation to standard form by completing the squares:

$$x^2 + y^2 - \frac{x}{2} + \frac{3y}{2} - \frac{15}{2} = 0$$

$$\left(x^2 - \frac{x}{2}\right) + \left(y^2 + \frac{3y}{2}\right) = \frac{15}{2}$$

$$\left(x^2 - \frac{x}{2} + \frac{1}{16}\right) + \left(y^2 + \frac{3y}{2} + \frac{9}{16}\right) = \frac{120}{16} + \frac{1}{16} + \frac{9}{16}$$

$$\left(x - \frac{1}{4}\right)^2 + \left(y + \frac{3}{4}\right)^2 = \left(\frac{\sqrt{130}}{4}\right)^2$$

So the center is $(h, k) = (\frac{1}{4}, -\frac{3}{4})$ and the radius is $r = \sqrt{130}/4$, as shown in Figure 4-3.

Check:
$$h = -\frac{D}{2} = -\left(\frac{-1/2}{2}\right) = \frac{1}{4}$$

$$k = -\frac{E}{2} = -\left(\frac{3/2}{2}\right) = -\frac{3}{4}$$

$$r = \frac{\sqrt{(-1/2)^2 + (3/2)^2 - 4(-15/2)}}{2} = \frac{\sqrt{130/4}}{2}$$

$$= \sqrt{130}/4$$

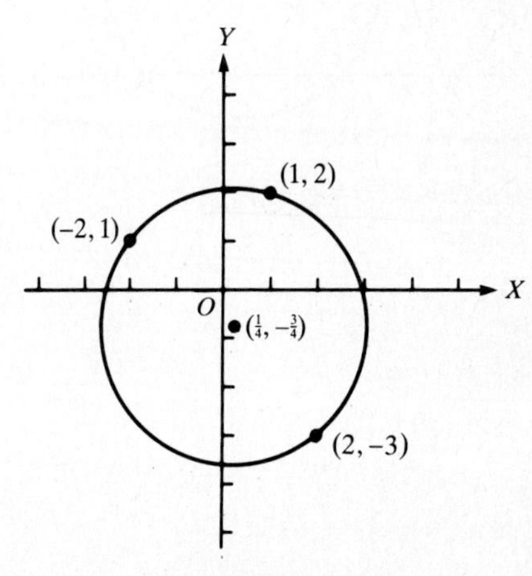

Figure 4-3

EXAMPLE 4-8: Find the equation of the circle passing through the points $(1, -2)$ and $(5, 3)$ and having its center on the line $x - y + 2 = 0$.

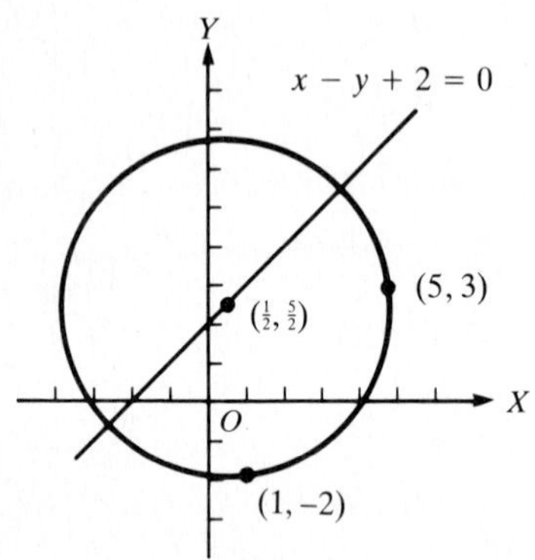

Figure 4-4

Solution: Given the equation of the line on which the center falls (aha! a shot at the radius!), choose the standard form (4-1). Substitute the given points to obtain two of the equations in h, k, and r:

$$(1 - h)^2 + (-2 - k)^2 = r^2$$

and

$$(5 - h)^2 + (3 - k)^2 = r^2$$

Then you can set up the third equation by substituting the coordinates of the center (h, k) into the equation of the line. You can do this because the line passes through the center of the circle; i.e., the center (h, k) is a point on the line, so the coordinates of (h, k) must satisfy the equation of the line. Thus

$$h - k + 2 = 0$$

Solving the three equations simultaneously for h, k, and r, you get $h = \frac{1}{2}$, $k = \frac{5}{2}$, and $r = \frac{1}{2}\sqrt{82}$ (see Figure 4-4). Therefore the required equation of the circle is

$$\left(x - \frac{1}{2}\right)^2 + \left(y - \frac{5}{2}\right)^2 = \left(\frac{\sqrt{82}}{2}\right)^2$$

or

$$x^2 + y^2 - x - 5y - 14 = 0$$

EXAMPLE 4-9: A circle is tangent to the line $2x - y + 1 = 0$ at the point $(2, 5)$, and the center of the circle falls on the line $x + y = 9$. What is the equation of the circle?

Solution: First, draw the graph that meets all the conditions given. Then draw the line r that passes through $(2, 5)$ perpendicular to the line $2x - y + 1 = 0$, so that r intersects $x + y = 9$ at the center of the circle, as shown in Figure 4-5. Now you're set up to find out more about r. Rearranging $2x - y + 1 = 0$ in the slope-intercept form (3-2), you have $y = mx + b = 2x + 1$; hence the slope of this line is 2. And since the slope of the line r, which is perpendicular to $2x - y + 1 = 0$, must have the negative reciprocal as its slope, the slope of r must be $-\frac{1}{2}$. Using this slope and the coordinates of the point $(2, 5)$ in the point-slope formula (3-1), you get

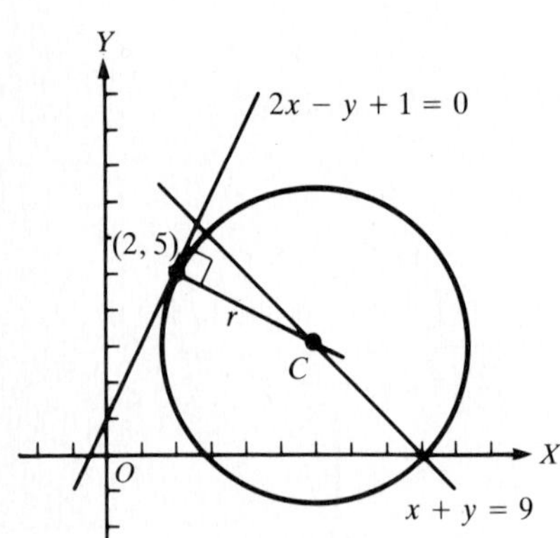

Figure 4-5

$$y - y_1 = m(x - x_1)$$

$$y - 5 = -\tfrac{1}{2}(x - 2)$$

so that $x + 2y = 12$ is the equation of the perpendicular line r. And the solution of the system

$$x + 2y = 12$$

$$x + y = 9$$

gives you the coordinates of the center, $C(6, 3)$. Finally, the distance d from point $C(6, 3)$ to $(2, 5)$—that is, the radius r of the circle—can be found from eq. (1-2):

$$\begin{aligned} r = d &= \sqrt{(x_2 - x_1)^2 + (y_2 - y_1)^2} \\ &= \sqrt{(6 - 2)^2 + (3 - 5)^2} \\ &= \sqrt{20} \end{aligned}$$

Thus, the equation of the circle can be written in standard form:

$$(x - 6)^2 + (y - 3)^2 = (\sqrt{20})^2 = 20$$

4-5. Families of Circles

A. Family of intersecting circles: $k \neq -1$

Given two fixed points, we can (if we are so disposed) draw a circle through them. We can, in fact, draw any number of circles through those same two points, thereby creating a family of circles defined by their mutual intersections. And we can write a relationship that describes this family of circles. Consider the equations of two intersecting circles, C_1 and C_2:

$$C_1: \quad x^2 + y^2 + D_1x + E_1y + F_1 = 0$$

$$C_2: \quad x^2 + y^2 + D_2x + E_2y + F_2 = 0$$

Then if we take k as a parameter, we can take the sum of the given equations to get the equation of the family of circles:

FAMILY OF CIRCLES

$$x^2 + y^2 + D_1x + E_1y + F_1 + k(x^2 + y^2 + D_2x + E_2y + F_2) = 0 \quad \textbf{(4-3)}$$

By collecting terms, we can rewrite eq. (4-3) in the form

$$(1 + k)x^2 + (1 + k)y^2 + (D_1 + kD_2)x + (E_1 + kE_2)y + F_1 + kF_2 = 0$$

which we recognize as the equation of a circle for every value of k—except $k = -1$.

Since we have a different circle whenever the value of k is changed, we can say that $C_1 = kC_2 = 0$ is the equation of a *family of circles.* Furthermore, *each* circle of this family will pass through the intersections of the given circles, because any pair of x and y values that will satisfy both $C_1 = 0$ and $C_2 = 0$ must likewise satisfy a particular $C_1 + kC_2 = 0$. And finally, if $C_1 = kC_2 = 0$ is the equation of a family of circles through the intersection of $C_1 = 0$ and $C_2 = 0$, then it doesn't matter *which* of the given circles is multiplied by the arbitrary constant.

Since we have already imposed two conditions on any circle of the family, namely, that it go through the two points that are the intersections of the given circles, we need only one further condition, or piece of information (a point or distance), in order to find the value of k—and hence the equation of a particular circle of the family.

note: A family of circles is defined by any two of the three conditions that define a specific circle. (See Example 4-4.)

EXAMPLE 4-10: **(a)** Find the equation of the circle that crosses the Y-axis at $(0, -4)$ and passes through the intersections of circles C_1 and C_2:

$$C_1: \quad x^2 + y^2 - 2x - 2y - 2 = 0$$

$$C_2: \quad x^2 + y^2 + 4x - 6y + 4 = 0$$

(b) Draw the three circles.

Solution:

(a) Letting k be a parameter of C_2, express the family of circles by eq. (4-3):

$$x^2 + y^2 - 2x - 2y - 2 + k(x^2 + y^2 + 4x - 6y + 4) = 0$$

Since the particular circle in which you're interested passes through the point $(0, -4)$, you can substitute these values of x and y into the equation to find the value of k:

$$44k + 22 = 0 \quad \text{or} \quad k = -\tfrac{1}{2}$$

Substituting this value of k into the equation of the family of circles and simplifying, you get the equation of the third circle:

$$x^2 + y^2 - 8x + 2y - 8 = 0$$

(b) Change the equations for C_1 and C_2 to standard form to find their centers and radii. Graph these two circles; then use their intersections and point $(0, -4)$ to draw $C_1 + kC_2$, as shown in Figure 4-6.

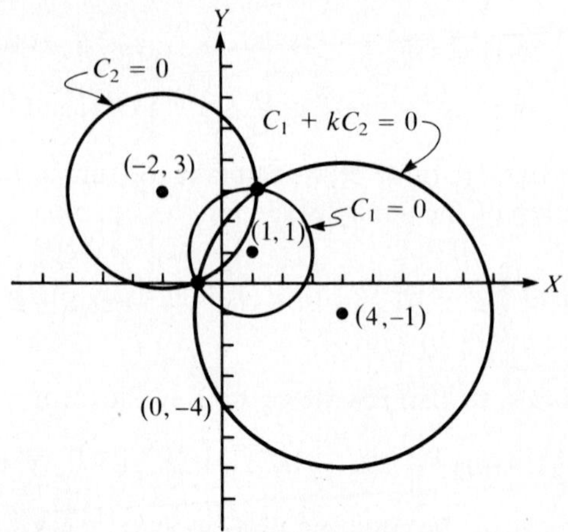

Figure 4-6. Family of circles: $C_1 = kC_2 = 0$.

$C_1 = 0$: $\quad x^2 + y^2 - 2x - 2y - 2 = 0$

$$(x^2 - 2x + 1) + (y^2 - 2y + 1) = 2 + 1 + 1$$

$$(x - 1)^2 + (y - 1)^2 = 2^2$$

$C_2 = 0$: $\quad x^2 + y^2 + 4x - 6y + 4 = 0$

$$(x + 2)^2 + (y - 3)^2 = 3^2$$

EXAMPLE 4-11: Find the equation of the circle that passes through the intersections of the circles $x^2 + y^2 - 4x + 2y = 0$ and $x^2 + y^2 = 4$ and through point (2, 1).

Solution: From eq. (4-3)

$$x^2 + y^2 - 4x + 2y + k(x^2 + y^2 - 4) = 0$$

Substitute (2, 1) into the equation to find k:

$$(-1) + k(1) = 0 \qquad \text{or} \qquad k = 1$$

Substitute $k = 1$ into the equation of the family of circles and simplify to get the equation of the particular circle:

$$x^2 + y^2 - 2x + y - 2 = 0$$

B. Radical axis of two circles: $k = -1$

In developing the equation for the family of circles passing through the intersection of two given circles, we excluded the value $k = -1$ as a parameter. We did this because when $k = -1$, the particular equation $C_1 + kC_2 = 0$ becomes $C_1 - C_2 = 0$ and assumes a *linear* form:

RADICAL AXIS OF TWO CIRCLES

$$(D_1 - D_2)x + (E_1 - E_2)y + F_1 - F_2 = 0 \qquad \textbf{(4-4)}$$

Since this equation is first-degree in x and y, it always represents a straight line called the **radical axis of two circles.**

The radical axis is a real line and may be plotted for any two circles that are not concentric. Thus, even if two circles have no real points in common, they may still have a radical axis. If two circles intersect at real points, the radical axis is called the *common chord*; and if the circles are tangent, it is called the *common tangent.*

EXAMPLE 4-12: (**a**) Find the radical axis of the circles

$$x^2 + y^2 + 4x + 2y - 1 = 0$$

and

$$x^2 + y^2 - 8x - 4y + 12 = 0$$

(**b**) Draw the circles and the radical axis.

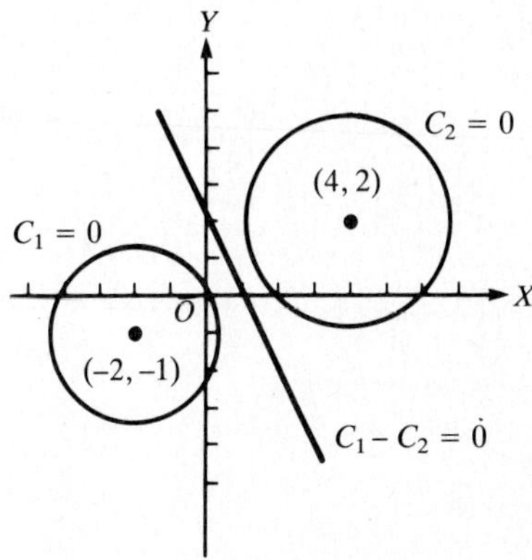

Figure 4-7

Solution:

(**a**) Call the second equation C_2 and subtract it from the first (C_1) to get

$$C_1 - C_2 = 12x + 6y - 13 = 0$$

as the equation of the radical axis.

(**b**) Figure 4-7 shows the circles (plotted from the standard forms of the given equations) and the line (plotted from the equation of the radical axis.)

SUMMARY

1. A circle is the locus of a point in a plane that moves in such a way that its distance from a fixed point is always a constant.
2. The standard form of the equation of a circle is

$$(x - h)^2 + (y - k)^2 = r^2$$

3. If the center of the circle is at the origin, the standard form of the equation reduces to $x^2 + y^2 = r^2$.
4. The general form of the equation of a circle is

$$x^2 + y^2 + Dx + Ey + F = 0$$

5. Every equation of the second degree in x and y, in which the xy term is missing and the coefficients of the x^2 and y^2 terms are the same, is the equation of a circle.
6. An equation of a circle in general form can be changed to standard form by completing the squares.
7. To obtain the equation of any particular circle, you need to set up three independent equations from which the values of three arbitrary constants (h, k, r or D, E, F) can be found. (These equations are the analytic expressions of *conditions* that the circle must satisfy.)
8. The equation that represents the family of circles is

$$x^2 + y^2 + D_1x + E_1y + F_1 + k(x^2 + y^2 + D_2x + E_2y + F_2) = 0$$

9. The equation for finding the radical axis of two circles is

$$(D_1 - D_2)x + (E_1 - E_2)y + F_1 - F_2 = 0$$

RAISE YOUR GRADES

Can you . . . ?

☑ determine the equation of a circle, given the coordinates of its center and its radius
☑ change the equation of a circle to the standard form and graph the circle
☑ find the equation of a circle, given the coordinates of its center and of a point through which it passes
☑ find the equation of a circle, given the coordinates of the end points of its diameter
☑ write the equation of a circle that passes through three given points
☑ find the equation of a circle passing through two given points and having its center on a line whose equation is known
☑ find the equation of a circle that is tangent to a given line (at a given point) and whose center lies on a given line
☑ find the equation of the family of circles that pass through the intersections of two circles whose equations are known
☑ find the equation of a circle that passes through the intersections of two circles whose equations are known and a given point
☑ find the radical axis of two given circles

SOLVED PROBLEMS

Standard Equation of a Circle

PROBLEM 4-1 Find the equation of the circle with center at $(2, -1)$ and radius 5.

Solution: Since $h = 2$, $k = -1$, and $r = 5$, the equation of the circle can be obtained directly by substituting these values into the standard form of the equation of a circle (4-1). Thus

$$(x - h)^2 + (y - k)^2 = r^2$$

$$(x - 2)^2 + (y + 1)^2 = 5^2$$

General Equation of a Circle

PROBLEM 4-2 Change $3x^2 + 6x + 3y^2 - 8y = 48$ to standard form, and give the radius of the circle and the coordinates of its center.

Solution: Dividing each member of the given equation by the coefficient of x^2, you get $x^2 + 2x + y^2 - 8y/3 = 16$. Then rearrange, and complete the square of each quadratic expression by adding the square of one-half of the coefficient of the proper first-degree term and adding same to the right-hand side:

$$x^2 + 2x + 1^2 + y^2 - \frac{8y}{3} + \left(-\frac{4}{3}\right)^2 = 16 + 1^2 + \frac{16}{9}$$

Then collect terms and put the equation in standard form (4-1):

$$(x+1)^2 + \left(y - \frac{4}{3}\right)^2 = \left(\frac{13}{3}\right)^2$$

Hence the radius is $\frac{13}{3}$ and the center is at $(-1, \frac{4}{3})$.

PROBLEM 4-3 Describe the circle represented by $x^2 + 2x + y^2 - 4y + 5 = 0$.

Solution: Completing the squares of the quadratics, you have

$$(x+1)^2 + (y-2)^2 = -5 + 1 + 4 = 0$$

Since $r^2 = 0$, the given equation is a point circle at $(-1, 2)$.

PROBLEM 4-4 Describe the circle represented by $x^2 + 2x + y^2 - 4y + 7 = 0$.

Solution: Completing the squares of the quadratics, you get

$$(x+1)^2 + (y-2)^2 = -7 + 1 + 4 = -2$$

Since $r^2 < 0$, the equation represents an imaginary circle.

Conditions That Determine a Circle

PROBLEM 4-5 Find the equation of the circle that passes through the points $(1, -2)$, $(3, -4)$, and $(5, 0)$.

Solution: Since you have no distance data, you choose the general form (4-2), which has the arbitrary constants D, E, and F. Now you want to set up three independent equations in these constants. If the circle is to pass through the point $(1, -2)$, the equation must be satisfied when $x = 1$ and $y = -2$. Making these substitutions, you get one linear equation:

$$1^2 + (-2)^2 + D(1) + E(-2) + F = D - 2E + F + 5 = 0$$

Similarly, using the points $(3, -4)$ and $(5, 0)$, you get two more linear equations:

$$3D - 4E + F + 25 = 0$$

$$5D \qquad + F + 25 = 0$$

Solving these three linear equations simultaneously gives you the values of the three constants:

$$D = -\frac{20}{3}, \qquad E = \frac{10}{3}, \qquad \text{and} \qquad F = \frac{25}{3}$$

Substitute these values into the general equation:

$$x^2 + y^2 - \frac{20}{3}x + \frac{10}{3}y + \frac{25}{3} = 0$$

So the equation of the circle is

$$3x^2 + 3y^2 - 20x + 10y + 25 = 0$$

PROBLEM 4-6 Find the equation of the circle that passes through $(-2, 3)$ and $(1, 4)$ in such a way that its center is on the line $3x + 4y = 5$.

Solution: Graph the given data: the center of the circle (h, k) on the line $3x + 4y = 5$ and the circle through $(-2, 3)$ and $(1, 4)$, as shown in Figure 4-8. This (possibly unnecessary) graph is a good way to see that you'll want to find the values of the standard-form constants h, k, and r. It shows you plainly that the coordinates of the point on the given line that is equidistant from the two given points must be the coordinates of the center (h, k), which is the same distance from *all* points on the

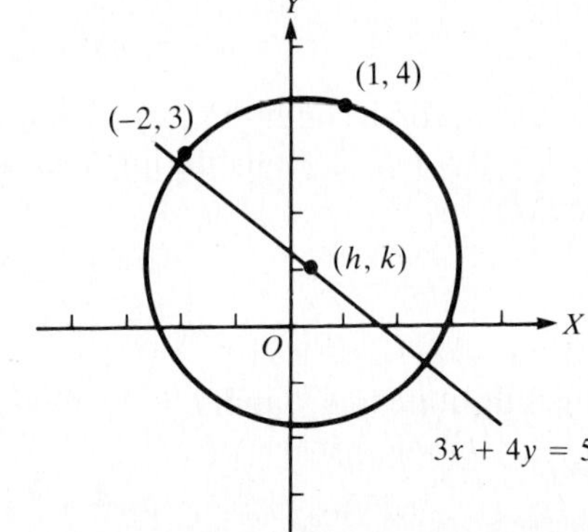

Figure 4-8

circle. Now you can set up two equations. Since (h, k) is on $3x + 4y = 5$,

$$3h + 4k = 5 \tag{1}$$

Also, since (h, k) is equidistant from $(-2, 3)$ and $(1, 4)$, the distance formula (1-2) gives you

$$\sqrt{(h + 2)^2 + (k - 3)^2} = \sqrt{(h - 1)^2 + (k - 4)^2}$$

Squaring, collecting terms, and dividing by 2, you get

$$3h + k = 2 \tag{2}$$

If you solve eqs. (1) and (2) for h and k, you find that $h = \frac{1}{3}$ and $k = 1$. (Two constants down, one to go!)

Now, using $(\frac{1}{3}, 1)$ as the coordinates of the center and $(1, 4)$ as the coordinates of one point on the circle, you can find the radius r by eq. (4-1):

$$r^2 = (x - h)^2 + (y - k)^2$$

$$r = \sqrt{\left(1 - \frac{1}{3}\right)^2 + (4 - 1)^2} = \frac{\sqrt{85}}{3}$$

You now have the values of all three constants, so the equation of the circle is

$$\left(x - \frac{1}{3}\right)^2 + (y - 1)^2 = \left(\frac{\sqrt{85}}{3}\right)^2 = \frac{85}{9}$$

Families of Circles

PROBLEM 4-7 **(a)** Find the equation of the family of circles in which each circle has radius 5 and center on the line $x = -2$. **(b)** Find the particular member(s) of this family that must pass through $(2, -5)$.

Solution:

(a) Here you know that $h = -2$ and you're given $r = 5$, so the standard form (eq. 4-1) becomes the equation of a one-parameter family of circles:

$$(x + 2)^2 + (y - k)^2 = 5^2 = 25$$

(b) Substituting $x = 2$ and $y = -5$ into the equation of the family of circles gives you $k = -2$ or -8, so there are two circles meeting the extra condition:

$$(x + 2)^2 + (y + 2)^2 = 25 \qquad \text{and} \qquad (x + 2)^2 + (y + 8)^2 = 25$$

PROBLEM 4-8 **(a)** Find the equation of the family of circles in which each circle is tangent to the line $x = 2$ and passes through $(3, 0)$. **(b)** Find the equation(s) of the member(s) that must go through $(4, 0)$.

Solution:

(a) The first condition (tangency to $x = 2$) requires that $r = h - 2$ or $r = 2 - h$. Either way, you get the following equation in two parameters:

$$(x - h)^2 + (y - k)^2 = (h - 2)^2 \tag{1}$$

By the second condition, $x = 3$ and $y = 0$ must satisfy **(1)**; so you can find h in terms of k: $h = (k^2 + 5)/2$. Substituting this value of h into **(1)** yields the equation of the family of circles:

$$\left(x - \frac{k^2 + 5}{2}\right)^2 + (y - k)^2 = \left(\frac{k^2 + 1}{2}\right)^2 \tag{2}$$

(b) Substitute $x = 4$ and $y = 0$ into **(2)**:

$$\left(4 - \frac{k^2 + 5}{2}\right)^2 + (0 - k)^2 = \left(\frac{k^2 + 1}{2}\right)^2$$

Clearing fractions in the first binomial term

$$\left(\frac{8 - k^2 + 5}{2}\right)^2 + k^2 = \left(\frac{k^2 + 1}{2}\right)^2$$

rewriting the two denominators outside the parentheses

$$\tfrac{1}{4}(3 - k^2)^2 + k^2 = \tfrac{1}{4}(k^2 + 1)^2$$

multiplying through by 4

$$(3 - k^2)^2 + 4k^2 = (k^2 + 1)^2$$

and, finally, expanding the binomial terms, you get

$$9 - 6k^2 + k^4 + 4k^2 = k^4 + 2k^2 + 1$$

$$4k^2 = 8$$

$$k = \pm\sqrt{2}$$

Use this value of k to solve for h and r^2:

$$h = \frac{(\sqrt{2})^2 + 5}{2} = \frac{7}{2} \quad \text{and} \quad r^2 = \left(\frac{7}{2} - 2\right)^2 = \frac{9}{4}$$

Thus the two special members of the family that meet the third condition are

$$\left(x - \frac{7}{2}\right)^2 + (y \pm \sqrt{2})^2 = \frac{9}{4}$$

PROBLEM 4-9 Find the equation of the two-parameter family of circles whose centers are on the line $3x - 4y = 6$.

Solution: The condition requires that $3h - 4k = 6$, or $k = (3h - 6)/4$. Using the standard form, you get the desired equation:

$$(x - h)^2 + (y - k)^2 = r^2$$

$$(x - h)^2 + \left(y - \frac{3h - 6}{4}\right)^2 = r^2$$

note: You can also write an equation for this family of circles by solving for h instead of k.

PROBLEM 4-10 Find the equation of the common chord of the two circles $C_1 = x^2 + y^2 + 3x - 2y - 7 = 0$ and $C_2 = x^2 + y^2 - x - y + 2 = 0$.

Solution: Since $C_1 - C_2 = 0$ when $k = -1$, you can simply subtract the second equation from the first to find the linear equation $4x - y - 9 = 0$, which is the straight line between two circles intersecting at real points.

PROBLEM 4-11 Find the points of intersection of the circles $x^2 + y^2 - 25 = 0$ and $x^2 + y^2 + x + y - 20 = 0$.

Solution: It's easiest to begin by solving from the radical axis (by subtracting the second equation from the first); this gives you $x + y + 5 = 0$. Then for y you get $y = -x - 5$. Substituting this value of y into the equation of the first circle yields

$$x^2 + (-x - 5)^2 - 25 = 0$$

$$x^2 + 5x = 0$$

so that $x = \{0, -5\}$. Substituting these values of x alternately into the equation of the radical axis, you get $y = \{-5, 0\}$. Thus the points of intersection are $(0, -5)$ and $(-5, 0)$.

Supplementary Exercises

PROBLEM 4-12 Find the equation of the circle with center at $(3, 4)$ and radius 2.

PROBLEM 4-13 Find the equation of the circle with center at $(2, 1)$ and radius 3.

PROBLEM 4-14 Find the equation of the circle for which $(h, k) = (4, -1)$ and $r = 4$.

PROBLEM 4-15 Find the radius and center of the circle $x^2 + y^2 - 2x + 4y - 4 = 0$.

PROBLEM 4-16 Find the radius and center of the circle $x^2 + y^2 - 4x - 6y - 12 = 0$.

PROBLEM 4-17 The equation of a circle is $x^2 + y^2 + 4x - 10y + 29 = 0$. Find its radius and the coordinates of its center.

PROBLEM 4-18 Find the equation of the circle that has center $(2, 3)$ and passes through $(5, -1)$.

PROBLEM 4-19 A circle has its center at $(6, -2)$ and passes through the point $(4, 0)$. What is its equation?

PROBLEM 4-20 If a circle has its center at $(-1, 3)$ and passes through the point $(0, 3)$, what is its equation?

PROBLEM 4-21 Write the equation for the circle in which the line segment joining $(-1, 5)$ and $(-5, -7)$ is a diameter.

PROBLEM 4-22 Write the equation of the circle in which the line segment joining the points $(-3, -4)$ and $(4, 3)$ is a diameter.

PROBLEM 4-23 What is the equation of a circle that is tangent to the Y-axis and whose center is at $(5, 3)$?

PROBLEM 4-24 A circle is tangent to the X-axis and $(h, k) = (-3, -4)$. What is its equation?

PROBLEM 4-25 Reduce the equation $x^2 + y^2 + 6x - 4y - 12 = 0$ to the center-radius (standard) form.

PROBLEM 4-26 Reduce the equation $x^2 + y^2 - 10x + 4y - 7 = 0$ to the center-radius form.

PROBLEM 4-27 Determine whether the equation $x^2 + y^2 - 6x + 2y + 10 = 0$ represents a real, imaginary, or point circle.

PROBLEM 4-28 Determine whether the equation $x^2 + y^2 + 4x - 8y - 5 = 0$ represents a real, imaginary, or point circle.

PROBLEM 4-29 Find the equation of the circle that is tangent to the line $x - y = 2$ at the point $(4, 2)$ and whose center is on the X-axis.

PROBLEM 4-30 Find the equation of the circle that is tangent to the line $x + 2y = 3$ at the point $(-1, 2)$ and whose center is on the Y-axis.

PROBLEM 4-31 Write an equation for the member of the family of circles passing through the intersection of the circles

$$x^2 + y^2 - 2x - 24 = 0 \qquad \text{and} \qquad x^2 + y^2 + 6x + 2y + 6 = 0$$

for which $k = 1$.

PROBLEM 4-32 Find the equation of the line passing through the points of intersection of the circles

$$x^2 + y^2 - 4x + 2y - 4 = 0 \qquad \text{and} \qquad x^2 + y^2 + 4x = 0$$

PROBLEM 4-33 Find the equation of the radical axis of the circles

$$x^2 + y^2 + 4x + 8y + 16 = 0 \qquad \text{and} \qquad x^2 + y^2 - 10y + 16 = 0$$

Answers to Supplementary Exercises

4-12: $(x-3)^2+(y-4)^2=4$

4-13: $(x-2)^2+(y-1)^2=9$

4-14: $(x-4)^2+(y+1)^2=16$

4-15: $r=3; (h,k)=(1,-2)$

4-16: $r=5; (h,k)=(2,3)$

4-17: $r=0; (h,k)=(-2,5)$

4-18: $(x-2)^2+(y-3)^2=25$

4-19: $(x-6)^2+(y+2)^2=8$

4-20: $(x+1)^2+(y-3)^2=1$

4-21: $(x+3)^2+(y+1)^2=40$

4-22: $(x-\frac{1}{2})^2+(y+\frac{1}{2})^2=\frac{49}{2}$

4-23: $(x-5)^2+(y-3)^2=25$

4-24: $(x+3)^2+(y+4)^2=16$

4-25: $(x+3)^2+(y-2)^2=25$

4-26: $(x-5)^2+(y+2)^2=36$

4-27: point circle

4-28: real circle

4-29: $(x-6)^2+y^2=8$

4-30: $x^2+(y-4)^2=5$

4-31: $x^2+y^2+2x+y-9=0$

4-32: $4x-y+2=0$

4-33: $2x+9y=0$

5 THE PARABOLA

THIS CHAPTER IS ABOUT

☑ Definition and Construction of the Parabola
☑ Standard Equations of the Parabola
☑ Other Equations of the Parabola
☑ Symmetry Theorems
☑ Properties of a Parabola: Applications

5-1. Definition and Construction of the Parabola

The parabola, like the circle, is one of the conic-section curves, which are described by second-degree (quadratic) equations in two variables.

- A **parabola** is the locus of a point in a plane that moves so that its distance from a fixed point is always equal to its distance from a fixed straight line.

The fixed point of the parabola is called the **focus** and the fixed line is the **directrix** of the parabola.

To construct a parabola, we let F be the given point (the *focus*) and DD' be the given line (the *directrix*). We can then draw a line through F perpendicular to DD' at C and let V be the midpoint of the segment CF, as shown in Figure 5-1a. Since the midpoint is equidistant from points C and F, point V is, by definition, a point of the parabola.

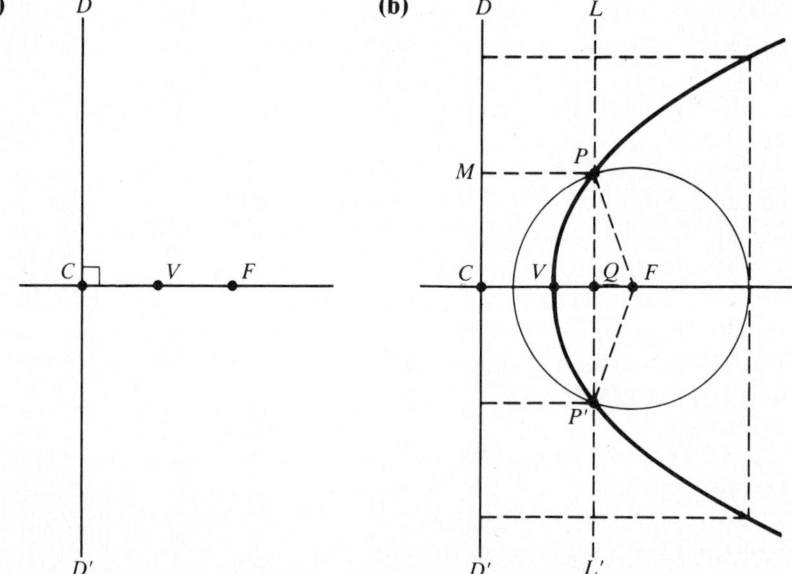

Figure 5-1. Construction of a parabola: (**a**) $CV = FV$; (**b**) $FP = CQ = MP$, etc.

To construct other points on the parabola, we draw a line LL' parallel to the directrix DD' through any point Q, so that Q lies on the segment CF and to the right of V. Then, using F as a center, we draw a circle with radius r

equal to the distance between C and Q. This circle intersects LL' at two points, P and P', as shown in Figure 5-1b. Now we know that since $r = FP = CQ = MP$, the point P is equidistant from the focus and the directrix. Therefore P lies on the parabola. And since $P'F = FP$, point P' is also on the parabola. This procedure can be repeated indefinitely.

The line through C and F (a line of symmetry) is called the *axis* of the parabola. The point V, where the curve intersects the axis, is called the *vertex* of the parabola.

5-2. Standard Equations of the Parabola

A. Standard forms: $V = (0, 0)$

The simplest form of the equation of a parabola is obtained by using one of the coordinate axes as the axis of the parabola and the origin as the vertex. So, if we start with a given parabola, as in Figure 5-2, we can let F have the coordinates $(a, 0)$ and $V = (0, 0)$. Then, since $|CV| = |VF|$, where C is on the directrix and the midpoint V is on the parabola, we can set $VF = a$ and $VC = -a$. So the equation of the directrix is $x = -a$. Similarly, for any point $P(x, y)$, you know that $|FP| = |MP|$ so

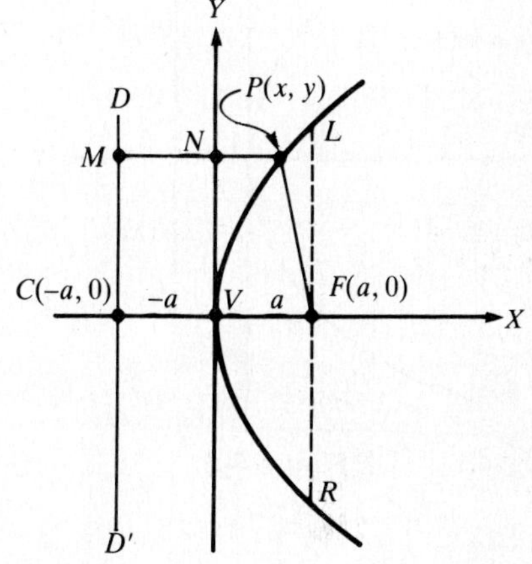

Figure 5-2. Standard equation of an X-parabola: $y^2 = 4ax$.

$$|FP| = \sqrt{(x - a)^2 + (0 - y)^2}$$

and

$$|MP| = x + a$$

Equating the right-hand members of these equations, squaring, and simplifying,

$$(x - a)^2 + y^2 = (x + a)^2$$

$$x^2 - 2ax + a^2 + y^2 = x^2 + 2ax + a^2$$

we get the standard equation of a parabola whose axis is on the X-axis:

X-PARABOLA, $V = (0, 0)$: STANDARD FORM

$$y^2 = 4ax \qquad \textbf{(5-1)}$$

This is the equation we want because it is true for every point on the curve; conversely, it is *not* true for any other point, because for points that are not on the curve $|FP| \neq |MP|$.

The equation $y^2 = 4ax$ consists of only two terms—the square of y and a constant times x. Therefore it is satisfied by $x = y = 0$ and remains unchanged when y is replaced by $-y$. This tells us that the locus of the equation passes through the origin and is symmetric with respect to the X-axis.

If we reduce the equation (take the square root of both sides) to the form $y = \pm 2\sqrt{ax}$, we see that a and x must be of like sign in order for y to be real. And for each value of x, there must be two values of y—numerically equal but opposite in sign. These values of y increase as x increases. Hence the curve opens to the right when a is positive and to the left when a is negative, and extends indefinitely away from both coordinate axes.

When $x = a$, we find that $y = \pm 2a$. Therefore the length of the chord that passes through the focus perpendicular to the axis of the parabola is $4a$, which is the coefficient of x in the equation $y^2 = 4ax$. This chord is known by its Latin name, **latus rectum** (or, sometimes, **focal chord**), and is shown in Figure 5-2 by the line LR.

If the focus is taken at the point $(0, a)$ on the Y-axis, the equation of the parabola is

Y-PARABOLA, $V = (0, 0)$: STANDARD FORM

$$x^2 = 4ay \qquad \textbf{(5-2)}$$

which represents a parabola with the origin as its vertex $V(0, 0)$, the Y-axis as its axis, the point $F(0, a)$ as its focus, and the line $y + a = 0$ as the equation of its directrix. It opens up or down according to whether a is positive or negative, respectively.

B. Graphing the standard equation

We can plot eq. (5-1) or (5-2) by computing a table of values. However, if we just want a sketch, we can obtain it by drawing the curve through the vertex and the ends of the latus rectum.

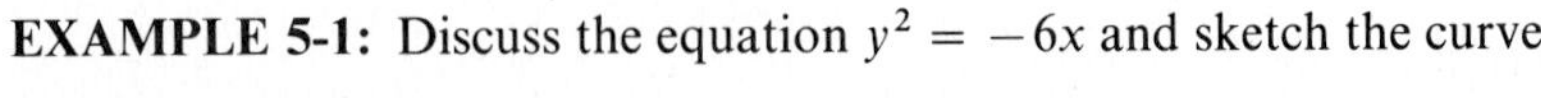

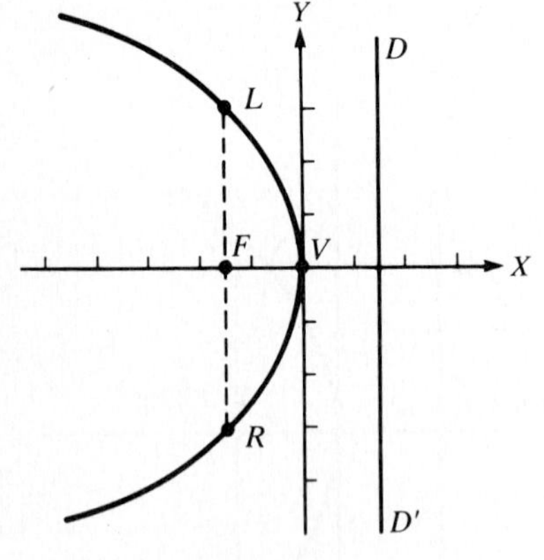

Figure 5-3

EXAMPLE 5-1: Discuss the equation $y^2 = -6x$ and sketch the curve.

Solution: The equation is satisfied by $x = y = 0$ and remains unchanged when $-y$ is substituted for y: Therefore, the curve passes through the origin $(0, 0)$ and is symmetric with respect to the X-axis. Comparing the equation with the standard form $y^2 = 4ax$, you see that $4a = -6$, or $a = -\frac{3}{2}$: Therefore, the curve has its focus at $(-\frac{3}{2}, 0)$ and opens to the left.

The equation of the directrix DD' is

$$x - \frac{3}{2} = 0 \qquad \text{or} \qquad 2x - 3 = 0$$

If $x = -\frac{3}{2}$, then $y = \pm 3$; so the coordinates of the end points of the latus rectum LR are $(-\frac{3}{2}, \pm 3)$ and the length of LR is six units. Knowing all these facts, you can easily draw the curve (see Figure 5-3).

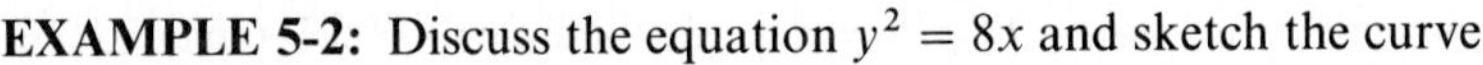

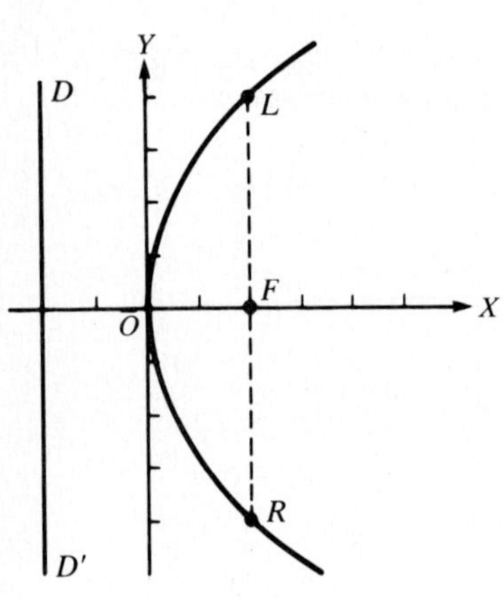

Figure 5-4

EXAMPLE 5-2: Discuss the equation $y^2 = 8x$ and sketch the curve.

Solution: Since you're given $y^2 = 8x$, you know that $4a = 8$, or $a = 2$. Therefore, the coordinates of the focus are $(2, 0)$. Substituting the x-coordinate of the focus into the equation of the curve gives you $y^2 = 8(2) = 16$; hence $y = \pm 4$. So, the coordinates of the latus rectum are $(2, \pm 4)$. And substituting $a = 2$ into the equation $x + a = 0$, you get $x + 2 = 0$ as the equation of the directrix. Your sketch of the equation should look like Figure 5-4.

EXAMPLE 5-3: A parabolic reflector is to be designed with a light source at its focus, which is $\frac{9}{4}$ inches from its vertex. If the reflector is to be 10 inches deep, how broad must it be and how far will the outer rim be from the source?

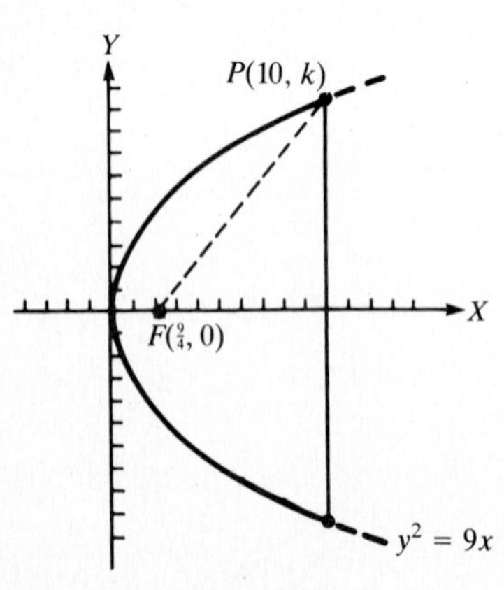

Figure 5-5

Solution:

(1) Draw a cross-sectional diagram of the reflector on a set of X,Y-axes, showing the vertex of the reflector's parabolic cross-section at the origin and the focus $\frac{9}{4}$ units from the vertex on the X-axis, so that $F = (\frac{9}{4}, 0)$, as shown in Figure 5-5.

(2) The standard equation for the parabola is $y^2 = 4ax$. So, since $a = \frac{9}{4}$, you can write $y^2 = 4(\frac{9}{4})x = 9x$. Hence the equation of the reflector's parabolic cross-section is $y^2 = 9x$.

(3) Since the reflector is to be 10 inches deep, you can designate a point on the parabola as $P(10, k)$, which represents the outer rim of the reflector. Substituting $x = 10$ and $y = k$ into the equation $y^2 = 9x$, you get $k^2 = 9(10) = 90$, or $k = \sqrt{90}$ inches. And since k is the distance from the outer rim to the axis, the total breadth is $2k = 2\sqrt{90}$ inches.

(4) By definition, the *focal radius* to any point on the curve of a parabola is equal to the distance of that point from the directrix; so you can find the distance of the point P (the outer rim) from the source (at the focus F) by this equality:

$$FP = x + a = 10 + \frac{9}{4} = \frac{49}{4} \text{ inches}$$

5-3. Other Equations of the Parabola

A. Standard forms: $V \neq (0, 0)$

Parabolas don't have to have vertices located at the origin (i.e., intersection of the coordinate axes)—it is possible to draw, and write a more general equation for, a parabola whose vertex is anywhere in the coordinate plane.

Starting with a parabola, as in Figure 5-6, we let the vertex of the desired parabola be at the point $O'(h, k)$ and take the line $O'X'$ parallel to the X-axis as its axis. Then we erect a perpendicular $O'Y'$ to this axis at O'. Now our parabola is referred to the axes $O'X'$ and $O'Y'$, so the equation of the parabola, with its focus a units from the vertex, is given by

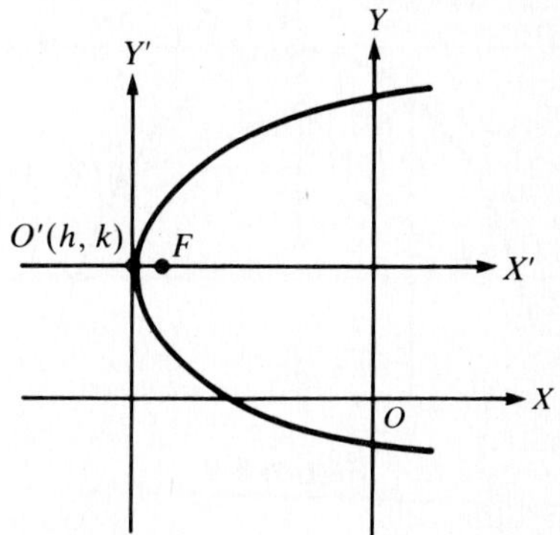

Figure 5-6. Parabola with vertex at (h, k).

$$(y')^2 = 4ax'$$

In order to find its equation with reference to the original axes, we make use of the translation formulas (2-1), so that

$$x' = x - h \quad \text{and} \quad y' = y - k$$

Making these substitutions, $(y')^2 = 4ax'$ becomes

X-PARABOLA, V = (h, k): STANDARD FORM
$$(y - k)^2 = 4a(x - h) \tag{5-3}$$

note: The curve opens to the right or the left according to whether a is positive or negative, respectively.

Similarly, if we draw a parabola $(x')^2 = 4ay'$, so that the axis is parallel to the Y-axis, we get

Y-PARABOLA, V = (h, k): STANDARD FORM
$$(x - h)^2 = 4a(y - k) \tag{5-4}$$

which is the equation of a parabola having the point (h, k) as its vertex, the line $x - h = 0$ as its axis, and a curve whose direction is determined by the sign of a.

B. General forms

If we expand eqs. (5-3) and (5-4), we can write the equations of the X- and Y-parabolas in general form:

X-PARABOLA GENERAL FORM
$$y^2 + Dx + Ey + F = 0 \tag{5-5a}$$

Y-PARABOLA GENERAL FORM
$$x^2 + Dx + Ey + F = 0 \tag{5-5b}$$

Conversely, any equation of the general form (5-5) may be reduced to one of the standard forms (5-3) or (5-4) by completing the square. Therefore,

- the equation $y^2 + Dx + Ey + F = 0$, where $D \neq 0$, represents a parabola with axis parallel to the X-axis; and
- the equation $x^2 + Dx + Ey + F = 0$, where $E \neq 0$, represents a parabola with axis parallel to the Y-axis.

But, when $D = 0$, eq. (5-5a) becomes $y^2 + Ey + F = 0$, which (by completing the square) may be written in the form $(2y + E)^2 = E^2 - 4F$. Hence the locus may consist of

- the line $2y + E = 0$ counted twice, if $E^2 - 4F = 0$.
- the pair of lines $2y = -E \pm \sqrt{E^2 - 4F}$ parallel to the X-axis, if $E^2 - 4F > 0$.
- an imaginary line, if $E^2 - 4F < 0$.

note: When $E = 0$, eq. (5-5b) can be written $(2x + D)^2 = E^2 - 4F$, so its loci will have the same forms as those of eq. (5-5a)—but a different axis.

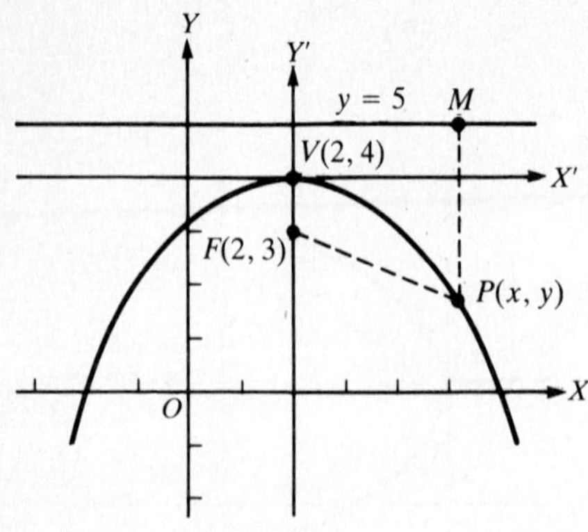

Figure 5-7

EXAMPLE 5-4: Find the equation of the parabola having the point $F(2, 3)$ as its focus and the line $y - 5 = 0$ as its directrix, as shown in Figure 5-7.

Solution: You know from the definition of a parabola that the point $P(x, y)$ must be equidistant from the focus $F(2, 3)$ and the point M on the directrix, so

$$|FP| = |MP|$$

or

$$\sqrt{(x-2)^2 + (y-3)^2} = y - 5$$

By squaring both sides and simplifying, you can write the equation of the parabola:

$$x^2 - 4x + 4 + y^2 - 6y + 9 = y^2 - 10y + 25$$

$$x^2 - 4x + 4y - 12 = 0$$

Alternative Solution: You know that the vertex of a parabola lies on its axis midway between the directrix and focus; therefore, the coordinates of the vertex of this parabola must be (2, 4). Since the focus (2, 3) of this particular parabola is two units below the directrix, the curve extends downward and $a = -1$. So the equation of the curve (referred to the lines through its vertex) is $(x')^2 = -4y'$. And since $h = 2$ and $k = 4$ (the coordinates of the vertex), this equation becomes

$$(x-2)^2 = -4(y-4) \qquad \text{or} \qquad x^2 - 4x + 4y - 12 = 0$$

when referred to the original axes.

C. Reduction to standard form

We can reduce the equation of a parabola in general form to one of the standard forms (5-3) or (5-4) by the following steps:

(1) Determine *which* standard form is wanted: If the second-degree term is in y, eq. (5-3) is wanted; if the second-degree term is in x, eq. (5-4) is wanted.

(2) Divide all the terms of the equation by the coefficient of the second-degree term if that coefficient is not equal to 1.

(3) Reduce the equation to standard form by completing the square.

EXAMPLE 5-5: Find the coordinates of the vertex and focus, the equations of the axis and directrix, and the length of the latus rectum of the parabola $2y^2 - 5x - 4y - 3 = 0$. Sketch the curve.

Solution: The second-degree term is in y, so we'll reduce the equation to the form of eq. (5-3). And since the coefficient of y^2 is 2, we divide all the terms of the equation by 2:

$$y^2 - \left(\frac{5}{2}\right)x - 2y - \frac{3}{2} = 0$$

Transposing all terms except those containing y to the left-hand side and completing the square, we get

$$y^2 - 2y + 1 = \left(\frac{5}{2}\right)x + \frac{3}{2} + 1$$

$$(y-1)^2 = \frac{5}{2}(x+1)$$

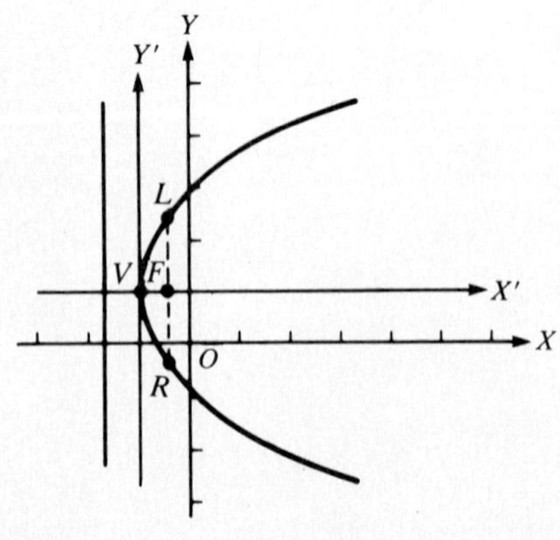

Figure 5-8

By comparing this equation with $(y - k)^2 = 4a(x - h)$, we see that the parabola has its axis parallel to the X-axis, opens to the right, and has its vertex at $(-1, 1)$, as shown in Figure 5-8. Also, since $4a = \frac{5}{2}$, we find that $a = \frac{5}{8}$; so the focus is at $(-1 + \frac{5}{8}, 1)$, or $(-\frac{3}{8}, 1)$. The equation of the axis is $y - 1 = 0$, and that of the directrix is $x = -1 - \frac{5}{8}$, or $8x + 13 = 0$. The length of the latus rectum is $\frac{5}{2}$ units; hence the coordinates of its end points are $(-\frac{3}{8}, 1 \pm \frac{5}{4})$, or $(-\frac{3}{8}, \frac{9}{4})$ and $(-\frac{3}{8}, -\frac{1}{4})$.

5-4. Symmetry Theorems

A. Symmetry revisited

The parabola must, by definition, be symmetric with respect to a line, but it cannot be symmetric with respect to the origin.

- A curve is symmetric with respect to a line L if, for each point A on the curve but not on L, there is a second point B on the curve, such that L is the perpendicular bisector of the segment AB. A curve is symmetric with respect to the origin O if O is the midpoint of the segment AB joining every pair of symmetric points A and B on the curve. (See Section 2-2B.)

In Figure 5-9a, for example, the parabola $y^2 = 4ax$ is symmetric with respect to the X-axis: For any point A (except O), there is another point B on the curve so that the X-axis is the perpendicular bisector of the segment AB. But the curve $y = x^3$, in Figure 5-9b, is symmetric with respect to the origin: The point O is the midpoint of every straight-line segment AB joining symmetrically located points A and B.

(a)

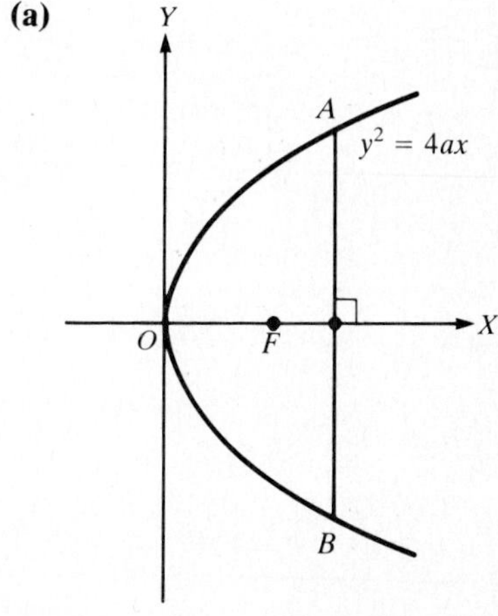

(b)

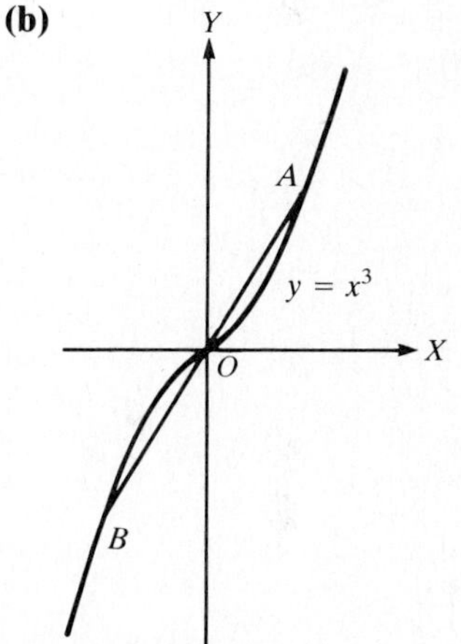

Figure 5-9. Symmetry: (**a**) Symmetry with respect to the X-axis; (**b**) symmetry with respect to the origin.

B. Symmetry theorems proved

We know that we can test the equation of a curve for symmetry with respect to an axis and symmetry with respect to the origin (see Section 2-2B). Now we can state these tests as theorems—and prove them.

Symmetry Theorem 1: *If the equation of a curve is unchanged when x is replaced by $-x$, the curve is symmetric with respect to the Y-axis. If the equation of a curve is unchanged when y is replaced by $-y$, the curve is symmetric with respect to the X-axis.*

Proof: Under the conditions given, if the equation is satisfied by a particular pair of values (x_1, y_1), it will also be satisfied by the coordinates of a second point $(-x_1, y_1)$. Furthermore, the Y-axis is the perpendicular bisector of the line segment joining $A(x_1, y_1)$ and $B(-x_1, y_1)$. Therefore the curve is symmetric with respect to the Y-axis.

Symmetry Theorem 2: *If the equation of a curve is unchanged when both x and y are replaced, respectively, by $-x$ and $-y$, the curve is symmetric with respect to the origin.*

Proof: In this case the second point used in the argument is $(-x, -y)$, and the origin is the midpoint of the line segment $A(x_1, y_1)B(-x_1, -y_1)$.

These theorems are helpful in plotting curves: When one part of a curve is obtained, any corresponding symmetric parts may be easily drawn.

note: An equation that has only *even* powers of one variable (such as x in $y = x^2$ or in $x^2y + x^4 = 1$) always indicates a curve that is symmetric with respect to a coordinate axis (the Y-axis in these examples). This condition is *sufficient* for such symmetry; but in the case of non-algebraic equations (such as $y = \cos x$), it is not *necessary*.

EXAMPLE 5-6: Test the equation $x^2 - 3x^2y + y^3 - 2 = 0$ for symmetry with respect to the origin and each coordinate axis.

Solution: Replacing both x and y by $-x$ and $-y$, respectively, we get

$$(-x)^2 - 3(-x)^2(-y) + (-y)^3 - 2 = 0$$
$$x^2 + 3x^2y - y^3 - 2 = 0$$

The equation is changed and so the curve is not symmetric with respect to the origin.

Replacing y with $-y$, we have

$$x^2 - 3x^2(-y) + (-y)^3 - 2 = 0$$
$$x^2 + 3x^2y - y^3 - 2 = 0$$

Again, the equation is changed and the curve is not symmetric with respect to the X-axis.

Finally, replacing x with $-x$ we get

$$(-x)^2 - 3(-x)^2y + y^3 - 2 = 0$$
$$x^2 - 3x^2y + y^3 - 2 = 0$$

so the curve is symmetric with respect to the Y-axis.

5-5. Properties of a Parabola: Applications

The parabola is a very practical curve: Its properties can be used to describe, explain, and predict many physical phenomena.

An object (such as a comet or a single stone) that falls toward the sun "from infinity" would travel in a parabola with the sun at its focus if there were no other bodies in the universe whose gravitational attraction might deflect its path. Moreover, projectiles in a vacuum on the surface of the earth travel in paths that are nearly parabolic, and projectiles in the air approximate this path with more or less precision (depending on their speed, shape, and weight).

Millions of parabolic surfaces are manufactured yearly to be used in automobile headlights, searchlights, reflecting telescopes, radar receivers, etc. Such surfaces are traced by a parabola that revolves upon its axis and hence are known as *paraboloids*. The paraboloid is important in devices that send or receive waves of any kind because of one simple property of the parabola:

- The angle FPT, where P is a point on the parabola with focus F and PT is parallel to OX, is exactly bisected by PN, which is the line *normal* to the curve at P. In other words, the angle FPT is exactly bisected by the line (PN) that is perpendicular to the line that can be drawn tangent to the curve at P. (See Figure 5-10.)

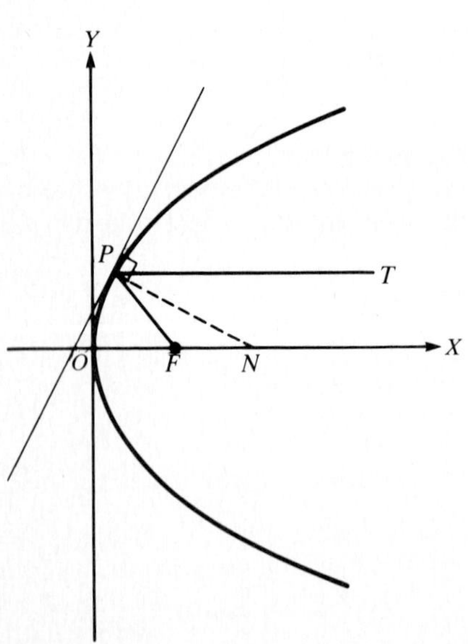

Figure 5-10. Reflective property of a parabola.

This property explains (to physicists) the familiar headlight effect: When a light source is placed at the focus F, the whole reflecting surface seems to be the source of light. Conversely, when the light comes from T to P to F, as in a reflecting telescope, the real image of the object viewed appears at F.

Another important role of the parabola derives from a principle of mechanics: The main cable of a suspension bridge would assume the form of a parabola—if the cable were perfectly flexible and of negligible mass and if the weight of the bridge were distributed uniformly per unit of horizontal length. Although these conditions are not met in practice, the approximation is sufficiently close to make knowledge of the properties of a parabola useful in construction designs for suspension bridges. Similarly, a somewhat analogous mechanical principle—acting in reverse—dictates the use of parabolic arches in certain construction problems rather than, say, semicircular ones.

EXAMPLE 5-7: The ends of a bridge suspension cable are 1000 feet apart and 100 feet above the horizontal road bed, while the center of the cable is level with the roadbed. Assuming that the cable suspends a load of equal weight for equal horizontal distances, find the height of the cable above the roadbed at a distance of 300 feet from the base of the cable-support tower at either end (see Figure 5-11).

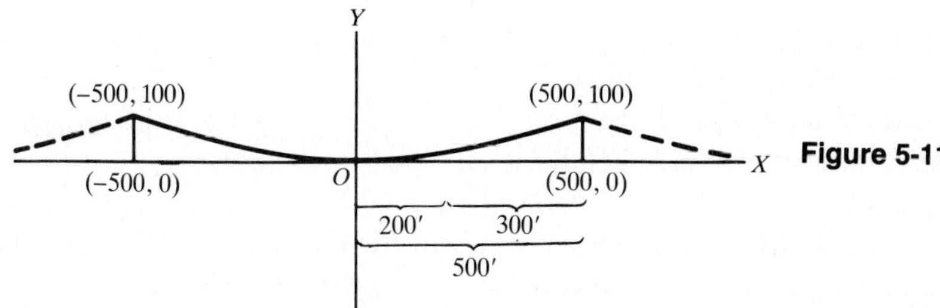

Figure 5-11

Solution: Since the cable (parabola) passes through the point (500, 100) while its center (vertex) is level with the roadbed (X-axis), you can substitute $(x, y) = (500, 100)$ into the standard equation for the parabola, $x^2 = 4ay$, where $V = (0,0)$ and the axis is the Y-axis. This gives you

$$(500)^2 = 4a(100) \qquad \text{or} \qquad 4a = \frac{250\,000}{100} = 2500.$$

and the equation for the parabola becomes

$$x^2 = 2500y \qquad \text{or} \qquad y = 0.0004x^2$$

So, when $x = 200$ (300 feet from the base of the support tower), the value of y is $y = 0.0004(200)^2$, or $y = 16$ feet.

SUMMARY

1. A parabola is the locus of a point that moves so that its distance from a fixed point, the focus, is always equal to its distance from a fixed straight line, the directrix.
2. The point at which a parabola intersects its axis is its vertex; the chord through the focus, perpendicular to the axis of the parabola, is the latus rectum, or focal chord. The length of the latus rectum $= 4a$.
3. There are two standard forms of the equation of a parabola whose vertex is at the origin: $y^2 = 4ax$ (symmetric with respect to the X-axis) and $x^2 = 4ay$ (symmetric with respect to the Y-axis).
4. There are two standard (translation) equations of the parabola whose vertex is not at the origin: $(y - k)^2 = 4a(x - h)$ and $(x - h)^2 = 4a(y - k)$, where (h, k) are the coordinates of the vertex.
5. The sign of a in the standard equations of the parabola determines the direction in which the curve extends: If a is positive, the curve opens to the right or up; if a is negative, the curve opens to the left or down.
6. There are two general forms of the equation of a parabola, derived by expanding the standard translation equations: $y^2 + Dx + Ey + F = 0$ and

$x^2 + Dx + Ey + F = 0$. The equation of a parabola in general form can be reduced to standard form by completing the square.

7. If the equation of a curve is unchanged when x is replaced by $-x$, or when y is replaced by $-y$, the curve is symmetric with respect to the Y-axis, or the X-axis, respectively.
8. If the equation of a curve is unchanged when both x and y are replaced by their negatives, the curve is symmetric with respect to the origin.

RAISE YOUR GRADES

Can you...?

☑ determine the axis of symmetry and the direction of the curve, given the equation of a parabola
☑ write the equation of the directrix, find the end points and length of the latus rectum, and sketch the curve of a parabola, given its equation
☑ find the equation of a parabola, given the coordinates of the focus and the equation of the directrix
☑ reduce the general form of the equation of a parabola to the standard form
☑ test an equation of second (or higher) degree for symmetry about the X- and Y-axes and the origin
☑ recognize the equation for a parabola in standard and general forms

SOLVED PROBLEMS

Standard Equations of the Parabola

PROBLEM 5-1 Discuss the equation $(x + 2)^2 = -8(y - 1)$ and sketch the curve.

Solution: Comparing the given equation with the standard (translation) form $(x - h)^2 = 4a(y - k)$, you see that it is a Y-parabola curve (i.e., its axis is parallel with the Y-axis) with vertex at $V(-2, 1)$. Then, since $4a = -8$, you know that $a = -2$, and so the focus F is two units below the vertex and $F = (-2, -1)$. The length of the latus rectum LR is $4a = -8$; so its ends lie four units to the right and four units to the left of the focus, and its coordinates are $L(-6, -1)$ and $R(2, -1)$. Finally, to sketch the curve quickly, you need to graph only the coordinates of the vertex, the focus, and the two ends of the latus rectum, as shown in Figure 5-12.

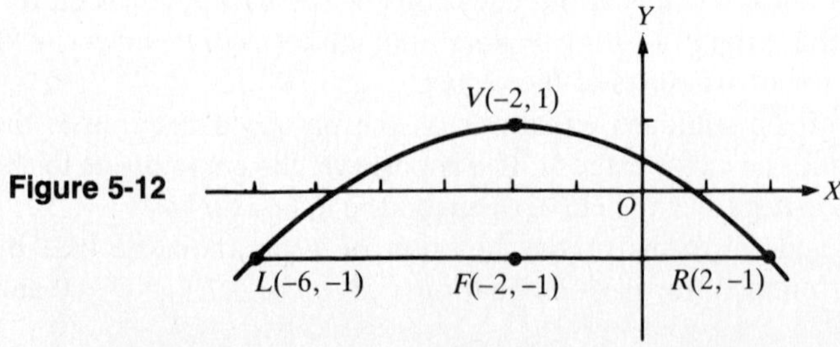

Figure 5-12

Other Equations of the Parabola

PROBLEM 5-2 Find the equation of the parabola with focus at $(-1, 2)$ and directrix $x = 1$.

Solution: Since the directrix is vertical and perpendicular to the axis, the curve is an X-parabola represented by the form $(y - k)^2 = 4a(x - h)$. So the problem consists of finding the unknowns h, k, and a.

The vertex (halfway between the focus and directrix) is at the point $(0, 2)$, so $h = 0$ and $k = 2$. Also, a must be negative (because the curve opens to the left) and equal to the distance from the focus to the vertex, so $a = -1$. Substituting $0, 2$, and -1 for h, k, and a, respectively, in the standard form (5-3), you get

$$(y - k)^2 = 4a(x - h)$$

$$(y - 2)^2 = -4(x - 0)$$

$$(y - 2)^2 = -4x$$

PROBLEM 5-3 Find the equation of the parabola with focus at the origin and directrix $2x + 3y + 6 = 0$ (see Figure 5-13).

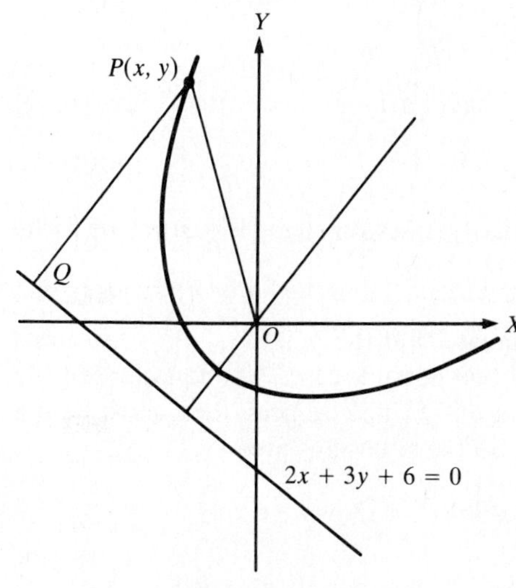

Figure 5-13

Solution: The axis of this parabola is not parallel to one of the coordinate axes, so neither of the standard forms is applicable. But you can derive the equation directly by using the definition of a parabola. By definition, $OP = QP$ in Figure 5-13. Then if you use the formulas for point-to-point (eq. 1-2) and line-to-point (eq. 3-8) distances, you can write the equation $OP = QP$ analytically:

$$\sqrt{x^2 + y^2} = \frac{2x + 3y + 6}{\sqrt{13}}$$

Square both sides

$$13x^2 + 13y^2 = 4x^2 + 12xy + 24x + 9y^2 + 36y + 36$$

and simplify to get the equation you want:

$$9x^2 - 12xy + 4y^2 - 24x - 36y - 36 = 0$$

note: This equation is of the general form

$$Ax^2 + Bxy + Cy^2 + Dx + Ey + F = 0$$

where $B \neq 0$. Except in the case of a circle, the xy term is always present when an axis of the conic section is not parallel to one of the coordinate axes.

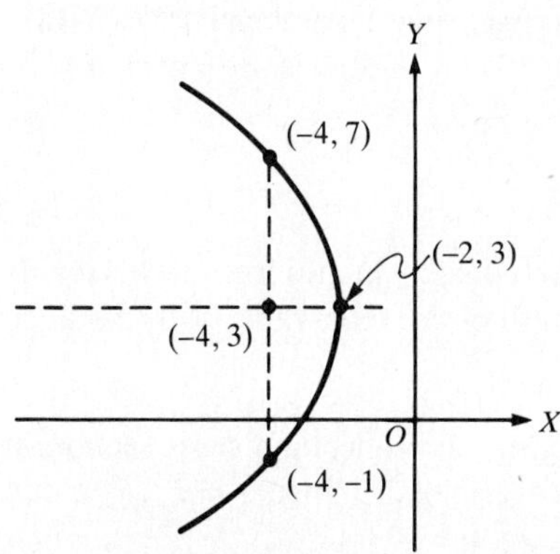

Figure 5-14

PROBLEM 5-4 Draw the graph of the following equation:

$$y^2 + 8x - 6y + 25 = 0$$

Solution: The equation represents a parabola because y appears as a second-degree term and x as a first-degree term. It will be easier to draw the graph if you reduce the equation to standard form by completing the square:

$$y^2 - 6y = -8x - 25$$

$$y^2 - 6y + 9 = -8x - 25 + 9$$

or

$$(y - 3)^2 = -8(x + 2)$$

Now you can see that the vertex is at $(-2, 3)$ and that $4a = -8$; so $a = -2$ and the focus is two units to the left of the vertex. The length of the latus rectum (being equal to the absolute value of $4a$) is eight units. Hence the latus rectum extends four units above and below the focus. Now you can draw the graph, as shown in Figure 5-14.

PROBLEM 5-5 Reduce the equation $3x^2 - 8x + 4y + 2 = 0$ to standard form and describe the parabola it represents.

Solution: Clear the coefficient of x^2 and complete the square:

$$3x^2 - 8x + 4y + 2 = 0$$

$$x^2 - \frac{8x}{3} + \frac{4y}{3} + \frac{2}{3} = 0$$

$$x^2 - \frac{8x}{3} + \frac{16}{9} = -\frac{4y}{3} - \frac{2}{3} + \frac{16}{9}$$

$$\left(x - \frac{4}{3}\right)^2 = -\frac{4y}{3} + \frac{10}{9}$$

$$\left(x - \frac{4}{3}\right)^2 = -\frac{4}{3}\left(y - \frac{5}{6}\right)$$

From this final form you can see that the given equation is that of a Y-parabola with vertex at $(\frac{4}{3}, \frac{5}{6})$ and with $a = -\frac{1}{3}$, so that it opens downward.

PROBLEM 5-6 Find the equation of the Y-parabola that passes through $(1, -3)$ whose focus is $(-2, 1)$.

Solution: From the distance formula (1-2), you can calculate that the point $(1, -3)$ is five units from the focus and hence also from the directrix in each of two possible cases. The equations of the directrices are therefore $y = -3 \pm 5$, so that $y = 2$ and $y = -8$. The vertices, then, must be the points $(-2, \frac{3}{2})$ when $a = -\frac{1}{2}$, and $(-2, -\frac{7}{2})$ when $a = \frac{9}{2}$. So the equations are

$$(x + 2)^2 = -2(y - \tfrac{3}{2}) \qquad \text{and} \qquad (x + 2)^2 = 18(y + \tfrac{7}{2})$$

note: The coordinates of the focus—like those of the vertex—supply in effect two of the necessary three conditions.

Symmetry Theorems

PROBLEM 5-7 Test the equation $x^8 - 1 = (y^2 - 1)(x^4 + 3)$ for symmetry.

Solution: Since both x and y appear only in even powers, their values will not be changed by substituting their negatives and hence the equation will not change. Therefore the given equation represents a curve that is symmetric with respect to the origin.

Properties of a Parabola: Applications

PROBLEM 5-8 A parabolic reflector has a light source at its focus, $2\frac{1}{4}$ inches from its vertex. If the reflector is 5 inches deep, how broad is it and what is the length of the focal radius (the distance from the focal point to the rim of the reflector)?

Solution: For the sake of simplicity, place the vertex of the parabolic reflector's cross-section at the origin and the focus at $(2\frac{1}{4}, 0)$ with symmetry about the X-axis. Then, since $a = 2\frac{1}{4}$, you can write

$$y^2 = 4ax = 4(\tfrac{9}{4})x = 9x$$

Since the reflector is 5 inches deep, you can designate a point on its outer rim as $(5, k)$. Substituting these coordinate values into the equation $y^2 = 9x$, you get $k^2 = 9(5) = 45$, so that $k = 3\sqrt{5}$, or $2k = 6\sqrt{5}$ inches for the breadth. The focal radius is given by $x + a$, or $5 + 2\frac{1}{4} = 7\frac{1}{4}$ inches.

Supplementary Exercises

PROBLEM 5-9 Determine the coordinates of the vertex V and the focus F, write the equation of the directrix DD', and find the length of the latus rectum LR for the following parabolas:

(a) $y^2 = 4x$ **(c)** $x^2 = 12y$
(b) $y^2 = -8x$ **(d)** $(x - 2)^2 = 12y$

PROBLEM 5-10 Find the equations of the parabolas that pass through the points given below. Assume $V = (0, 0)$, and use the X-axis as the axis of the parabola.

(a) $(3, 1)$ **(c)** $(4, 6)$
(b) $(-4, -5)$ **(d)** $(-2, -5)$

PROBLEM 5-11 Find the equations of the parabolas that pass through the points given below. Assume $V = (0, 0)$, and use the Y-axis as the axis of the parabola.

(a) $(-3, 3)$ **(c)** $(3, -5)$
(b) $(-3, -5)$ **(d)** $(3, -4)$

PROBLEM 5-12 Find the equations of the following parabolas by means of the definition.

(a) Focus at $(0, 2)$; directrix $y + 2 = 0$
(b) Focus at $(0, 0)$; directrix $4x - 6 = 0$
(c) Focus at $(-4, -5)$; directrix $3x + 4 = 0$

PROBLEM 5-13 Find the equations of the following parabolas:

(a) Focus at $(6, 8)$; directrix $y - 2 = 0$
(b) Focus at $(4, -2)$; directrix $x + 4 = 0$
(c) Focus at $(0, 0)$; vertex at $(-2, 0)$

PROBLEM 5-14 For the parabola $y^2 + 8y + 8x = 0$, find **(a)** the coordinates of the vertex, **(b)** the coordinates of the focus, **(c)** the coordinates of the ends of the latus rectum, **(d)** the equation of the axis, and **(e)** the equation of the directrix.

PROBLEM 5-15 Find the equations of the following parabolas:

(a) Vertex at $(3, 4)$, axis parallel to the X-axis, $a = 8$
(b) Vertex at $(1, 2)$, axis parallel to the X-axis, curve passing through $(3, -1)$
(c) Axis parallel to the X-axis, vertices at $(-2, -1)$, latus rectum five units in length

PROBLEM 5-16 Reduce the following equations to the standard form:

(a) $x^2 - 8y + 8 = 0$ **(c)** $y^2 + 12x = 24$
(b) $y^2 - 4x - 4 = 0$ **(d)** $y^2 - 2y - 8x + 1 = 0$

PROBLEM 5-17 Test the following equations for symmetry with respect to the X- and Y-axes and the origin: **(a)** $y = \cos x$, **(b)** $y^3 - 3xy - y^5 = 3$, and **(c)** $x = (y^2 - 1)^{1/4}$.

PROBLEM 5-18 If a ball is thrown vertically upward with a velocity of 30 feet per second, the path the ball describes is given (approximately) by the equation $s = 30t - 16t^2$, where s is the number of feet above the ground at time t. When will the ball reach the ground? [*Hint:* Write this equation in a standard form, where the coordinates of a point on the parabolic curve are (t, s); you might want to sketch the curve.]

Answers to Supplementary Exercises

5-9: **(a)** $V(0,0)$; $F(1,0)$; DD' is $x = -1$; $|LR| = 4$
(b) $V(0,0)$; $F(-2,0)$; DD' is $x = 2$; $|LR| = 8$
(c) $V(0,0)$; $F(0,3)$; DD' is $y = -3$; $|LR| = 12$
(d) $V(2,0)$; $F(2,3)$; DD' is $y = -3$; $|LR| = 12$

5-10: **(a)** $3y^2 = x$ **(c)** $y^2 = 9x$
(b) $4y^2 + 25x = 0$ **(d)** $2y^2 = -25x$

5-11: **(a)** $x^2 = 3y$ **(c)** $5x^2 + 9y = 0$
(b) $5x^2 + 9y = 0$ **(d)** $4x^2 + 9y = 0$

5-12: **(a)** $x^2 = 8y$
(b) $y^2 + 12x - 9 = 0$
(c) $9y^2 + 48x + 90y + 353 = 0$

5-13: **(a)** $x^2 - 12x - 12y + 96 = 0$
(b) $y^2 + 4y - 16x + 4 = 0$
(c) $y^2 - 8x - 16 = 0$

5-14: **(a)** $V(2, -4)$ **(d)** $y + 4 = 0$
(b) $F(0, -4)$ **(e)** $x - 4 = 0$
(c) $L(0,0)$, $R(0, -8)$

5-15: **(a)** $y^2 - 8y - 32x + 112 = 0$
(b) $2y^2 - 9x - 8y + 17 = 0$
(c) $y^2 + 2y - 5x - 9 = 0$
$y^2 + 2y + 5x + 11 = 0$

5-16: **(a)** $x^2 = 8(y - 1)$ **(c)** $y^2 = -12(x - 2)$
(b) $y^2 = 4(x + 1)$ **(d)** $(y - 1)^2 = 8x$

5-17: **(a)** Y-axis **(c)** X-axis
(b) no symmetry

5-18: $1\frac{7}{8}$ seconds later $[(t - \frac{15}{16})^2 = \frac{225 - 16s}{256}]$

6 THE ELLIPSE

THIS CHAPTER IS ABOUT

- ☑ Definition and Standard Equation of the Ellipse
- ☑ Properties of the Ellipse ($C = (0, 0)$)
- ☑ Construction of an Ellipse
- ☑ Other Equations of the Ellipse ($C = (h, k)$)

6-1. Definition and Standard Equation of the Ellipse

- An **ellipse** is the locus of a point that moves so that the sum of the distances from the moving point to two fixed points is a constant.

Each fixed point in an ellipse is a *focus*, and the midpoint of the line segment joining these fixed points is the *center* of the ellipse.

To obtain a simple form of the equation of the ellipse, we'll use as foci the fixed points F and F' on the X-axis, and as the center we'll use the midpoint of FF' at the origin O, as shown in Figure 6-1. Now we can say that the distance between the foci F' and F is $2c$ units, so the coordinates of these points are $F'(-c, 0)$ and $F(c, 0)$, respectively. Then, invoking the definition of an ellipse, we can denote the sum of the distances of any point $P(x, y)$ on the ellipse from the two foci by $2a$; i.e., by definition

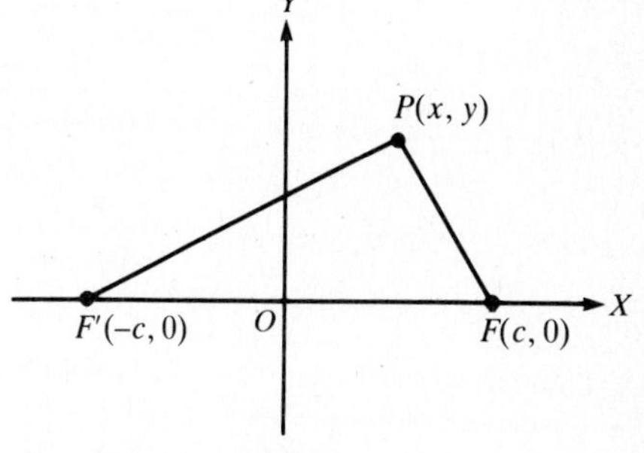

Figure 6-1

$$|F'P| + |FP| = 2a$$

So far, we have the triangle $F'PF$, from which we can see that $2a$ must be greater than $2c$ for any point not on the segment $F'F$ (since the sum of two sides of a triangle is always greater than the third side). So, we'll take $a > c$ as given in the discussion that follows.

Expressing the relation $F'P + FP = 2a$ in terms of distances by eq. (1-2), we have

X-ELLIPSE: SUM OF POINT-TO-FOCI DISTANCES

$$\sqrt{(x + c)^2 + y^2} + \sqrt{(x - c)^2 + y^2} = 2a \qquad \textbf{(6-1)}$$

Transposing the second radical (or the first), squaring, and reducing, we get

$$x^2 + 2xc + c^2 + y^2 = 4a^2 - 4a\sqrt{(x - c)^2 + y^2} + x^2 - 2xc + c^2 + y^2$$

$$a^2 - cx = a\sqrt{(x - c)^2 + y^2}$$

Squaring again and simplifying:

$$(a^2 - c^2)x^2 + a^2y^2 = a^2(a^2 - c^2)$$

But $a^2 - c^2$ is a positive number because $a > c > 0$; therefore, $a^2 > c^2$. If we let $a^2 - c^2 = b^2$, where b is real, and make this substitution, our equation becomes

$$b^2x^2 + a^2y^2 = a^2b^2$$

Dividing both sides by a^2b^2, we get a simple equation for an ellipse whose foci are on the X-axis:

X-ELLIPSE (STANDARD FORM): $C = (0, 0)$; $F = (\pm c, 0)$

$$\frac{x^2}{a^2} + \frac{y^2}{b^2} = 1 \tag{6-2}$$

In deriving this formula, we have shown that every point that satisfies the condition $F'P + FP = 2a$ has coordinates that satisfy eq. (6-2). The converse is also true: Every point whose coordinates satisfy eq. (6-2) must also satisfy eq. (6-1) and must, therefore, be a point on the ellipse.

6-2. Properties of the Ellipse ($C = (0, 0)$)

A. Symmetry

The ellipse represented algebraically by eq. (6-2) is symmetric with respect to both coordinate axes and to the origin. Its symmetry can be verified by the symmetry tests: The equation $x^2/a^2 + y^2/b^2 = 1$ remains unaltered when x is replaced by $-x$, when y is replaced by $-y$, and when both x and y are replaced by their negatives.

B. Excluded values

Solving the equation of the ellipse for y in terms of x, and for x in terms of y, we find that

$$y = \pm\frac{b}{a}\sqrt{a^2 - x^2} \qquad \text{and} \qquad x = \pm\frac{a}{b}\sqrt{b^2 - y^2}$$

The first of these equations shows that the only values of x that give real values of y are those for which $x^2 \leq a^2$. Likewise, from the second equation, values of y such that $y^2 \leq b^2$ are the only ones that give real values of x. And since values that are not real are excluded from the curve, the curve must lie between the lines $x = \pm a$ and $y = \pm b$. Then, if $x = \pm a$, we find that $y = 0$; and if $y = \pm b$, we have $x = 0$. So the curve crosses the X-axis at $(\pm a, 0)$ and the Y-axis at $(0, \pm b)$, as shown in Figure 6-2.

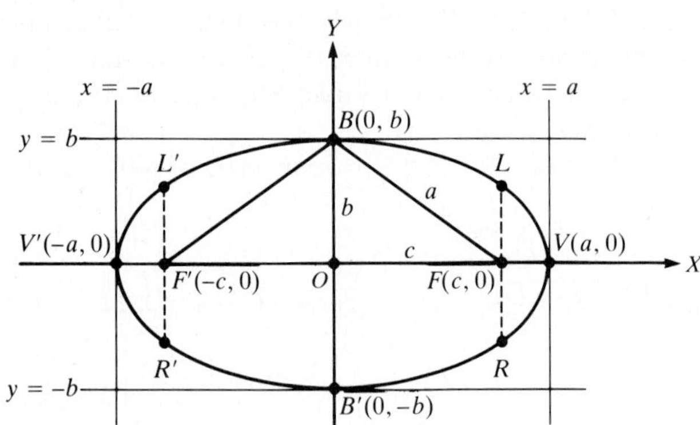

Figure 6-2. Properties of the ellipse $x^2/a^2 + y^2/b^2 = 1$: Symmetry about the X- and Y-axes and the origin; excluded values $|x| > a$ and $|y| > b$; Pythagorean relationship $a^2 = b^2 + c^2$; eccentricity $e = c/a$.

C. Geometric relationships

The line segment $V'V$ of length $2a$ passing through the foci is the **major axis**, while the chord $B'B$ of length $2b$ passing through the center perpendicular to the major axis is the **minor axis**. The lengths a and b are the **semi-major** and

semi-minor axes, respectively. The end points V' and V of the major axis are the *vertices* of the ellipse. (The end points B' and B of the minor axis are the *covertices* of the ellipse. The end points V', V and B', B are sometimes referred to collectively as *vertices.*)

The relationship between the constants a, b, and c is expressed by the equation $a^2 = b^2 + c^2$ from the Pythagorean theorem. Geometrically, this means that a line drawn from a focus to an end of the minor axis has the same length as the semi-major axis, so that $FB = OV$, for example. Also, the length of the chord through the ellipse at either focus perpendicular to the major axis, called the *latus rectum* (pl. *latera recta*), may be found by substituting $x = c$ or $x = -c$ into the equation of the ellipse and solving for y:

$$y = \pm\frac{b}{a}\sqrt{a^2 - c^2} = \pm\frac{b^2}{a}$$

since $a^2 - c^2 = b^2$. Hence the length of the latus rectum is $2(b^2/a)$, since it is the double ordinate (twice the length of the ordinate to the curve at that point) at a focus.

D. Eccentricity

The value of the ratio c/a indicates the shape of the ellipse: For a of fixed length, the curve flattens out as c approaches a ($c \to a$) and the curve approaches a circle of radius a as $c \to 0$. This ratio, which takes values between 0 and 1 since $c < a$, is called the **eccentricity** and is designated by the letter e, so that $e = c/a$.

E. *Y*-Axis as major axis

The equation of an ellipse with its major axis along the *Y*-axis and foci at $(0, \pm c)$ is

Y-ELLIPSE (STANDARD FORM): $C = (0, 0)$; $F = (0, \pm c)$

$$\frac{y^2}{a^2} + \frac{x^2}{b^2} = 1 \qquad \textbf{(6-3)}$$

note: Remember that $a > b$, so you can always tell which axis is the major axis and which equation to use: If the term containing x has the larger denominator, then that denominator is a and the major axis is along the X-axis (eq. 6-2); if the term containing y has the larger denominator, then that denominator is a and the major axis is along the Y-axis (eq. 6-3).

EXAMPLE 6-1: Find the equation of an ellipse with foci at $(0, \pm 4)$ and a vertex at $(0, 6)$.

Solution: The location of the foci shows that the center of the ellipse is at the origin, that $c = 4$, and that the equation you want may be expressed in the form of eq. (6-3). The given vertex, six units from the origin, makes $a = 6$. Now you can use the Pythagorean relation $b^2 = a^2 - c^2 = 36 - 16 = 20$. Thus the equation of the ellipse is

$$\frac{y^2}{36} + \frac{x^2}{20} = 1$$

6-3. Construction of an Ellipse

An ellipse may be constructed by means of points in the following way (see Figure 6-3):

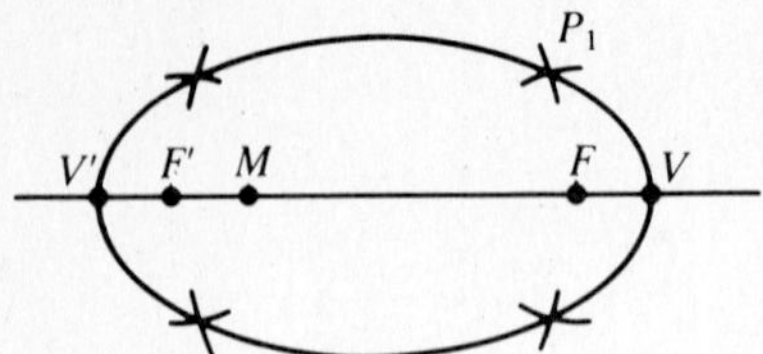

Figure 6-3. Construction of an ellipse.

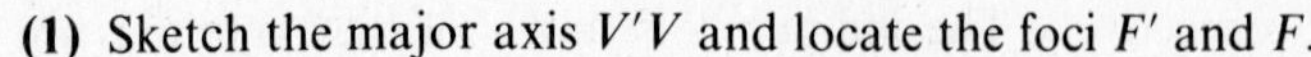

(1) Sketch the major axis $V'V$ and locate the foci F' and F.
(2) Let M be any point on the line segment $F'F$.
(3) Draw arcs above and below the major axis, using the foci as centers and a radius equal to MV. Then, using the same centers and radius equal to MV', draw arcs intercepting those just found, thus producing four points on the ellipse. (Other points can be found by varying the position of M.)

To prove the validity of this construction, call one of the points P_1 and observe that $MV = F'P_1$ and $MV' = FP_1$; therefore

$$F'P_1 + FP_1 = MV + MV' = V'V$$

which is the length of the major axis. And this length remains constant; that is, $V'M + MV$ always equals $V'V$, so the sum of the distances from the foci to any point on the curve is constant.

note: For just a sketch of the ellipse, draw the curve through the X- and Y-intercepts and the end points of the latera recta.

EXAMPLE 6-2: Find **(a)** the lengths of the semi-major and semi-minor axes and the coordinates of the vertices; **(b)** the coordinates of the foci; **(c)** the lengths and coordinates of the latera recta; and **(d)** the eccentricity of the ellipse $9x^2 + 4y^2 = 36$. Graph the curve.

Solution: First, reduce the equation to standard form by dividing both sides by 36:

$$\frac{9x^2}{36} + \frac{4y^2}{36} = \frac{36}{36} = \frac{x^2}{4} + \frac{y^2}{9} = 1$$

(a) Since the larger of the two denominators 9 and 4 appears in the term containing y^2, you know that the major axis lies along the Y-axis and that you need eq. (6-3), which tells you that $a^2 = 9$ and $b^2 = 4$. So you know that the length of the semi-major axis is $a = \sqrt{9} = 3$ and that of the semi-minor axis is $b = \sqrt{4} = 2$. And you know that the coordinates of the vertices are $(0, a) = (0, \pm 3)$ and those of the ends of the minor axis are $(\pm b, 0) = (\pm 2, 0)$.

(b) From the Pythagorean relationship $a^2 = b^2 + c^2$, you can find the value of the constant c:

$$c = \sqrt{a^2 - b^2} = \sqrt{3^2 - 2^2} = \sqrt{5}$$

so the coordinates of the foci are $(0, \pm c) = (0, \pm\sqrt{5})$.

(c) Substitute $a = 3$ and $b = 2$ into the formula for the length of the latus rectum:

$$LR = \frac{2b^2}{a} = \frac{2(2^2)}{a} = \frac{8}{3}$$

so the length of each latus rectum is $8/3$ and the coordinates of the latera recta are $(\pm b^2/a, \pm c) = (\pm 4/3, \pm\sqrt{5})$.

(d) The eccentricity e is the ratio c/a, so

$$e = \frac{c}{a} = \frac{\sqrt{5}}{3}$$

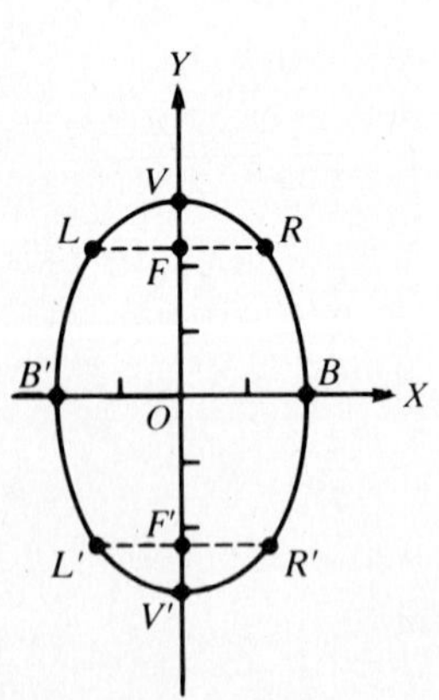

Figure 6-4

Putting all these data together, you can graph the ellipse shown in Figure 6-4.

EXAMPLE 6-3: Find the semi-axes, the foci, the vertices, the length of the latus rectum, and the eccentricity of the ellipse $x^2 + 2y^2 = 4$. Sketch the curve.

Solution: Reduce the equation to standard form: $x^2/4 + y^2/2 = 1$. Since $a > b$, you know that $a^2 = 4$ and $b^2 = 2$, or $a = 2$ and $b = \sqrt{2}$ (the lengths of the semi-axes). The vertices are $V(\pm 2, 0)$ and $B(0, \pm\sqrt{2})$. Also, $c = \sqrt{a^2 - b^2} = \sqrt{4-2} = \sqrt{2}$; thus the foci are $F(\pm\sqrt{2}, 0)$. The length of the latus rectum is $2b^2/a = 2(2)/2 = 2$, so $L = (\pm\sqrt{2}, 1)$ and $R = (\pm\sqrt{2}, -1)$. The eccentricity is $e = c/a = \sqrt{2}/2$.

The sketch of the curve, shown in Figure 6-5, can be made by graphing the points V and B (the X- and Y-intercepts) and the points L and R (the end points of the latus rectum), then assuming symmetry.

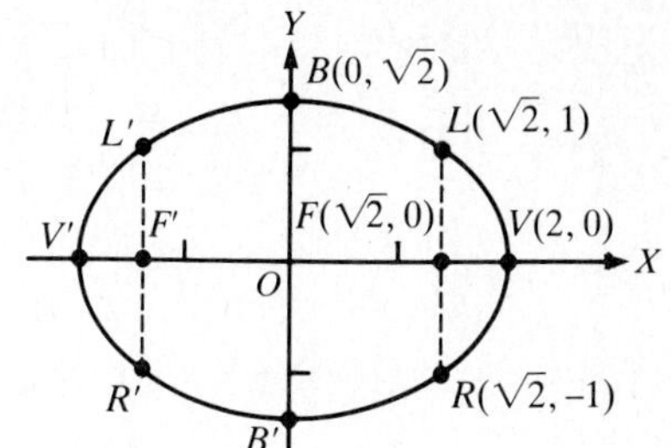

Figure 6-5

6-4. Other Equations of the Ellipse ($C = (h, k)$)

A. Standard (translation) forms

There are (of course) ellipses whose centers are not on the origin—and we can write equations for them. Referring to Figure 6-6, let (h, k) be the center of an ellipse and let the axes of the ellipse be on the lines $O'X'$ and $O'Y'$, drawn parallel to the coordinate axes. Then, if the major axis, of length $2a$, is contained within $O'X'$ and the foci are c units to the right and left of O' on this line, we know that the equation of the curve, referred to its axes, is

$$\frac{(x')^2}{a^2} + \frac{(y')^2}{b^2} = 1$$

So, making use of the translation formulas $x' = x - h$ and $y' = y - k$ to translate the center (h, k) to the point O, we have

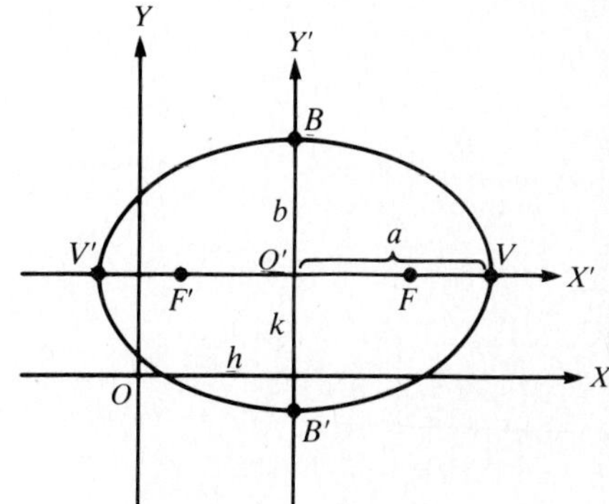

Figure 6-6. X-Ellipse: $\frac{(x-h)^2}{a^2} + \frac{(y-k)^2}{b^2} = 1.$

X-ELLIPSE (STANDARD FORM): C = (h, k)

$$\frac{(x-h)^2}{a^2} + \frac{(y-k)^2}{b^2} = 1 \qquad \textbf{(6-4)}$$

which is the standard equation translated to the X- and Y-axes. Similarly, if the major axis is taken parallel to the Y-axis, the equation becomes

Y-ELLIPSE (STANDARD FORM): C = (h, k)

$$\frac{(y-k)^2}{a^2} + \frac{(x-h)^2}{b^2} = 1 \qquad \textbf{(6-5)}$$

B. General form

By expanding the binomial terms and clearing fractions, we can rewrite either of the translation equations in general form:

ELLIPSE (GENERAL FORM) $\quad Ax^2 + Cy^2 + Dx + Ey + F = 0 \qquad$ **(6-6)**

note: The constants A and C MUST have the same sign, and $A \neq C$. (See Section 7-7B: If A and C have DIFFERENT signs, your "ellipse" is a hyperbola!)

Every equation of the form (6-6), in which A and C have the same sign and are not zero, represents an ellipse with axes parallel to the coordinate axes.

We can reduce the general form to standard form by completing the squares:

$$Ax^2 + Cy^2 + Dx + Ey + F = 0$$

$$A\left(x^2 + \frac{Dx}{A} + \frac{D^2}{4A^2}\right) + C\left(y^2 + \frac{Ey}{C} + \frac{E^2}{4C^2}\right) = \frac{D^2}{4A} + \frac{E^2}{4C} - F$$

$$A\left(x + \frac{D}{2A}\right)^2 + C\left(y + \frac{E}{2C}\right)^2 = \frac{D^2}{4A} + \frac{E^2}{4C} - F$$

Then, if we let $h = -(D/2A)$, $k = -(E/2C)$, and $H = D^2/4A + E^2/4C - F$, this equation becomes

$$A(x-h)^2 + C(y-k)^2 = H$$

or

$$\frac{(x-h)^2}{H/A}+\frac{(y-k)^2}{H/C}=1$$

which is in standard form (6-4) or (6-5), depending on whether H/A is greater or less than H/C. It therefore represents an ellipse with axes parallel to the coordinate axes.

note: For the ellipse to be real, the constant H must have the same sign as A and C; if $H = 0$, the locus is a *point ellipse.*

EXAMPLE 6-4: The foci of an ellipse are at $(2, 4)$ and $(2, -6)$ and the semi-major axis is $a = 6$. **(a)** Determine the elements b and c; **(b)** find the general equation of the ellipse and sketch the curve.

Solution:

(a) Since the foci are on the line $x = 2$, you know that the major axis is parallel to the Y-axis. And the center of the ellipse (h, k) must be $(2, -1)$, which is the midpoint of the line segment joining $(2, 4)$ and $(2, -6)$. The distance between the foci is therefore $2c = 10$; so $c = 5$. And since you're given $a = 6$, you can write $b^2 = a^2 - c^2 = 11$; so $b = \sqrt{11}$.

(b) The standard equation of the ellipse referred to the X'- and Y'-axes is

$$\frac{(y')^2}{a^2}+\frac{(x')^2}{b^2}=\frac{(y')^2}{36}+\frac{(x')^2}{11}=1$$

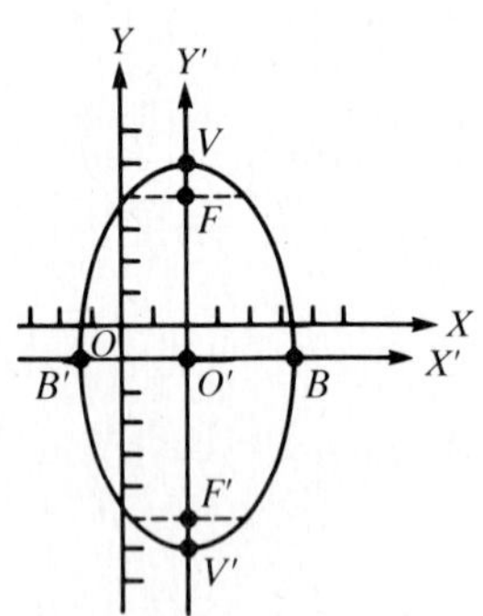

Figure 6-7

and when referred to the X- and Y-axes (eq. 6-5), it becomes

$$\frac{(y+1)^2}{36}+\frac{(x-2)^2}{11}=1$$

so the general form is

$$11(y^2+2y+1)+36(x^2-4x+4)=11(36)$$

$$36x^2+11y^2-144x+22y-241=0$$

You can sketch the ellipse by using the known elements ($a = 6$, $b = \sqrt{11}$, $c = 5$, and the length of the latus rectum $2b^2/a = 11/3$), as shown in Figure 6-7.

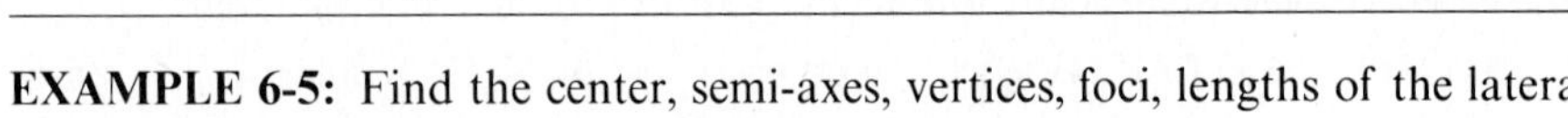

EXAMPLE 6-5: Find the center, semi-axes, vertices, foci, lengths of the latera recta, and the eccentricity of the ellipse whose equation is

$$49x^2+144y^2-196x-720y-668=0$$

Solution: By completing the squares the equation may be written as

$$49(x^2-4x+4)+144\left(y^2-5y+\frac{25}{4}\right)=1764$$

which can be reduced to standard form:

$$\frac{(x-2)^2}{36}+\frac{(y-5/2)^2}{49/4}=1$$

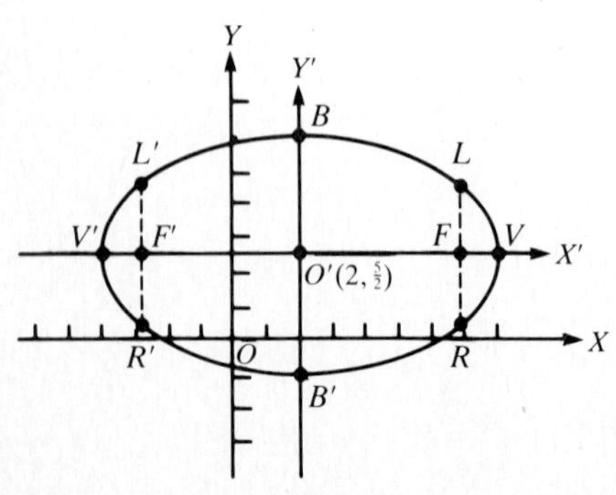

Figure 6-8

From the equation in standard form, you can see that the center of the curve is at the point $(2, \frac{5}{2})$ and that the major and minor axes coincide with the lines $2y - 5 = 0$ and $x - 2 = 0$, respectively. The semi-axes are $a = 6$ and $b = \frac{7}{2}$, and the coordinates of the vertices V are $(2 \pm 6, \frac{5}{2})$, or $(8, \frac{5}{2})$ and $(-4, \frac{5}{2})$.

Then, since $c^2 = a^2 - b^2 = \frac{95}{4}$, you have $c = \frac{1}{2}\sqrt{95}$; so the foci are at $(2 \pm \frac{1}{2}\sqrt{95}, \frac{5}{2})$. The length of the latus rectum is $2b^2/a = 49/12$, and the eccentricity is $e = c/a = \sqrt{95}/12$. Figure 6-8 shows the sketch.

SUMMARY

1. An ellipse is the locus of a point that moves so that the sum of its distances from two fixed points is a constant. The two fixed points are called foci, and the midpoint of the line segment joining them is the center of the ellipse.
2. The line passing through the foci of an ellipse is its major axis; the chord passing through the center perpendicular to the major axis is its minor axis.
3. The end points of the major axis are the vertices of the ellipse.
4. The length a, from the center of an ellipse to its vertex, is the semi-major axis; the length b, from the center of an ellipse to the end of its minor axis, is the semi-minor axis.
5. The chord through either focus, perpendicular to the major axis, is the latus rectum. The length of the latus rectum is $2b^2/a$.
6. The two standard forms of the equation of the ellipse are $x^2/a^2 + y^2/b^2 = 1$ (foci on the X-axis) and $y^2/a^2 + x^2/b^2 = 1$ (foci on the Y-axis).
7. The two translation equations of the ellipse are

$$\frac{(x-h)^2}{a^2} + \frac{(y-k)^2}{b^2} = 1 \qquad \text{and} \qquad \frac{(y-k)^2}{a^2} + \frac{(x-h)^2}{b^2} = 1$$

   where (h, k) represent the coordinates of the center.
8. The general equation of the ellipse is

$$Ax^2 + Cy^2 + Dx + Ey + F = 0 \qquad (A \neq C, \quad AC > 0)$$

   The equation of the ellipse in general form may be reduced to standard form by completing the square.

RAISE YOUR GRADES

Can you...?

☑ determine the equation of an ellipse, given the coordinates of the foci and a vertex

☑ find the semi-major and semi-minor axes, the coordinates of the foci and vertices, the length of the latus rectum, and the eccentricity of an ellipse, given its equation

☑ sketch the curve of an ellipse, given its equation

☑ determine the elements b and c, find the equation, and sketch the curve of an ellipse, given the foci and the length of the semi-major axis

☑ find the center, semi-axes, vertices, foci, latera recta, and eccentricity of an ellipse, given its equation in general form

SOLVED PROBLEMS

Properties of the Ellipse ($C = (0, 0)$)

PROBLEM 6-1 Write the equation of the ellipse with foci at $(\pm 5, 0)$ and vertices at $(0, \pm 6)$.

Solution: The coordinates of the foci show that the curve is an X-ellipse with center at $(0, 0)$ and that $c = 5$. The coordinates of the vertices show that $b = 6$. Hence, $a = \sqrt{b^2 + c^2} = \sqrt{61}$.

Substituting these values into the standard form (6-2), you get

$$\frac{x^2}{a^2} + \frac{y^2}{b^2} = 1$$

$$\frac{x^2}{61} + \frac{y^2}{36} = 1$$

as the desired equation.

PROBLEM 6-2 Find the equation of the ellipse whose center is (0, 0) and whose curve passes through (4, −1) and (−2, 3).

Solution: In this case, you'll find it convenient to use the general form

$$Ax^2 + Cy^2 = 1$$

where A and C replace $1/a^2$ and $1/b^2$ of the standard form (6-2) of an ellipse with center at the origin. Then, substitution of the two pairs of coordinates in the equation produces two linear equations that can be solved simultaneously:

$$16A + C = 1 \quad \text{and} \quad 4A + 9C = 1$$

$$A = \frac{2}{35} \quad \text{and} \quad C = \frac{3}{35}$$

Hence the required equation is

$$\frac{2x^2}{35} + \frac{3y^2}{35} = 1$$

an X-ellipse for which $a = \sqrt{35/2}$ and $b = \sqrt{35/3}$.

Construction of an Ellipse

PROBLEM 6-3 Sketch the ellipse represented by the equation $9x^2 + 25y^2 = 225$.

Solution: Dividing by 225 gives you the equation in standard form:

$$\frac{x^2}{25} + \frac{y^2}{9} = 1$$

Since $a > b$, and the denominator of x^2 is greater than the denominator of y^2, you know that the major axis is along the X-axis. You can also see that

$$a^2 = 25, \qquad b^2 = 9, \qquad c = \sqrt{a^2 - b^2} = 4$$

Hence the vertices are $V(\pm 5, 0)$, the ends of the minor axis are $B(0, \pm 3)$, and the foci are $F(\pm 4, 0)$. The length of each latus rectum LR is $2b^2/a = 18/5$, and their ends are $(\pm c, \pm b^2/a) = (\pm 4, \pm 9/5)$.

The locations of the ends of the axes and the ends of each latus rectum are sufficient for you to make a sketch of the ellipse. Figure 6-9 shows the curve with several important points indicated.

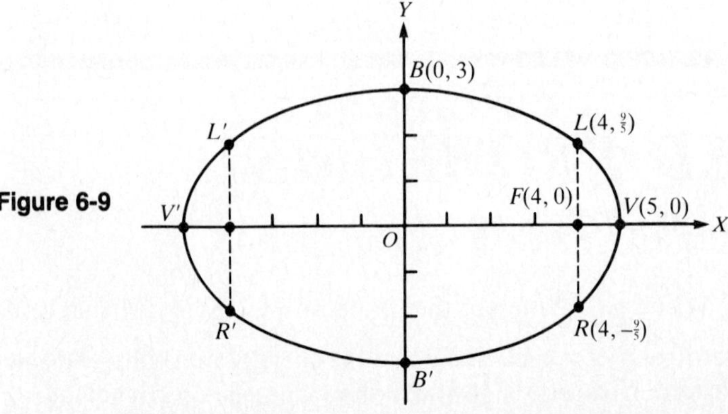

Figure 6-9

PROBLEM 6-4 Sketch the ellipse represented by the equation

$$2x^2 + y^2 = 4$$

Solution: In standard form the equation is

$$\frac{x^2}{2} + \frac{y^2}{4} = 1$$

Since the denominator of y^2 is the larger, the major axis lies along the Y-axis (eq. 6-3) and $a^2 = 4$; so $a = 2$, $b = \sqrt{2}$, and $c = \sqrt{2}$. The center is $(0, 0)$, the vertices are $(0, \pm 2)$, and the foci are at $(0, \pm\sqrt{2})$, as shown in Figure 6-10.

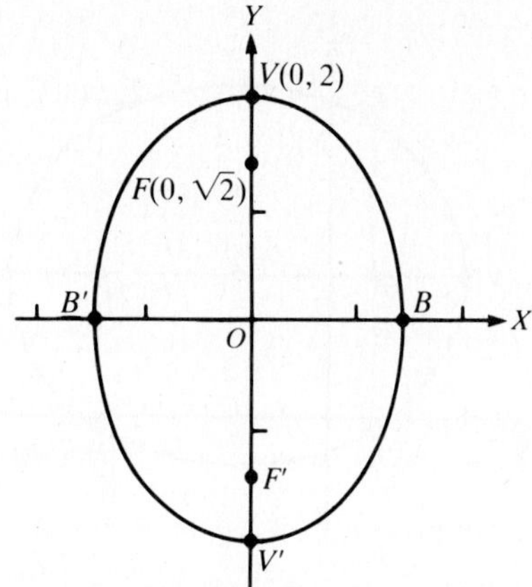

Figure 6-10

Other Equations of the Ellipse $(C = (h, k))$

PROBLEM 6-5 Graph the curve

$$9(x + 2)^2 + 4(y - 1)^2 = 36$$

Determine the coordinates of the vertices and the ends of the minor axis, the ends of the latera recta, and the foci. Find the eccentricity of the ellipse.

Solution: Division by 36 gives you the standard form

$$9(x + 2)^2 + 4(y - 1)^2 = 36$$

$$\frac{(x + 2)^2}{4} + \frac{(y - 1)^2}{9} = 1$$

which you recognize as an ellipse with center at (h, k) and major axis parallel to the Y-axis (eq. 6-5), since $9 > 4$. Therefore, its center is at $(-2, 1)$, $a = 3$, $b = 2$, $c = \sqrt{a^2 - b^2} = \sqrt{5}$, and $LR = 2b^2/a = 2(4)/3 = 8/3$. Now you can find the coordinates of the vertices, the ends of the minor axis, the foci, and the ends of the latera recta (shown in Figure 6-11):

$V, V' = (-2, \pm a + 1)$ $\qquad$ $B, B' = (\pm b - 2, 1)$

$V = (-2, 4)$ $\qquad$ $B = (0, 1)$

$V' = (-2, -2)$ $\qquad$ $B' = (-4, 1)$

$F, F' = (-2, 1 \pm c)$

$F = (-2, 1 + \sqrt{5})$

$F' = (-2, 1 - \sqrt{5})$

$L, L' = (-2 - b^2/a, 1 \pm c)$

$L = (-10/3, 1 + \sqrt{5})$

$L' = (-10/3, 1 - \sqrt{5})$

$R, R' = (-2 + b^2/a, 1 \pm c)$

$R = (-2/3, 1 + \sqrt{5})$

$R' = (-2/3, 1 - \sqrt{5})$

Finally, the eccentricity is $e = c/a = \sqrt{5}/3$.

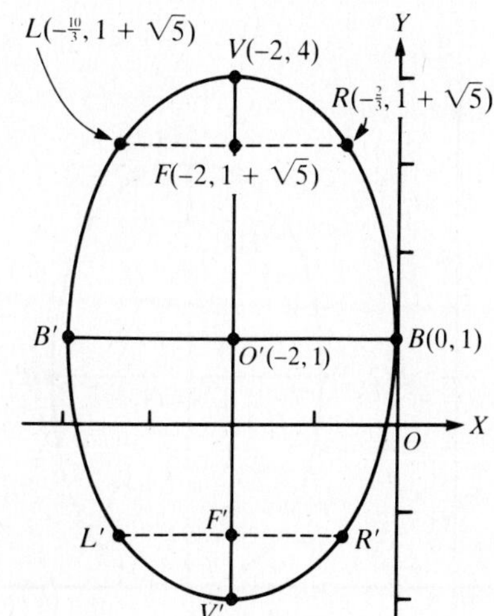

Figure 6-11

PROBLEM 6-6 Find the equation of the ellipse with center at $(2, 3)$, focus at $(5, 3)$, and corresponding vertex at $(7, 3)$. Sketch the curve.

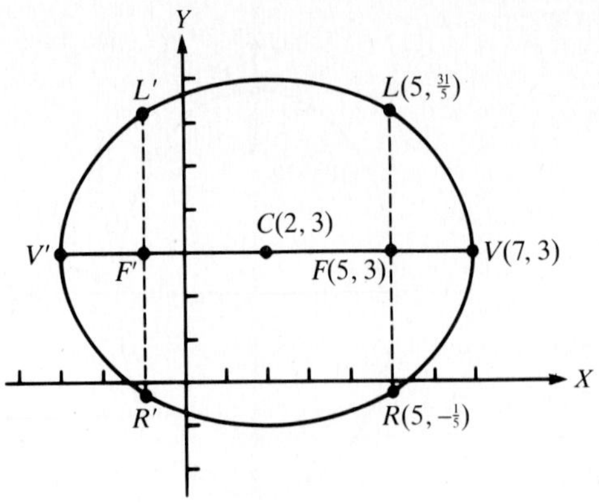

Figure 6-12

Solution: It will help to draw a sketch first (see Figure 6-12), and then find the equation of the ellipse. The distance from center to vertex is always a; so in this problem $a = 5$ and $CF = c = 3$. Therefore, $b^2 = a^2 - c^2 = 5^2 - 3^2 = 4^2$. Now you're set up to find the equation.

You know you have to use eq. (6-4), because the major axis is parallel to the X-axis. And you know the coordinates of the center, $h = 2$ and $k = 3$; so you can write

$$\frac{(x-2)^2}{5^2} + \frac{(y-3)^2}{4^2} = 1$$

To finish sketching the curve, use the given vertex, the opposite vertex, and the ends of the latera recta. The given vertex and focus are respectively 5 and 3 units to the right of center; hence the other vertex and focus are respectively 5 and 3 units to the left of center as shown in Figure 6-12. The length of each latus rectum is $2b^2/a = 2(4^2)/5 = 32/5$, so you know that $L = (5, 3 + 16/5)$ and $R = (5, 3 - 16/5)$ and that L', R' are their opposites through $F'(-1, 3)$.

PROBLEM 6-7 Find the equation of the ellipse with foci at $(4, -2)$ and $(10, -2)$ and a vertex at $(12, -2)$.

Solution: The center, which is midway between the foci, is at $(7, -2)$, so the distance between the foci must be 6 units. And the given vertex must be 5 units from the center. Hence $c = 3$, $a = 5$, and $b^2 = a^2 - c^2 = 16$. Since the major axis is parallel to the X-axis, you substitute $a^2 = 25$ and $b^2 = 16$ into eq. (6-4) to get the equation of the ellipse:

$$\frac{(x-7)^2}{25} + \frac{(y+2)^2}{16} = 1$$

PROBLEM 6-8 Reduce the following equation to standard form:

$$4y^2 + 9x^2 - 24y - 72x + 144 = 0$$

Sketch the curve.

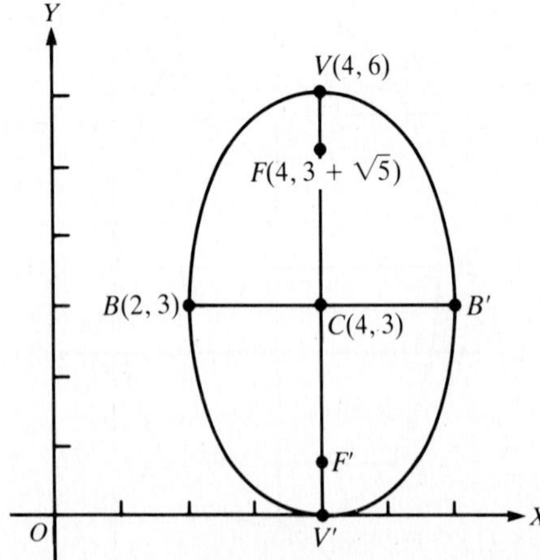

Figure 6-13

Solution: Collecting terms in y and x sets you up for completing the square:

$$4(y^2 - 6y + 9) + 9(x^2 - 8x + 16)$$
$$= -144 + 4(9) + 9(16)$$
$$4(y-3)^2 + 9(x-4)^2 = 36$$

and dividing through by 36 gives you the equation in standard form:

$$\frac{(y-3)^2}{9} + \frac{(x-4)^2}{4} = 1$$

where $a^2 = 9$ and $b^2 = 4$, since $9 > 4$. So you can see that you have a Y-ellipse the coordinates of whose center are $(4, 3)$. Hence

$$a = 3, \qquad b = 2, \quad \text{and} \quad c = \sqrt{a^2 - b^2} = \sqrt{5}$$

The vertices are at $(4, 0)$ and $(4, 6)$, and the ends of the minor axis are at $(2, 3)$ and $(6, 3)$. The coordinates of the foci are $(4, 3 - \sqrt{5})$ and $(4, 3 + \sqrt{5})$. Sketch the curve as shown in Figure 6-13.

PROBLEM 6-9 Reduce $x^2 + 4y^2 + 4x = 0$ to standard form.

Solution:

$$x^2 + 4x + 4 + 4y^2 = 4$$

$$(x + 2)^2 + 4y^2 = 4$$

$$\frac{(x + 2)^2}{4} + y^2 = 1$$

PROBLEM 6-10 Reduce $5x^2 - 10x + 9y^2 - 54y + 41 = 0$ to standard form.

Solution: Complete the square:

$$5(x^2 - 2x \qquad) + 9(y^2 - 6y \qquad) = -41$$

$$5(x^2 - 2x + 1) + 9(y^2 - 6y + 9) = -41 + 5(1) + 9(9) = 45$$

$$\frac{(x - 1)^2}{9} + \frac{(y - 3)^2}{5} = 1$$

Supplementary Exercises

PROBLEM 6-11 Find the center C, semi-axes a and b, vertices V, foci F, lengths of the latera recta LR, and eccentricity e of the following ellipses:

(a) $x^2 + 9y^2 - 4x - 5 = 0$
(b) $25x^2 + 9y^2 - 10x - 12y - 220 = 0$
(c) $3x^2 + 4y^2 - 12x + 24y = 0$

PROBLEM 6-12 In each of the following, find the equation of the ellipse having its axes parallel to the coordinate axes and satisfying the given conditions: **(a)** vertices at $(-3, 6)$ and $(-3, -2)$, $e = \frac{2}{3}$; **(b)** foci at $(6, 3)$ and $(6, -9)$, $a = 10$; **(c)** center at $(1, 2)$, major axis parallel to X-axis, ellipse passes through $(1, 1)$ and $(3, 2)$.

PROBLEM 6-13 Find the equations of the following ellipses:

(a) The X-ellipse with center at $(-1, 3)$ and major and minor axes of length 10 and 6, respectively
(b) The Y-ellipse with center at $(3, -4)$ and major and minor axes of length 18 and 12, respectively
(c) The X-ellipse with center at $(-2, -5)$ and with major and minor axes of length 9 and 6, respectively
(d) The ellipse with vertices $(-5, 2)$ and $(3, 2)$ and covertices $(-1, 5)$ and $(-1, -1)$
(e) The ellipse with vertices $(6, 8)$ and $(6, -2)$ and covertices $(10, 3)$ and $(2, 3)$
(f) The ellipse in which one axis is 18 units in length and the coordinates of the end points of the other axis are $(2, 5)$ and $(2, -3)$

PROBLEM 6-14 Write the equation of the ellipse that satisfies the given conditions:

(a) Center at $(5, 1)$, vertex at $(5, 4)$, end of minor axis at $(3, 1)$
(b) Vertex at $(6, 3)$, foci at $(-4, 3)$ and $(4, 3)$
(c) Vertices at $(-1, 3)$ and $(5, 3)$, minor axis 4 units in length
(d) Center at $(0, 0)$, one vertex at $(0, -6)$, end point of minor axis at $(4, 0)$
(e) Foci at $(0, -8)$ and $(0, 8)$, major axis 34 units in length
(f) Foci at $(-5, 0)$ and $(5, 0)$, minor axis 8 units in length

PROBLEM 6-15 Find the equation that is satisfied by the coordinates of each point in the following:

(a) The sum of the distances of each point from $(5, 3)$ and $(4, -2)$ is 6
(b) The sum of the distances of each point from $(2, 3)$ and $(5, -1)$ is 7
(c) The sum of the distances of each point from $(3, -3)$ and $(0, 5)$ is 9

PROBLEM 6-16 The earth's orbit is an ellipse with the sun at one focus. The length of the major axis is 1.86×10^8 miles, and the eccentricity 1.67×10^{-2}. Find the greatest and least distances from the earth to the sun.

Answers to Supplementary Exercises

6-11: **(a)** $C(2,0)$; $a = 3$; $b = 1$; $V'(-1,0)$, $V(5,0)$; $F,F' = (2 \pm 2\sqrt{2}, 0)$; $LR = \frac{2}{3}$; $e = \frac{2}{3}\sqrt{2}$

(b) $C(\frac{1}{5}, \frac{2}{3})$; $a = 5$; $b = 3$; $V'(\frac{1}{5}, -4\frac{1}{3})$, $V(\frac{1}{5}, 5\frac{2}{3})$; $F(\frac{1}{5}, 4\frac{2}{3})$; $F'(\frac{1}{5}, -3\frac{1}{3})$; $LR = \frac{18}{5}$; $e = \frac{4}{5}$

(c) $C(2, -3)$; $a = 4$; $b = 2\sqrt{3}$; $V'(-2, -3)$, $V(6, -3)$; $F'(0, -3)$, $F(4, -3)$; $LR = 6$; $e = \frac{1}{2}$

6-12: **(a)** $9x^2 + 5y^2 + 54x - 20y + 21 = 0$
(b) $25x^2 + 16y^2 - 300x + 96y - 556 = 0$
(c) $x^2 + 4y^2 - 2x - 16y + 13 = 0$

6-13: **(a)** $\frac{(x+1)^2}{25} + \frac{(y-3)^2}{9} = 1$

(b) $\frac{(x-3)^2}{36} + \frac{(y+4)^2}{81} = 1$

(c) $\frac{4(x+2)^2}{81} + \frac{(y+5)^2}{9} = 1$

(d) $\frac{(x+1)^2}{16} + \frac{(y-2)^2}{9} = 1$

(e) $\frac{(x-6)^2}{16} + \frac{(y-3)^2}{25} = 1$

(f) $\frac{(x-2)^2}{81} + \frac{(y-1)^2}{16} = 1$

6-14: **(a)** $\frac{(x-5)^2}{4} + \frac{(y-1)^2}{9} = 1$

(b) $\frac{x^2}{36} + \frac{(y-3)^2}{20} = 1$

(c) $\frac{(x-2)^2}{9} + \frac{(y-3)^2}{4} = 1$

(d) $\frac{y^2}{36} + \frac{x^2}{16} = 1$

(e) $\frac{y^2}{289} + \frac{x^2}{225} = 1$

(f) $\frac{x^2}{41} + \frac{y^2}{16} = 1$

6-15: **(a)** $35x^2 + 11y^2 - 10xy - 310x + 34y = -599$
(b) $40x^2 + 33y^2 + 24xy - 304x - 150y + 313 = 0$
(c) $72x^2 + 17y^2 + 48xy - 264x - 106y + 89 = 0$

6-16: 91.4×10^6 miles and 94.6×10^6 miles

EXAM 2 (chapters 4–6)

1. If the center of a circle is at $(-4, 2)$ and a point on the circle touches the Y-axis, what is the equation of the circle? Draw the figure. [*Hint:* You know the radius r from the fact that the abscissa of the center is -4 and the circle touches the Y-axis.]

2. Find the center C and radius r of the circle $3x^2 + 3y^2 + 8x + 4y = 0$.

3. Find the equation of the circle that touches both axes and passes through the point $(6, 3)$.

4. Write the equations of the circles that meet the following conditions: **(a)** center at $(0, 0)$, $r = 4$; **(b)** center at $(2, -2)$, $r = 6$.

5. Find the center and radius of each of the following circles: **(a)** $x^2 + y^2 - 2x + 4y - 11 = 0$; **(b)** $4x^2 + 4y^2 - 4x + 8y + 5 = 0$.

6. Find the equations of the circles that satisfy the following conditions:

   (a) Passing through $(0, 0)$, $(-2, -1)$, $(4, 5)$
   (b) Passing through $(-1, 3)$, $(7, -1)$, $(2, 9)$
   (c) Having intercepts of 2 and 3 on the X- and Y-axes, respectively, and passing through the origin
   (d) Passing through $(5, 0)$ and $(0, -3)$; center on the line $x - y = 0$

7. **(a)** Determine the equation of the family of circles that pass through the intersection of the circle $x^2 + y^2 - 6x + 9 = 0$ and the line $x - 2y + 3 = 0$. **(b)** Give the equation of the member of the family that passes through $(6, 0)$.

8. Write the equation of **(a)** the family of circles that pass through the intersection of the two circles $x^2 + y^2 - 6x + 4y + 36 = 0$ and $x^2 + y^2 - 3x + 10y - 9 = 0$ and **(b)** the particular member of the family that passes through $(0, 0)$.

9. Find the radical axis of the pair of circles $x^2 + y^2 + 4x - 2y - 11 = 0$ and $x^2 + y^2 - 2x + 8y + 8 = 0$.

10. **(a)** The fixed point of a parabola is called the ____________.
    (b) The fixed line of a parabola is called the ____________.
    (c) The line of symmetry of a parabola is called the ____________.
    (d) The point at which the parabola intersects its axis is called the ____________.

11. Find the coordinates of the focus F and ends of the latus rectum LR, and determine the equation of the directrix DD' of the curve $y^2 - 2x = 0$. Sketch the curve.

12. Identify the coordinates of the vertex and focus, find the equation of the directrix, and determine the length of the latus rectum for the curve $(y - 4)^2 = 4x$.

13. Find the coordinates of the vertex and focus, the equation of the directrix, and the length of the latus rectum for the curve $x^2 = 24(y + 2)$.

14. Derive the equation of the parabolas determined by the following data:

    (a) Vertex at $(0, 0)$, focus at $(0, 5)$
    (b) Focus at $(4, 0)$, directrix $x = -4$
    (c) Focus at $(0, 5)$, length of the latus rectum is 12, curve opens to the left

15. Reduce the equation $y^2 + 25 = 10y - 16x$ to standard form.

16. Find the coordinates of the axis intersections and of the vertex of the parabola $x = y^2 - 2y - 3$.

17. Find the equation of the X-parabola that passes through $(0, 2)$, $(0, -3)$, and $(-3, 0)$.

18. Test the equation $x^2 - 3y^2 = 1$ for symmetry.

19. Find the lengths of the semi-axes a and b, the coordinates of the foci and vertices, the length of the latera recta, and the eccentricity of the ellipse $16x^2 + 36y^2 = 576$.

20. Write the equation of the ellipse whose major axis is 10 units in length and whose foci are at $(0, \pm 3)$.

21. If the center is at the origin, the major axis is 6, the latus rectum is $\frac{8}{3}$, and the foci are on the Y-axis, what is the equation of the ellipse?

22. Find the equation for the locus of a point that moves so that the sum of its distances from $(0, \pm 3)$ is 12.

23. Find the center, lengths of the semi-axes, coordinates of the vertices and foci, length of the latus rectum, and eccentricity of the ellipse $4x^2 + 25y^2 - 8x + 50y - 171 = 0$. Sketch the graph.

24. Find the equation of the ellipse with axes parallel to the coordinate axes, vertices at $(1, -4)$ and $(1, 6)$, and one focus on the line $2y - x - 7 = 0$.

25. Find the coordinates of the foci, the end points of the major and minor axes, and the end points of each latus rectum of the curve $x^2/25 + y^2/9 = 1$.

26. Reduce $16x^2 + 25y^2 + 160x + 200y + 400 = 0$ to standard form.

Answers to Exam 2

1. $x^2 + y^2 + 8x - 4y + 4 = 0$

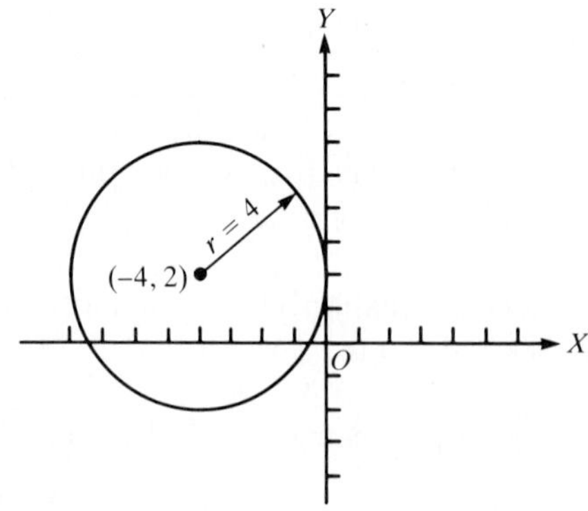

2. $C(-\frac{4}{3}, -\frac{2}{3}), r = \frac{2}{3}\sqrt{5}$

3. $x^2 + y^2 - 6x - 6y + 9 = 0$

4. **(a)** $x^2 + y^2 = 16$
(b) $x^2 + y^2 - 4x + 4y - 28 = 0$

5. **(a)** $C(1, -2), r = 4$
(b) $C(\frac{1}{2}, -1), r = 0$ (a point circle)

6. **(a)** $x^2 + y^2 + 11x - 17y = 0$
(b) $x^2 + y^2 - 9x - 8y + 5 = 0$
(c) $x^2 + y^2 - 2x - 3y = 0$
(d) $x^2 + y^2 - 2x - 2y - 15 = 0$

7. **(a)** $x^2 + y^2 - 6x + 9 + k(x - 2y + 3) = 0$
(b) $x^2 + y^2 - 7x + 2y + 6 = 0$

8. **(a)** $x^2 + y^2 - 6x + 4y + 36 + k(x^2 + y^2 - 3x + 10y - 9) = 0$
(b) $5x^2 + 5y^2 - 18x + 44y = 0$

9. $6x - 10y - 19 = 0$

10. **(a)** focus
(b) directrix
(c) axis
(d) vertex

11. $F(\frac{1}{2},0)$; $L,R = (\frac{1}{2}, \pm 1)$; DD' is $2x + 1 = 0$.

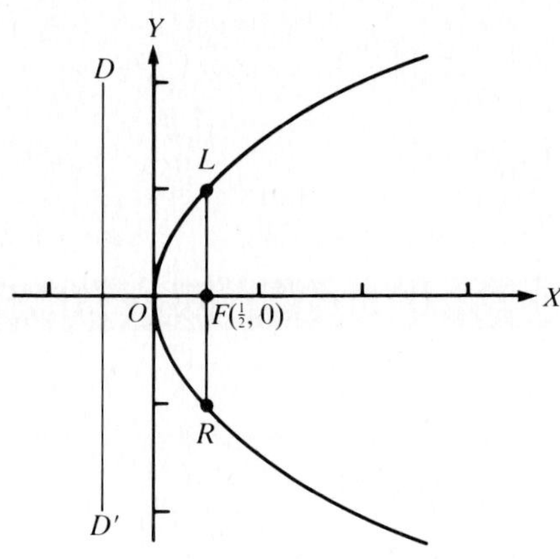

12. $V(0,4)$; $F(1,4)$; DD' is $x + 1 = 0$; $LR = 4$

13. $V(0,-2)$; $F(0,4)$; DD' is $y + 8 = 0$; $LR = 24$

14. **(a)** $x^2 = 20y$
(b) $y^2 = 16x$
(c) $(y-5)^2 = -12(x-3)$

15. $(y-5)^2 = -16x$

16. $(0,3)$, $(0,-1)$, $(-3,0)$; $V(-4,1)$

17. $y^2 - 2x + y - 6 = 0$

18. symmetric with respect to both axes and to the origin

19. $a = 6, b = 4$; $F,F' = (\pm 2\sqrt{5}, 0)$;
$V,V' = (\pm 6, 0)$; $LR = \frac{16}{3}$; $e = \frac{1}{3}\sqrt{5}$

20. $25x^2 + 16y^2 = 400$

21. $9x^2 + 4y^2 = 36$

22. $36x^2 + 27y^2 = 972$

23. $O'(1,-1)$; $a = 5\sqrt{2}$, $b = 2\sqrt{2}$;
$V,V' = (1 \pm 5\sqrt{2}, -1)$; $FF' = (1 \pm \sqrt{42}, -1)$;
$LR = \frac{8}{5}\sqrt{2}$; $e = \frac{1}{5}\sqrt{21}$

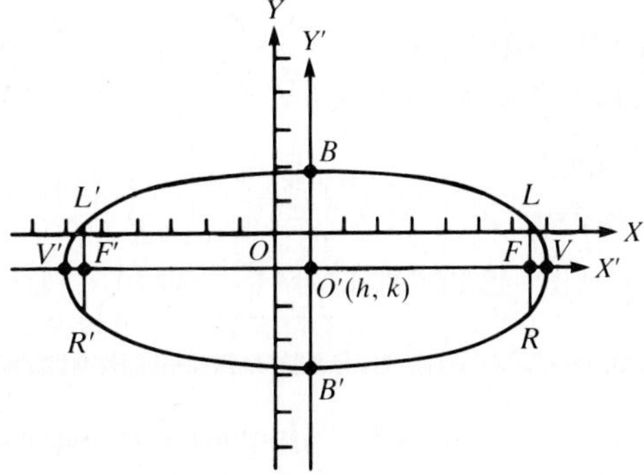

24. $25x^2 + 16y^2 - 50x - 32y - 359 = 0$

25. $F,F' = (\pm 4, 0)$; $V,V' = (\pm 5, 0)$, $B,B' = (0, \pm 3)$,
$L,R = (4, \pm \frac{9}{5})$, $L',R' = (-4, \pm \frac{9}{5})$

26. $\dfrac{(x+5)^2}{25} + \dfrac{(y+4)^2}{16} = 1$

7 THE HYPERBOLA

THIS CHAPTER IS ABOUT

- ☑ Simple Equation of the Hyperbola ($C = (0, 0)$)
- ☑ Properties of the Hyperbola
- ☑ Construction of a Hyperbola
- ☑ Asymptotes of a Hyperbola
- ☑ Conjugate Hyperbolas
- ☑ Equilateral Hyperbolas
- ☑ Other Equations of the Hyperbola ($C = (h, k)$)

7-1. Simple Equation of the Hyperbola ($C = (0, 0)$)

- A **hyperbola** is the locus of a point that moves so that the absolute value of the difference of the distances from the moving point to two fixed points is a constant.

The two fixed points are called the *foci*, and the midpoint of the line segment joining them is called the *center* of the hyperbola.

We can obtain a simple form of the equation of the hyperbola by taking the foci on the X-axis and the center at the origin. Thus if, as is shown in Figure 7-1, the foci are $F'(-c, 0)$ and $F(c, 0)$ and if $P(x, y)$ is any point on the hyperbola such that the difference of its distances from the foci is $2a$, then, by definition, we have the condition $F'P - FP = \pm 2a$. In terms of coordinates, this condition becomes

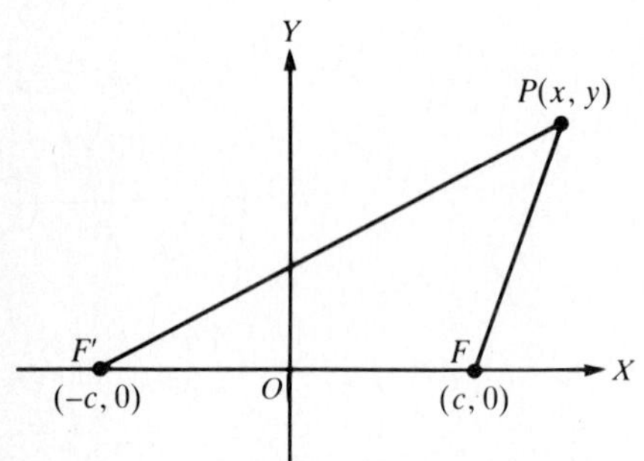

Figure 7-1. Obtaining a simple form for the equation of a hyperbola:

$$\sqrt{(x + c)^2 + y^2} - \sqrt{(x - c)^2 + y^2} = \pm 2a$$

which can be reduced (by squaring, reducing, and simplifying) to the form

$$(c^2 - a^2)x^2 - a^2y^2 = a^2(c^2 - a^2)$$

Then, since the difference of two sides of a triangle is always less than the third side, we have $|F'P| - |FP| < |F'F|$, or $2a < 2c$, for triangle $F'PF$; hence $a < c$ and $c^2 - a^2$ is a positive number. And finally, if we let b^2 represent this number (where b is real) and make the substitution $b^2 = c^2 - a^2$ into our equation, we get

$$b^2x^2 - a^2y^2 = a^2b^2$$

which can be divided through by a^2b^2 to give us the standard form of a hyperbola with its center on the origin and its axis on the X-axis:

X-HYPERBOLA (STANDARD FORM): C = (0, 0)

$$\frac{x^2}{a^2} - \frac{y^2}{b^2} = 1 \qquad \textbf{(7-1)}$$

Every point on the hyperbola has coordinates that satisfy eq. (7-1); and conversely, every point whose coordinates satisfy eq. (7-1) lies on the hyperbola.

7-2. Properties of the Hyperbola

A. Symmetry and excluded values

As in the corresponding case of the ellipse, the hyperbola represented algebraically by eq. (7-1) is symmetric with respect to both axes and to the

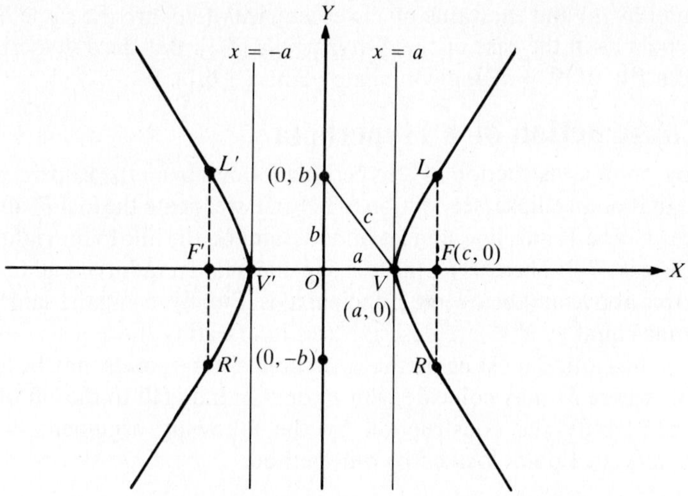

Figure 7-2. Properties of a hyperbola.

origin. That is, when x and y are replaced by their respective negatives in eq. (7-1), the equation is unchanged (see Section 6-2A).

To find excluded values, we solve eq. (7-1) for y and then for x:

$$y = \pm\frac{b}{a}\sqrt{x^2 - a^2} \qquad \text{and} \qquad x = \pm\frac{a}{b}\sqrt{y^2 + b^2}$$

So we can see that in order for y to be real, x must have values such that $x^2 \geq a^2$; i.e., no values of x BETWEEN $x = -a$ and $x = a$ $(-a < x < a)$ will give a point on the curve. We also see that x is real for all real values of y. But if $y = 0$, we find that $x = \pm a$; and if $x = 0$, then y is imaginary. So an X-hyperbola with center at the origin intersects the X-axis at $(\pm a, 0)$, but does not intersect the Y-axis. The curve therefore consists of two branches lying outside of the lines $x = \pm a$ and extending indefinitely away from both coordinate axes, as shown in Figure 7-2.

B. Geometric relationships

Hyperbolas have three axes: The line $F'F$ through the foci is the **principal axis**; the segment $V'V$, of length $2a$, is the **transverse axis**; and the line segment on the Y-axis between the points $(0, b)$ and $(0, -b)$, of length $2b$, is the **conjugate axis**. Then, of course, there are the half-axes: The lengths a and b are the **semi-transverse axis** and **semi-conjugate axis**, respectively. The points V' and V, at the ends of the transverse axis, are the *vertices* of the hyperbola. (See Figure 7-2.)

Looking at Figure 7-2, we can see from the Pythagorean relationship $c^2 = a^2 + b^2$ that the distance from the center $(0, 0)$ to a focus $(\pm c, 0)$ is the same as the distance from a vertex $(\pm a, 0)$ to an end of the conjugate axis $(0, \pm b)$. We can also see that the *latera recta*, the chords LR and $L'R'$ through the foci perpendicular to the principal axis, have coordinates $(\pm c, \pm y)$ and length $2b^2/a$. [Note that $y = (\pm b/a)(\sqrt{c^2 - a^2}) = \pm b^2/a$, since $c^2 - a^2 = b^2$; see Section 6-2C.] Finally, the eccentricity $e = c/a$, the value of which indicates the shape of the curve, must obviously be greater than 1 for the hyperbola because $c > a$.

C. Transverse axis on Y-axis

The equation of the hyperbola with transverse axis along the Y-axis and foci at $(0, \pm c)$ is given by

Y-HYPERBOLA (STANDARD FORM): C = (0, 0)

$$\frac{y^2}{a^2} - \frac{x^2}{b^2} = 1 \tag{7-2}$$

so that the lengths of the transverse axis ($2a$), conjugate axis ($2b$), and latus rectum ($2b^2/a$) and the value of the eccentricity (c/a) are the same in the Y-hyperbola as in the case of the X-hyperbola (7-1). But the Y-hyperbola has vertices VV' at $(0, \pm a)$ and conjugate points $(\pm b, 0)$.

7-3. Construction of a Hyperbola

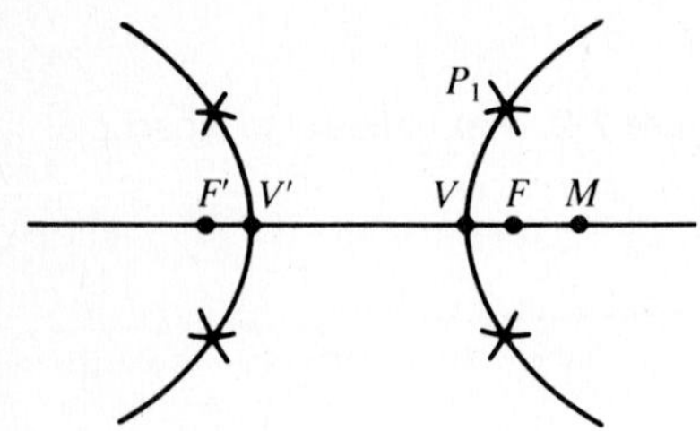

Figure 7-3. Construction of a hyperbola.

A point-by-point construction of a hyperbola follows from its properties, and is similar to that of an ellipse (see Section 6-3). First, we locate the foci F' and F and the vertices V' and V on a line, and let M be a point on the line to the right of F, as shown in Figure 7-3. Then, using the foci as centers and a radius equal to MV, we describe arcs above and below the principal axis. Finally, using the same centers and a radius equal to MV', we describe arcs intersecting those just drawn. The four points thus found must lie on the hyperbola. Other points may be found by varying M, where M may coincide with F' or F or may fall to the left of F'.

We can verify the construction by the following argument, where P_1 represents a typical point located by our method:

If $\quad MV' = F'P_1 \quad$ and $\quad MV = FP_1$

then $\quad F'P_1 - FP_1 = MV' - MV = VV'$

VV' is the length of the transverse axis and a constant value.

7-4. Asymptotes of a Hyperbola

The hyperbola $b^2x^2 - a^2y^2 = a^2b^2$ consists of two branches opening outward to the right and left of the Y-axis. Now let's begin with a hyperbola and draw a line through the origin intersecting its branches at the points P and P' (see Figure 7-4). The equation of this line in slope-intercept form (eq. 3-2) is $y = mx$ (because $b = 0$). We then substitute mx for y in the equation of the hyperbola, and simplify:

$$b^2x^2 - a^2(mx)^2 = a^2b^2$$

$$x^2(b^2 - a^2m^2) = a^2b^2$$

$$x = \pm\frac{ab}{\sqrt{b^2 - a^2m^2}}$$

So we have an expression for the abscissas of the points of intersection of the line and the curve.

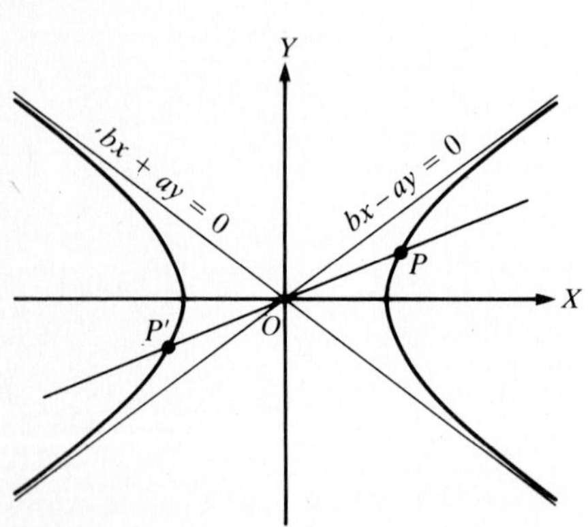

Figure 7-4. Asymptotes of a hyperbola.

Looking at Figure 7-4, we can see that, as P moves to the right along the curve (or as P' moves to the left), the numerical value of x increases without limit. And since we know that a and b are fixed numbers, we therefore know that the denominator $\sqrt{b^2 - a^2m^2}$ approaches zero as x increases without bound. So, when $b^2 - a^2m^2 = 0$, we have $m = \pm b/a$, and the equation $y = mx$ becomes $y = \pm bx/a$, or $bx \pm ay = 0$. Thus, as the numerical value of x increases, the hyperbola gradually approaches two lines, $bx - ay = 0$ and $bx + ay = 0$, that pass through the origin with respective slopes b/a and $-b/a$. But the gradually approaching curve never approaches close enough to touch, so the lines $bx \pm ay = 0$ are *asymptotes* of the hyperbola $b^2x^2 - a^2y^2 = a^2b^2$:

- An **asymptote** of a curve is a straight line such that the perpendicular distance from the line to a point on the curve becomes—and remains—less than any assignable positive value as the point on the curve recedes indefinitely from the origin.

There's an easy way to find the equations of the asymptotes: Make the right member of the equation zero and then factor. Thus

$$\frac{x^2}{a^2} - \frac{y^2}{b^2} = 0 \qquad \text{or} \qquad b^2x^2 - a^2y^2 = 0$$

factors into

$$bx - ay = 0 \qquad \text{and} \qquad bx + ay = 0$$

which are the equations of the asymptotes. And if the equation of the hyperbola is $b^2y^2 - a^2x^2 = a^2b^2$ (with the foci on the Y-axis), the equations of the asymptotes are $by \pm ax = 0$.

- All hyperbolas are asymptotic—virtually by definition: The asymptotes define the shape the curve may take as it recedes indefinitely from the origin.

Asymptotes are therefore very useful in sketching a hyperbola. For example, if we take the transverse axis $2a$ and the conjugate axis $2b$, as shown in Figure 7-5, we can construct a rectangle whose center is the center of the hyperbola and whose sides are $2a$ and $2b$, parallel to the transverse and conjugate axes, respectively. And the diagonals of this rectangle have slopes b/a and $-b/a$, so they become—when extended—the asymptotes of the hyperbola. Thus to sketch a hyperbola, we draw the asymptotes first, and then use them as guidelines for the curve. The curve is tangent to the rectangle at each vertex, passes through the end points of the latera recta, and recedes from the origin within the bounds defined by the asymptotes. And if we draw a circle around the rectangle, using the diagonals of the rectangle as diameters, we see that the circle passes through the foci of the hyperbola.

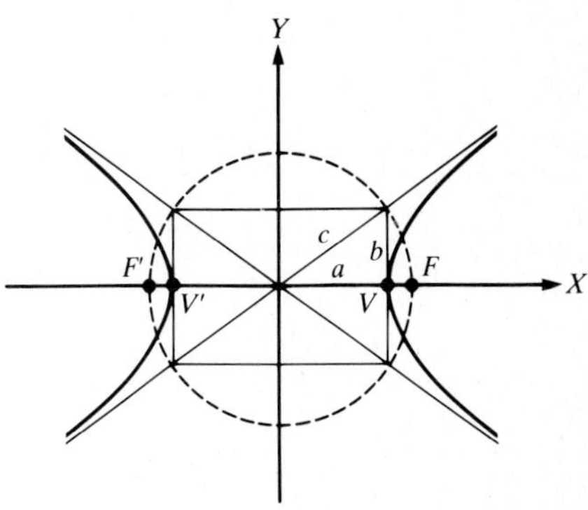

Figure 7-5. Sketching a hyperbola.

EXAMPLE 7-1: Given the hyperbola $49y^2 - 16x^2 = 196$, find **(a)** the values of a, b, c, and e; **(b)** the coordinates of the foci, the vertices, and the end points of the latera recta; **(c)** the length of a latus rectum; and **(d)** the equations of the asymptotes. **(e)** Sketch the curve.

Solution:

(a) Reduce the equation to standard form:

$$\frac{49y^2}{196} - \frac{16x^2}{196} = \frac{y^2}{4} - \frac{x^2}{49/4} = 1$$

Hence $a = \sqrt{4} = 2$ and $b = \sqrt{49/4} = 7/2$, so

$$c = \sqrt{a^2 + b^2} = \sqrt{\frac{16}{4} + \frac{49}{4}} = \frac{1}{2}\sqrt{65} \qquad \text{and} \qquad e = \frac{c}{a} = \frac{1}{4}\sqrt{65}$$

(b) Since the term containing y is positive, you know that the transverse axis is along the Y-axis. Now you can find the coordinates of the desired points:

$$\text{foci:} \quad F,F' = (0, \pm c) = (0, \pm\tfrac{1}{2}\sqrt{65})$$

$$\text{vertices:} \quad V,V' = (0, \pm a) = (0, \pm 2)$$

$$\text{ends of the latera recta:} \quad L,R \text{ and } L',R' = \left(\pm\frac{b^2}{a}, \pm c\right) = \left(\pm\frac{49}{8}, \pm\frac{1}{2}\sqrt{65}\right)$$

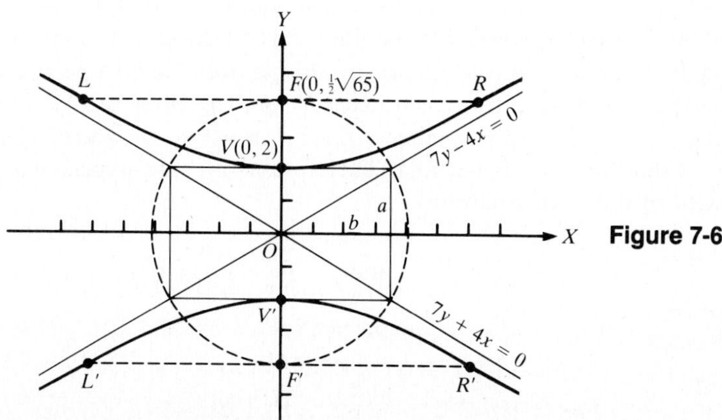

Figure 7-6

(c) The length of a latus rectum is $2b^2/a = 49/4$.
(d) The equations of the asymptotes can be found by factoring $49y^2 - 16x^2 = 0$, which gives you $7y - 4x = 0$ and $7y + 4x = 0$ as the asymptotes.
(e) These data, taken together, give you everything you could ever want to know about this hyperbola, so you can construct the hyperbola shown in Figure 7-6. [*Note: Do* draw the asymptotes first, and all the rest will follow.]

EXAMPLE 7-2: Given the hyperbola $9x^2 - 16y^2 = 144$, find **(a)** the values of a, b, c, and e; **(b)** the coordinates of the foci, the vertices, and the ends of the latera recta; **(c)** the length of a latus rectum; and **(d)** the equations of the asymptotes. **(e)** Sketch the curve.

Solution:
(a) If $9x^2 - 16y^2 = 144$, then $\dfrac{9x^2}{144} - \dfrac{16y^2}{144} = 1$ and

$$\frac{x^2}{16} - \frac{y^2}{9} = 1 \qquad \text{(standard form)}$$

The term containing x is positive, so the transverse axis is the X-axis, and

$$a = \sqrt{16} = 4, \qquad b = \sqrt{9} = 3, \qquad c = \sqrt{a^2 + b^2} = 5, \qquad e = \frac{c}{a} = \frac{5}{4}$$

(b) By definition,

$$F,F' = (\pm c, 0) = (\pm 5, 0) \qquad V,V' = (\pm a, 0) = (\pm 4, 0)$$

$$L,R = \left(c, \pm\frac{b^2}{a}\right) = \left(5, \pm\frac{9}{4}\right) \qquad L',R' = \left(-c, \pm\frac{b^2}{a}\right) = \left(-5, \pm\frac{9}{4}\right)$$

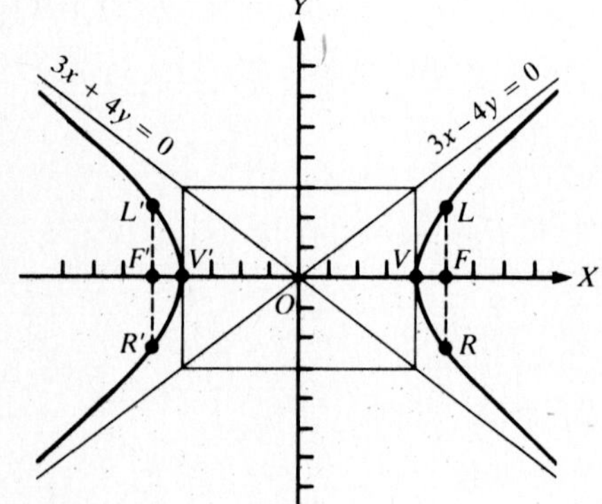

Figure 7-7

(c) $LR = \dfrac{2b^2}{a} = \dfrac{9}{2}$

(d) Factor:

$$9x^2 - 16y^2 = 0$$
$$(3x + 4y)(3x - 4y) = 0$$

Therefore the asymptotes are $3x \pm 4y = 0$.
(e) Draw the rectangle with sides $2a = 8$ and $2b = 6$ parallel to the X,Y-axes; then draw the asymptotes as the extended diagonals of the rectangle. Plot the points L and R at $(5, \pm\frac{9}{4})$. Finally, draw *half* the hyperbola—tangent to the vertical side of the rectangle at the X-axis, passing through L and R, and receding from the origin with the asymptotes as guidelines. Do the other half by symmetry. See Figure 7-7.

7-5. Conjugate Hyperbolas

- Two hyperbolas are **conjugate hyperbolas** when the transverse axis of each is the conjugate axis of the other.

In other words, two hyperbolas are conjugate when the semi-transverse and the semi-conjugate axes a_1 and b_1 of one hyperbola are equal, *respectively*, to the semi-conjugate and semi-transverse axes b_2 and a_2 of a second hyperbola. Thus, when $a_1 = b_2$ and $b_1 = a_2$, then $a_1{}^2 + b_1{}^2 = b_2{}^2 + a_2{}^2$, and so $a^2 + b^2$ has the same value for each hyperbola. Therefore, conjugate hyperbolas may be represented by a pair of equations

CONJUGATE HYPERBOLAS

$$\frac{x^2}{a^2} - \frac{y^2}{b^2} = 1 \qquad \text{and} \qquad \frac{y^2}{b^2} - \frac{x^2}{a^2} = 1$$

or

$$\frac{x^2}{a^2} - \frac{y^2}{b^2} = 1 \qquad \text{and} \qquad \frac{x^2}{a^2} - \frac{y^2}{b^2} = -1$$

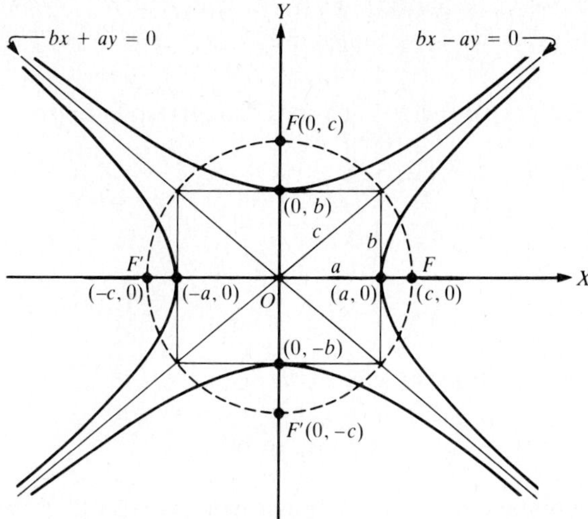

Figure 7-8. Conjugate *X*- and *Y*-hyperbolas:

$$\frac{x^2}{a^2} - \frac{y^2}{b^2} = 1 \quad \text{and} \quad \frac{y^2}{b^2} - \frac{x^2}{a^2} = 1$$

[Note that the coordinates labeled in the figure are referred to the *X*-hyperbola—except for $F(0, c)$ and $F'(0, -c)$.]

Axis	X-Hyperbola	Y-Hyperbola
Transverse	$(\pm a_X, 0)$	$(0, \pm b_X)$, where $b_X = a_Y$
Conjugate	$(0, \pm b_X)$	$(\pm a_X, 0)$, where $a_X = b_Y$
Principal	$(\pm c, 0)$	$(0, \pm c)$, where $c = c_X = c_Y$

Because $\sqrt{a^2 + b^2}$ has the same value in both conjugate hyperbolas, their foci must be equidistant ($\pm c$ units) from the center, as we see in Figure 7-8. And conjugate hyperbolas have common asymptotes $bx \pm ay = 0$, which we verify by setting the left-hand sides of each equation equal to zero and factoring.

note: $y^2/b^2 - x^2/a^2 = 1$ is exactly the same as $x^2/a^2 - y^2/b^2 = -1$; so you can easily write the conjugate of a simple hyperbola by changing the sign of the constant term in its standard equation.

7-6. Equilateral Hyperbolas

- When the transverse and conjugate axes of a hyperbola are the same length, the hyperbola is an **equilateral hyperbola**.

Thus, when $b = a$, the hyperbolas $b^2x^2 - a^2y^2 = a^2b^2$ and $b^2y^2 - a^2x^2 = a^2b^2$ become

EQUILATERAL HYPERBOLAS

$$x^2 - y^2 = a^2 \quad \text{and} \quad y^2 - x^2 = a^2$$

with center at the origin and foci on the *X*- and *Y*-axes, respectively.

note: A circle is to the ellipse what an equilateral hyperbola is to the hyperbola. When the center is at the origin and the major and minor axes *a* and *b* are equal, the ellipses $b^2x^2 + a^2y^2 = a^2b^2$ and $b^2y^2 + a^2x^2 = a^2b^2$ both become the circle $x^2 + y^2 = r^2$ because $a^2 = r^2$ when $C = (0, 0)$.

The asymptotes of an equilateral hyperbola must meet at right angles, as we see in Figure 7-9, where the asymptotes of $x^2 - y^2 = a^2$ are $x \pm y = 0$—two perpendicular lines. (Because of this 'right-angled-ness', an equilateral hyperbola is often called "*rectangular.*") Figure 7-9 also shows that the rectangle associated with equilateral hyperbolas is a square.

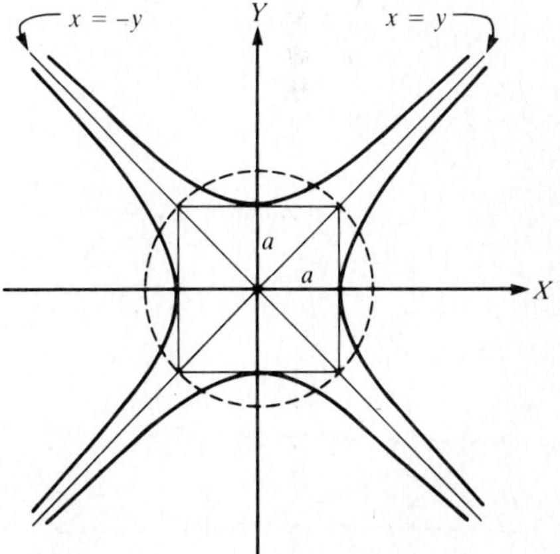

Figure 7-9. Conjugate equilateral hyperbolas.

The hyperbola *conjugate* to an equilateral hyperbola is the same curve, although it is differently placed. Thus, the conjugate of $x^2 - y^2 = a^2$ is $x^2 - y^2 = -a^2$ or $y^2 - x^2 = a^2$, which represents the original curve with foci on the *Y*-axis. (See good old Figure 7-9 again.)

7-7. Other Equations of the Hyperbola ($C = (h, k)$)

A. Standard (translation) forms

By making use of the translation formulas $x' = x - h$ and $y' = y - k$, as in the case of the ellipse (see Section 6-4), we can find the equation of the hyperbola having center $C(h, k)$ and transverse axis parallel to the *X*-axis:

X-HYPERBOLA (STANDARD FORM): C = (h, k)

$$\frac{(x-h)^2}{a^2} - \frac{(y-k)^2}{b^2} = 1 \qquad \textbf{(7-3)}$$

And if the transverse axis is parallel to the Y-axis, the corresponding equation is

Y-HYPERBOLA (STANDARD FORM): C = (h, k)

$$\frac{(y-k)^2}{a^2} - \frac{(x-h)^2}{b^2} = 1 \qquad \textbf{(7-4)}$$

B. General form

Either of the standard equations may be expressed as

HYPERBOLA (GENERAL FORM)

$$Ax^2 + Cy^2 + Dx + Ey + F = 0 \qquad \textbf{(7-5)}$$

by expanding the binomial terms and clearing fractions in eqs. (7-3) or (7-4). Conversely, every equation in the general form (7-5)—in which the constants A and C must have DIFFERENT signs—represents a hyperbola with axes parallel to the coordinate axes. (If A and C have the SAME sign, your "hyperbola" is an *ellipse*: See Section 6-4B.) And every general equation (7-5) can be converted to standard form (7-3) or (7-4) by completing the squares.

EXAMPLE 7-3: Given the hyperbola $4x^2 - 9y^2 - 16x + 18y - 29 = 0$, determine **(a)** the values of a, b, c, and e; **(b)** the coordinates of the center, foci, and vertices; **(c)** the lengths of the latus rectum and the transverse and conjugate axes; **(d)** the equations of the principal axis and asymptotes for the hyperbola. **(e)** Find the equation of the conjugate hyperbola and sketch both curves.

Solution: Completing the squares, you can express the equation in standard form (always a good first move!):

$$4(x-2)^2 - 9(y-1)^2 = 36$$

$$\frac{(x-2)^2}{9} - \frac{(y-1)^2}{4} = 1$$

(a) The term containing x being positive, you know that the transverse axis is parallel to the X-axis, and so the equation is of the form (7-3):

$$\frac{(x-h)^2}{a^2} - \frac{(y-k)^2}{b^2} = 1$$

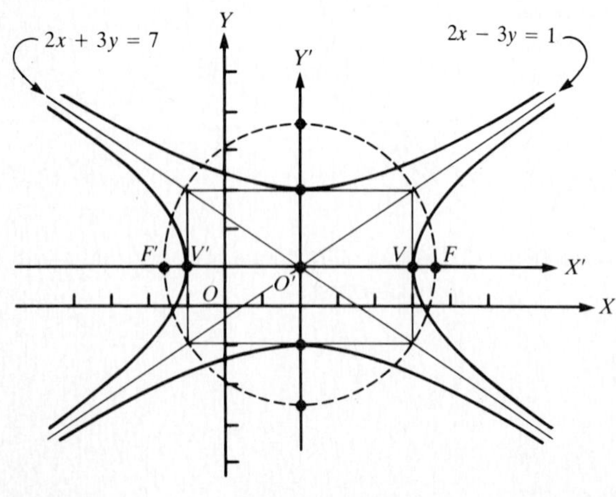

Figure 7-10

Thus

$$a = \sqrt{9} = 3, \qquad b = \sqrt{4} = 2,$$

$$c = \sqrt{a^2 + b^2} = \sqrt{13}, \qquad e = \frac{c}{a} = \frac{1}{3}\sqrt{13}$$

(b) The coordinates of the center are $(h, k) = (2, 1)$, and so the foci are $F, F' = (h \pm c, k) = (2 \pm \sqrt{13}, 1)$, and the vertices are $V = (h + a, k) = (5, 1)$ and $V' = (h - a, k) = (-1, 1)$.

(c) The lengths of the latus rectum and the transverse and conjugate axes are, respectively,

$$LR = \frac{2b^2}{a} = \frac{8}{3}, \qquad 2a = 6, \qquad 2b = 4$$

(d) The equation of the principal axis is $y - 1 = 0$. The asymptotes are the factors of the left-hand member of the standard equation, set equal to zero:

$$4(x-2)^2 - 9(y-1)^2 = (2x - 3y - 1)(2x + 3y - 7)$$

so the asymptotes are

$$2x - 3y - 1 = 0 \qquad \text{and} \qquad 2x + 3y - 7 = 0$$

(e) The standard form of the equation of the conjugate hyperbola is

$$\frac{(y-1)^2}{4} - \frac{(x-2)^2}{9} = 1 \qquad \text{or} \qquad \frac{(x-2)^2}{9} - \frac{(y-1)^2}{4} = -1$$

which has the general form

$$4x^2 - 9y^2 - 16x + 18y + 43 = 0$$

The sketch is shown in Figure 7-10.

SUMMARY

1. The hyperbola is the locus of a point P that moves in such a way that the absolute value of the difference of its distances from two fixed points—foci F, F'—is a constant. (The midpoint of the line segment joining F and F' is the center C of the hyperbola.)

2. Any hyperbola has three axes—
- the principal axis FF'; length $2c$
- the transverse axis VV': a line segment lying on FF'; length $2a$; $2a < 2c$
- the conjugate axis: the perpendicular bisector of FF'; length $2b$

—such that $c^2 = a^2 + b^2$.

3. The end points of the transverse axis are the two vertices V and V' of the curve, and the length a (from the vertex to the center) is the semi-transverse axis. The length b is the semi-conjugate axis.

4. The standard forms of the equation of a hyperbola are

	FF' on X-axis	FF' on Y-axis
$C = (0, 0)$:	$\frac{x^2}{a^2} - \frac{y^2}{b^2} = 1$	$\frac{y^2}{a^2} - \frac{x^2}{b^2} = 1$
	FF' parallel to X-axis	FF' parallel to Y-axis
$C = (h, k)$:	$\frac{(x-h)^2}{a^2} - \frac{(y-k)^2}{b^2} = 1$	$\frac{(y-k)^2}{a^2} - \frac{(x-h)^2}{b^2} = 1$

5. The general equation of the hyperbola is

$$Ax^2 + Cy^2 + Dx + Ey + F = 0$$

where A and C differ in sign.

6. An asymptote of a curve is a straight line such that the perpendicular distance from the line to a point on the curve becomes—and remains—less than any assignable positive value as the curve recedes indefinitely from the origin. Hyperbolas are asymptotic curves.

7. The asymptotes of a hyperbola, which can be determined by factoring the left-hand side of the standard equation of the hyperbola, serve as guidelines for sketching the curve.

8. Two hyperbolas are said to be conjugate hyperbolas when the transverse axis of each is the conjugate axis of the other.

9. A hyperbola is said to be an equilateral hyperbola when its transverse and conjugate axes are of the same length.

10. The equation of the hyperbola in general form may be reduced to standard form by completing the square.

RAISE YOUR GRADES

Given the equation of a hyperbola containing no linear terms in x and y, can you...?

☑ reduce it to standard form
☑ find the values of a, b, c, and e
☑ find the coordinates of the foci, the vertices, and the end points of the latera recta
☑ find the length of the latus rectum and the equations of the asymptotes

Given the equation of a hyperbola in general form, can you...?

☑ put it in standard form
☑ find the values of a, b, c, and e
☑ find the coordinates of the center, foci, and vertices
☑ determine the lengths of the latus rectum, transverse axis, and conjugate axis
☑ write the equations of the principal axis and the asymptotes

SOLVED PROBLEMS

Simple Equation of the Hyperbola

Asymptotes of a hyperbola

PROBLEM 7-1 Given the hyperbola $81y^2 - 144x^2 = 11\,664$, find (**a**) the values of $a, b, c,$ and e; (**b**) the coordinates of the foci, the vertices, and the end points of the latera recta; (**c**) the length of a latus rectum; and (**d**) the equations of the asymptotes. (**e**) Sketch the curve.

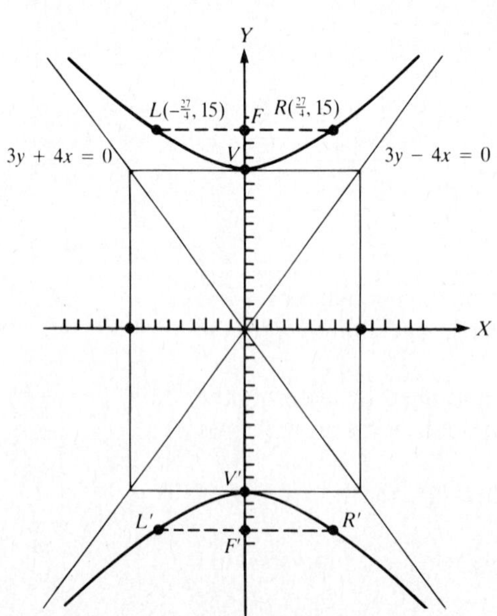

Figure 7-11

Solution:

(**a**) Divide the terms of the given equation by 11 664 to get the standard form (7-2):

$$\frac{y^2}{144} - \frac{x^2}{81} = 1$$

from which you see that the transverse axis is on the Y-axis and $a = \sqrt{144} = 12$, $b = \sqrt{81} = 9$, so

$$c = \sqrt{a^2 + b^2} = \sqrt{144 + 81} = 15, \quad e = \frac{c}{a} = \frac{5}{4}$$

(**b**) The foci F,F' are at $(0, \pm c) = (0, \pm 15)$; the vertices V,V' are at $(0, \pm a) = (0, \pm 12)$; the ends of the latera recta L,R and L',R' are at

$$L,R = \left(\pm\frac{b^2}{a}, c\right) = \left(\pm\frac{27}{4}, 15\right)$$

$$L',R' = \left(\pm\frac{b^2}{a}, -c\right) = \left(\pm\frac{27}{4}, -15\right)$$

(**c**) The length of the latus rectum is $|LR| = 2b^2/a = 27/2$.

(d) Setting $81y^2 - 144x^2$ equal to zero and factoring, you get $(3y + 4x)(3y - 4x) = 0$, so the equations of the asymptotes are $3y \pm 4x = 0$.

(e) To sketch the figure (Figure 7-11), draw the rectangle with sides $2a = 24$ and $2b = 18$ and diagonals $3y \pm 4x = 0$. Plot the points L and R, and extend the diagonals (asymptotes) beyond these points. Finally, sketch the hyperbola, so that its vertex is tangent to the rectangle at the Y-axis and its curve recedes from the origin, passing through L and R and extending indefinitely within the guidelines of the asymptotes. Do the other half of the curve by symmetry.

PROBLEM 7-2 Sketch the curve $36x^2 - 64y^2 = 2304$.

Solution: Dividing through by 2304 reduces the equation to standard form (7-1):

$$\frac{x^2}{64} - \frac{y^2}{36} = 1$$

This is the equation of a hyperbola in which the transverse axis is on the X-axis and $a = 8$, $b = 6$, and $c = \sqrt{64 + 36} = 10$. So the vertices are $V, V' = (\pm 8, 0)$, the foci are $F, F' = (\pm 10, 0)$, and each latus rectum has a length of $2b^2/a = 9$. The equations of the asymptotes (found by factoring $9x^2 - 16y^2 = 0$) are $3x - 4y = 0$ and $3x + 4y = 0$. From these data, you can draw the curve shown in Figure 7-12.

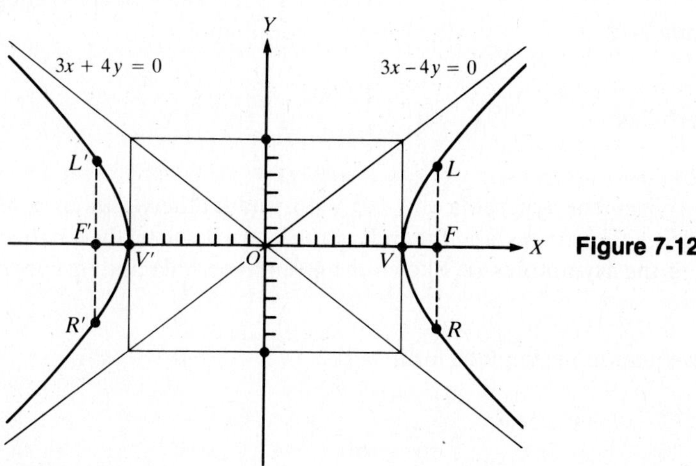

Figure 7-12

Conjugate hyperbolas

PROBLEM 7-3 Determine the equations of the hyperbolas that are conjugate to the hyperbolas **(a)** $4x^2 - 9y^2 = 36$; **(b)** $x^2 - y^2 = 1$; **(c)** $y^2 - x^2/4 = 1$; **(d)** $9y^2 - x^2 + 8x - 7 = 0$.

Solution:

(a) In standard form $4x^2 - 9y^2 = 36$ is $x^2/9 - y^2/4 = 1$. And, since the conjugate of $x^2/a^2 - y^2/b^2 = 1$ is $y^2/b^2 - x^2/a^2 = 1$, the conjugate of the given equation is

$$\frac{y^2}{4} - \frac{x^2}{9} = 1$$

(b) The conjugate of $x^2 - y^2 = 1$ is $y^2 - x^2 = 1$.

(c) The conjugate of $y^2 - x^2/4 = 1$ is $x^2/4 - y^2 = 1$.

(d) Change the equation to standard form by completing the square:

$$9y^2 - x^2 + 8x - 7 = 0$$

$$9y^2 - (x^2 - 8x + 16) = -9$$

$$(x - 4)^2 - 9y^2 = 9$$

$$\frac{(x - 4)^2}{9} - y^2 = 1$$

So the conjugate is $y^2 - \dfrac{(x - 4)^2}{9} = 1$.

PROBLEM 7-4 Given the hyperbola $4x^2 - y^2 + 36 = 0$, write the equation of its conjugate hyperbola and sketch the two conjugates.

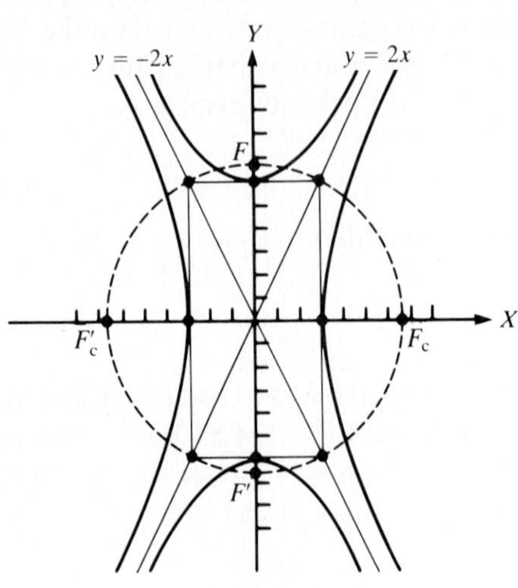

Figure 7-13

Solution: In standard form the equations of the conjugates are

$$\frac{y^2}{36} - \frac{x^2}{9} = 1 \qquad \text{and} \qquad \frac{x^2}{9} - \frac{y^2}{36} = 1$$

Thus the given hyperbola has its transverse axis on the Y-axis and $a = 6, b = 3, c = 3\sqrt{5}$; so its vertices and foci are respectively $V,V' = (0, \pm 6)$ and $F,F' = (0, \pm 3\sqrt{5})$, and its asymptotes are $y = \pm 2x$ (found by factoring $y^2/36 - x^2/9 = 0$).

The conjugate hyperbola must therefore have $a = 3$ and $b = 6$ (by definition), which means that the value of c is the same as that of the given hyperbola ($c = 3\sqrt{5}$), and its vertices and foci are at $(\pm 3, 0)$ and $(\pm 3\sqrt{5}, 0)$, respectively. The conjugate hyperbola has the same asymptotes as the given hyperbola. The sketch of the conjugate hyperbolas is shown in Figure 7-13.

Equilateral hyperbolas

PROBLEM 7-5 Given the hyperbola $y^2 - x^2 = 16$, find **(a)** the values of a, b, c, and e; **(b)** the coordinates of the foci, the vertices, and the ends of the latera recta; **(c)** the length of a latus rectum; **(d)** the equations of the asymptotes. **(e)** Sketch the given hyperbola and its conjugate.

Solution:

(a) Rewriting the equation in standard form

$$\frac{y^2}{16} - \frac{x^2}{16} = 1$$

you see that

$$a = 4, \qquad b = 4, \qquad c = 4\sqrt{2}, \qquad e = \sqrt{2}$$

so the hyperbola must be equilateral, since $a = b = 4$.

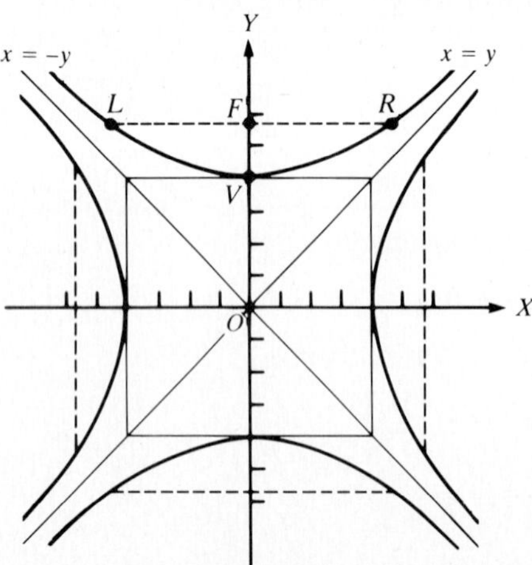

Figure 7-14

(b) $F,F' = (0, \pm c) = (0, \pm 4\sqrt{2})$

$V,V' = (0, \pm a) = (0, \pm 4)$

$$L,R = \left(\pm\frac{b^2}{a}, c\right) = (\pm 4, 4\sqrt{2})$$

$$L',R' = \left(\pm\frac{b^2}{a}, -c\right) = (\pm 4, -4\sqrt{2})$$

(c) $LR = \dfrac{2b^2}{a} = 8$

(d) Since $y^2 - x^2 = (y + x)(y - x)$, the equations of the asymptotes are $y \pm x = 0$.

(e) The sketch of the equilateral hyperbola $y^2 - x^2 = 16$ and its conjugate $x^2 - y^2 = 16$ is shown in Figure 7-14. Notice that the conjugate hyperbola is the same curve on a different axis.

PROBLEM 7-6 Find the equation of the equilateral hyperbola with center at $(2, -5)$ and a vertex at $(6, -5)$.

Solution: Here you know that $a = 4$, since that is the distance between the center and vertex. And you also know that the axis is parallel to the X-axis. So the equation you can write from the definition is

$$(x-2)^2 - (y+5)^2 = 4^2 \qquad \text{or} \qquad \frac{(x-2)^2}{16} - \frac{(y+5)^2}{16} = 1$$

Other Equations of the Hyperbola $(C = (h, k))$

PROBLEM 7-7 Change the equation $25x^2 - 16y^2 + 150x + 32y - 191 = 0$ to standard form.

Solution: Since this equation is in the general form $Ax^2 + Cy^2 + Dx + Ey + F = 0$ where A and C have opposite signs, the graph of this equation must be a hyperbola. And the general equation of a hyperbola can be changed to standard form by completing the squares:

$$25x^2 + 150x - 16y^2 + 32y - 191 = 0$$

$$25(x^2 + 6x) - 16(y^2 - 2y) - 191 = 0$$

$$25(x^2 + 6x + 9) - 16(y^2 - 2y + 1) = 191 + 225 - 16$$

$$25(x+3)^2 - 16(y-1)^2 = 400$$

Finally, by dividing through by 400 and writing 4^2 for 16 and 5^2 for 25, you can write

$$\frac{(x+3)^2}{4^2} - \frac{(y-1)^2}{5^2} = 1$$

which is the standard form $(x-h)^2/a^2 - (y-k)^2/b^2 = 1$ (eq. 7-3) of the given equation.

PROBLEM 7-8 Draw the curve defined by $9(x+3)^2 - 4(y-2)^2 = 36$, showing **(a)** the coordinates of the vertices, the foci, and the ends of the conjugate axis and **(b)** the asymptotes of the hyperbola. **(c)** Write the equations of the asymptotes. **(d)** Find the eccentricity.

Solution: In standard form $(x-h)^2/a^2 - (y-k)^2/b^2 = 1$ the equation becomes

$$\frac{(x+3)^2}{4} - \frac{(y-2)^2}{9} = 1$$

which indicates that you have an X-hyperbola (eq. 7-3) with center O' at $(h, k) = (-3, 2)$ and that $a = \sqrt{4} = 2$, $b = \sqrt{9} = 3$, $c = \sqrt{4+9} = \sqrt{13}$.

Now you can draw the hyperbola shown in Figure 7-15, so that its principal axis FF' is $2c = 2\sqrt{13}$ units long, its transverse axis VV' (lying on FF') is $2a = 4$ units long, its conjugate axis (perpendicular to FF') is $2b = 6$ units long, and all three axes have a midpoint at $O'(-3, 2)$.

(a) The coordinates shown in Figure 7-15 are

vertices V, V': $(h \pm a, k) = (-3 \pm 2, 2)$
foci F, F': $(h \pm c, k) = (-3 \pm \sqrt{13}, 2)$
ends of conjugate axis: $(h, k \pm b) = (-3, 2 \pm 3)$

(b) Figure 7-15 also shows the asymptotes of the hyperbola, which are drawn as the extended diagonals of a rectangle whose sides have lengths $2a = 4$ and $2b = 6$ (parallel and equal to the transverse and conjugate axes, respectively) and whose diagonals intersect at $O'(-3, 2)$. These asymptotes prescribe—and proscribe—the shape the curve may take as it recedes

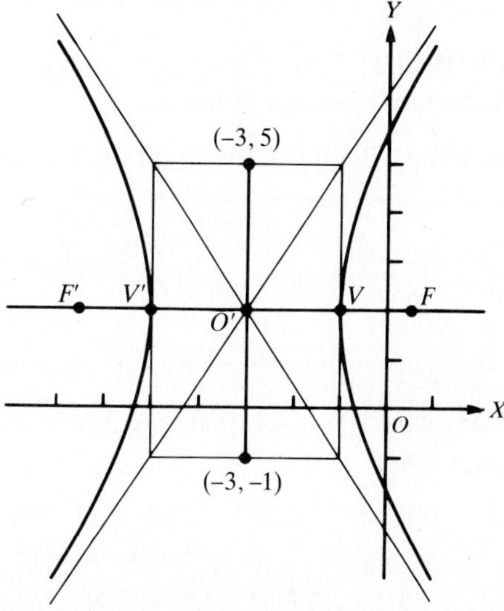

Figure 7-15

indefinitely from the origin; i.e., the locus approaches—but never touches—the asymptotes.

(c) The equations of the asymptotes, found by setting the right-hand side of the standard equation of the hyperbola equal to zero and factoring are $9(x + 3)^2 = 4(y - 2)^2$ or $x + 3 = \pm\frac{2}{3}(y - 2)$.

(d) The eccentricity is $e = c/a = \sqrt{13}/2$.

PROBLEM 7-9 Sketch the locus of the hyperbola $16x^2 - 9y^2 - 32x - 18y = 137$.

Solution: Completing the squares in x and y

$$16x^2 - 32x - 9y^2 - 18y = 137$$

$$16(x^2 - 2x) - 9(y^2 + 2y) = 137$$

$$16(x^2 - 2x + 1) - 9(y^2 + 2y + 1) = 137 + 16 - 9$$

$$16(x - 1)^2 - 9(y + 1)^2 = 144$$

and dividing through by 144, you get the standard form (7-3):

$$\frac{(x-1)^2}{9} - \frac{(y+1)^2}{16} = 1$$

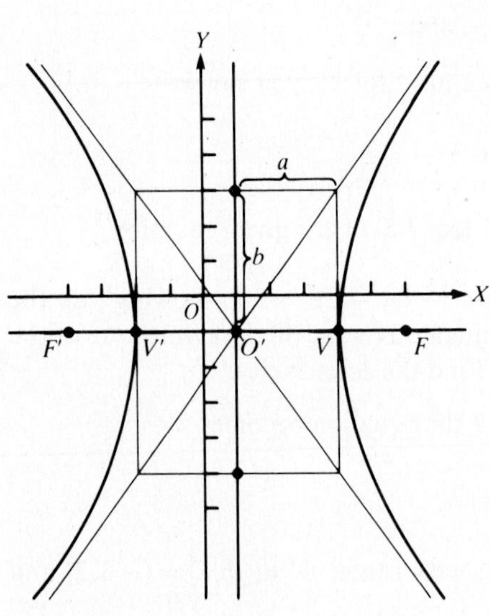

Figure 7-16

So the center $O'(h, k) = (1, -1)$, and $a = 3$, $b = 4$, $c = 5$. The principal axis FF' of length $2c = 10$ and the transverse axis VV' of length $2a = 6$ are parallel to the X-axis; and the conjugate axis of length $2b = 8$ is parallel to the Y-axis. The asymptotes have the equations

$$y + 1 = \pm\frac{4}{3}(x - 1)$$

Now you can sketch the locus, as shown in Figure 7-16. Check your sketch against the following points:

vertices:	$V' = (-2, -1)$	$V = (4, -1)$
foci:	$F' = (-4, -1)$	$F = (6, -1)$
ends of conjugate axis:	$(1, -5)$	$(1, 3)$

PROBLEM 7-10 Draw the graph of $12y^2 - 4x^2 + 72y + 16x + 44 = 0$ and determine all the important elements of the curve.

Solution: Reducing the equation to standard form, you get

$$12(y^2 + 6y + 9) - 4(x^2 - 4x + 4) = -44 + 108 - 16$$

$$12(y + 3)^2 - 4(x - 2)^2 = 48$$

$$\frac{(y+3)^2}{4} - \frac{(x-2)^2}{12} = 1$$

from which you see that $a = 2$, $b = 2\sqrt{3}$, $c = \sqrt{4 + 12} = 4$, and $(h, k) = (2, -3)$. Hence $O' = (2, -3)$ and

foci $F, F' = (2, -3 \pm c)$:	$F(2, 1)$	$F'(2, -7)$
vertices $V, V' = (2, -3 \pm a)$:	$V(2, -1)$	$V'(2, -5)$
ends of conjugate axis $= (2 \pm b, -3)$:	$(2 + 2\sqrt{3}, -3)$	$(2 - 2\sqrt{3}, -3)$

The sides $2a = 4$ and $2b = 4\sqrt{3}$ pass through the ends of the conjugate axis and the vertices, respectively, as shown in Figure 7-17. The length of each latus rectum is $2b^2/a = 12$, and therefore the ends of each latus rectum are 6 units from a focus:

$$F(2, 1): \quad L = (-6 + 2, 1) = (-4, 1)$$
$$R = (6 + 2, 1) = (8, 1)$$
$$F'(2, -7): \quad L' = (-6 + 2, -7) = (-4, -7)$$
$$R' = (6 + 2, -7) = (8, -7)$$

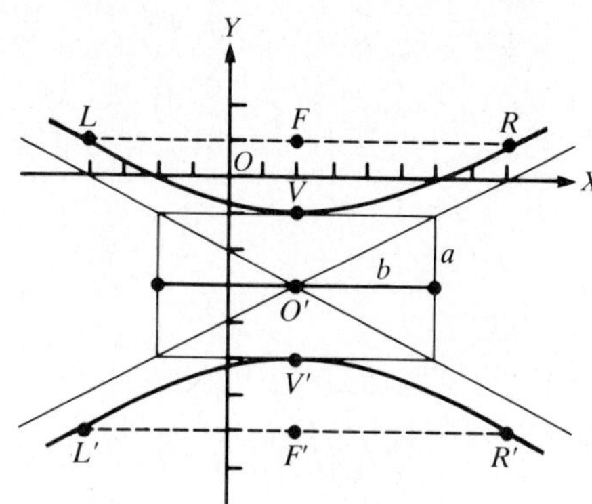

Figure 7-17

The extended diagonals of the rectangle are the asymptotes

$$\frac{y+3}{2} + \frac{x-2}{2\sqrt{3}} = 0 \quad \text{and} \quad \frac{y+3}{2} - \frac{x-2}{2\sqrt{3}} = 0$$

PROBLEM 7-11 Find the equation of the curve described by a point that moves so that the difference of its distance from $(4, -3)$ and $(4, 10)$ is always 10 units.

Solution: Since the difference of the point's distance from two fixed points is constant, you know that the curve is a hyperbola—and it must be a Y-hyperbola since the given points, or foci, are in a vertical line $x = 4$. Also, since the difference of the distance between the foci is given as 10, you know that $2a = 10$, and the distance between the foci $2c = 10 + 3 = 13$. So

$$a = 5, \qquad c = \frac{13}{2}, \qquad b = \sqrt{\left(\frac{13}{2}\right)^2 - 5^2} = \frac{\sqrt{69}}{2}$$

The center, halfway between the foci on the line $x = 4$, is the point $(4, 10 - \frac{13}{2}) = (4, \frac{7}{2})$. Now you can write the equation:

$$\frac{(x-4)^2}{69/4} - \frac{(y-7/2)^2}{25} = -1$$

PROBLEM 7-12 If the center of a hyperbola is at $(2, -3)$ and the curve passes through $(3, 1)$ and $(6, 8)$, what is its equation?

Solution: You can't tell in advance whether the required curve will be parallel to the X- or Y-axis. But you can write each of the standard (translation) equations (7-3) and (7-4) in the form $A(x-h)^2 + B(y-k)^2 = 1$ with the understanding that one of the constants, either A or B, is negative. Then, since you're given that $h = 2$ and $k = -3$, you can start with $A(x-2)^2 + B(y+3)^2 = 1$. Substituting the coordinates of the given points and solving the simultaneous equations in A and B, you get $A = -\frac{7}{9}$ and $B = \frac{1}{9}$, so the equation is $7(x-2)^2 - (y+3)^2 = 9$.

PROBLEM 7-13 Write the equation of the hyperbola with center at $(-2, 1)$, transverse axis 6 units long and parallel to the X-axis, and conjugate axis 8 units long. Also find the equations of the asymptotes.

Solution: Knowing the coordinates of the center $(-2, 1)$, the length of the semi-transverse axis $a = 3$, and the length of the semi-conjugate axis $b = 4$, you can write the equation at once as

$$\frac{(x+2)^2}{9} - \frac{(y-1)^2}{16} = 1$$

and the equations of the asymptotes are the factors of $(x+2)^2/9 - (y-1)^2/16 = 0$:

$$y - 1 = \pm\frac{4}{3}(x+2)$$

PROBLEM 7-14 Reduce the following equation to standard form and sketch the curve:

$$x^2 - y^2 - 2x - y + 1 = 0$$

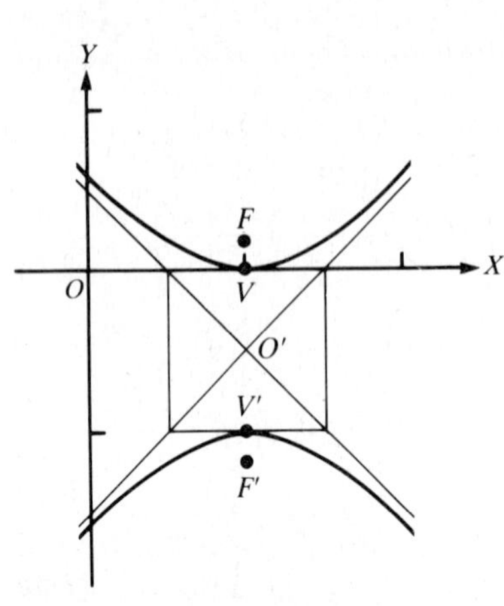

Figure 7-18

Solution:

$$x^2 - 2x + 1 - \left(y^2 + y + \frac{1}{4}\right) = -1 + 1 - \frac{1}{4}$$

$$(x-1)^2 - \left(y + \frac{1}{2}\right)^2 = -\frac{1}{4}$$

$$\frac{(y+1/2)^2}{1/4} - \frac{(x-1)^2}{1/4} = 1$$

Since $a = b = \frac{1}{2}$, this is an equilateral hyperbola, for which $c = \frac{1}{2}\sqrt{2}$ and the transverse axis is parallel to the Y-axis. Thus the vertices are $V(1, 0)$ and $V'(1, -1)$, the foci are $F(1, -\frac{1}{2} + \frac{1}{2}\sqrt{2})$ and $F'(1, -\frac{1}{2} - \frac{1}{2}\sqrt{2})$, and the asymptotes are $y + \frac{1}{2} = \pm(x - 1)$, as shown in Figure 7-18.

note: The rectangle associated with an equilateral hyperbola is a square.

Supplementary Exercises

PROBLEM 7-15 Determine the equations of the asymptotes and the coordinates of the vertices V, V' and foci F, F' of the hyperbolas represented by **(a)** $x^2 - y^2 = 1$; **(b)** $x^2/9 - y^2/9 = 1$; **(c)** $2x^2 - y^2 = 8$; **(d)** $y^2/1 - x^2/4 = 1$.

PROBLEM 7-16 Determine the center (C) and the vertices of the following hyperbolas:

(a) $9y^2 - x^2 + 8x - 7 = 0$
(b) $5x^2 - 4y^2 - 15x - 6y + 10 = 0$
(c) $16y^2 - 4x^2 + 4x + 48y = 1$
(d) $x^2 - 4x - 4y^2 - 8y = 0$

PROBLEM 7-17 Find the equations of the hyperbolas whose foci and vertices are **(a)** $F, F' = (\pm 3, 0)$, $V, V' = (\pm 2, 0)$; **(b)** $F, F' = (0, \pm 1)$, $V, V' = (0, \pm \frac{1}{2})$; **(c)** $F' = (-5, 1)$, $F = (7, 1)$; $V' = (-3, 1)$, $V = (5, 1)$.

PROBLEM 7-18 Determine the equations of the hyperbolas conjugate to **(a)** $4x^2 - 9y^2 = 36$; **(b)** $x^2 - y^2 = 1$; **(c)** $y^2 - x^2/4 = 1$; **(d)** $9y^2 - x^2 + 8x - 7 = 0$

PROBLEM 7-19 Determine the equation of the hyperbola from the information given below:

(a) Foci at $(0, 3)$ and $(0, -3)$; transverse axis of length 4
(b) Transverse axis of length 5 parallel to the Y-axis; conjugate axis of length 3; center at $(-2, 3)$
(c) Transverse and conjugate axes of equal length on coordinate axes; hyperbola passes through $(3, -1)$

PROBLEM 7-20 Write the equation of the hyperbola whose foci are symmetrically situated on the X-axis with respect to the origin such that the following conditions are satisfied:

(a) $2a = 10$, $2b = 8$
(b) The distance between the foci is 10 units, and the conjugate axis is 8 units long
(c) The eccentricity is $3/2$, and $2c = 6$
(d) The transverse axis is 16 units long, and $e = 5/4$

PROBLEM 7-21 Find the equation of the hyperbola whose foci are symmetrically situated on the Y-axis with respect to the origin such that the following conditions are satisfied:

(a) $a = 6$, $b = 18$
(b) The distance between the foci is 10 units, and the eccentricity is $5/3$
(c) The equations of the asymptotes are $y = \pm\frac{12}{5}x$, and the distance between the vertices is 48 units

PROBLEM 7-22 Determine the lengths of the semi-axes a and b of each of the following hyperbolas: **(a)** $x^2/9 - y^2/4 = 1$; **(b)** $x^2/16 - y^2 = 1$; **(c)** $x^2 - 4y^2 = 16$; **(d)** $x^2 - y^2 = 1$.

PROBLEM 7-23 Given the hyperbola $16x^2 - 9y^2 = 144$, find **(a)** the lengths of the semi-axes; **(b)** the coordinates of the foci; **(c)** the eccentricity; **(d)** the equations of the asymptotes.

PROBLEM 7-24 Given the hyperbola $16x^2 - 9y^2 = -144$, find **(a)** the lengths of the semi-axes; **(b)** the coordinates of the foci; **(c)** the eccentricity; **(d)** the equations of the asymptotes.

PROBLEM 7-25 Write the equation of a hyperbola whose foci are symmetrically situated on the X-axis with respect to the origin such that the following conditions are satisfied:

(a) The points $(6, -1)$ and $(-8, 2\sqrt{2})$ are on the curve
(b) The point $(-5, 3)$ is on the curve, and the eccentricity is $\sqrt{2}$
(c) The point $(\frac{9}{2}, -1)$ is on the curve, and the equations $y = \pm\frac{2}{3}x$ are the asymptotes

PROBLEM 7-26 Write the equations of the hyperbolas having centers at the origin and axes along the coordinate axes such that the following conditions are satisfied:

(a) One vertex at $(0, 8)$; $e = 2$
(b) Vertices at $(\pm 4, 0)$; latus rectum 18 units long
(c) Eccentricity 5/3; transverse axis 12 units; foci on X-axis
(d) Foci on X-axis; curve passes through $(-3, 1)$ and $(9, 5)$

PROBLEM 7-27 Find the coordinates of the center (C), foci (F,F'), and vertices (V,V'); the length of a latus rectum (LR); the equations of the asymptotes; and the conjugate hyperbola for each of the following hyperbolas:

(a) $\dfrac{(x-1)^2}{4} - \dfrac{(y+2)^2}{1} = 1$

(b) $\dfrac{(y+3)^2}{4} - \dfrac{(x+4)^2}{25} = 1$

(c) $9y^2 - 4x^2 - 8x + 18y + 41 = 0$

(d) $9x^2 - y^2 + 36x + 6y + 18 = 0$

PROBLEM 7-28 Find the equations of the hyperbolas that satisfy the following conditions:

(a) Foci at $(4, 0)$ and $(10, 0)$; one vertex at $(6, 0)$
(b) Conjugate axis 12 units long; vertices at $(-3, 2)$ and $(5, 2)$
(c) One vertex at $(3, -1)$; nearest focus at $(5, -1)$; eccentricity 3/2
(d) Axes parallel to the coordinate axes; curve passes through $(0, 1)$, $(0, -5)$, $(2, -2)$, and $(6, -2)$

Answers to Supplementary Exercises

7-15: **(a)** $y = \pm x$; $V,V' = (\pm 1, 0)$; $F,F' = (\pm\sqrt{2}, 0)$
(b) $y = \pm x$; $V,V' = (\pm 3, 0)$; $F,F' = (\pm 3\sqrt{2}, 0)$
(c) $y = \pm\sqrt{2}x$; $V,V' = (\pm 2, 0)$; $F,F' = (\pm 2\sqrt{3}, 0)$
(d) $y = \pm\frac{1}{2}x$; $V,V' = (0, \pm 1)$; $F,F' = (0, \pm\sqrt{5})$

7-16: **(a)** $C(4, 0)$; $V(7, 0)$, $V'(1, 0)$
(b) $C(\frac{3}{2}, -\frac{3}{4})$; $V(\frac{3}{2}, -\frac{1}{4})$, $V'(\frac{3}{2}, -\frac{5}{4})$
(c) $C(\frac{1}{2}, -\frac{3}{2})$; $V(\frac{1}{2}, 0)$, $V'(\frac{1}{2}, -3)$
(d) $C(2, -1)$: This hyperbola is a *degenerate hyperbola* that consists of the two straight lines $y + 1 = \pm\frac{1}{2}(x - 2)$.

7-17: **(a)** $\dfrac{x^2}{4} - \dfrac{y^2}{5} = 1$
(b) $12y^2 - 4x^2 = 3$
(c) $\dfrac{(x-1)^2}{16} - \dfrac{(y-1)^2}{20} = 1$

7-18: **(a)** $\dfrac{y^2}{4} - \dfrac{x^2}{9} = 1$ **(b)** $y^2 - x^2 = 1$ **(c)** $\dfrac{x^2}{4} - y^2 = 1$ **(d)** $\dfrac{(x-4)^2}{9} - y^2 = 1$

7-19: **(a)** $\dfrac{y^2}{4} - \dfrac{x^2}{5} = 1$ **(b)** $4(y-3)^2 - 4(x+2)^2 = 225$ **(c)** $x^2 - y^2 = 8$

7-20: **(a)** $\dfrac{x^2}{25} - \dfrac{y^2}{16} = 1$ **(b)** $\dfrac{x^2}{9} - \dfrac{y^2}{16} = 1$ **(c)** $\dfrac{x^2}{4} - \dfrac{y^2}{5} = 1$ **(d)** $\dfrac{x^2}{64} - \dfrac{y^2}{36} = 1$

7-21: **(a)** $\dfrac{y^2}{36} - \dfrac{x^2}{324} = 1$
(b) $\dfrac{x^2}{16} - \dfrac{y^2}{9} = -1$
(c) $\dfrac{x^2}{100} - \dfrac{y^2}{576} = -1$

7-22: **(a)** $a = 3, b = 2$ **(b)** $a = 4, b = 1$ **(c)** $a = 4, b = 2$ **(d)** $a = 1, b = 1$

7-23: **(a)** $a = 3, b = 4$ **(b)** $F,F' = (\pm 5, 0)$ **(c)** $e = \frac{5}{3}$ **(d)** $y = \pm\frac{4}{3}x$

7-24: **(a)** $a = 4, b = 3$ **(b)** $F,F' = (0, \pm 5)$ **(c)** $e = \frac{5}{4}$ **(d)** $y = \pm\frac{4}{3}x$

7-25: **(a)** $\dfrac{x^2}{32} - \dfrac{y^2}{8} = 1$

(b) $x^2 - y^2 = 16$

(c) $\dfrac{x^2}{18} - \dfrac{y^2}{8} = 1$

7-26: **(a)** $3y^2 - x^2 = 192$
(b) $9x^2 - 4y^2 = 144$
(c) $16x^2 - 9y^2 = 576$
(d) $x^2 - 3y^2 = 6$

7-27: **(a)** $C(1, -2)$; $F,F' = (1 \pm \sqrt{5}, -2)$; $V(3, -2)$, $V'(-2, -2)$; $LR = 1$; $x - 2y - 5 = 0$, $x + 2y + 3 = 0$; $4(y + 2)^2 - (x - 1)^2 = 4$
(b) $C(-4, -3)$; $F,F' = (-4, -3 \pm \sqrt{29})$; $V(-4, -1)$, $V'(-4, -5)$; $LR = 25$; $2x - 5y - 7 = 0$, $2x + 5y + 23 = 0$; $4(x + 4)^2 - 25(y + 3)^2 = 100$
(c) $C(-1, -1)$; $F,F' = (-1 \pm \sqrt{13}, -1)$; $V(-4, -1)$, $V'(2, -1)$; $LR = \frac{8}{3}$; $2x + 3y + 5 = 0$, $2x - 3y - 1 = 0$; $4x^2 - 9y^2 + 8x - 18y + 31 = 0$
(d) $C(-2, 3)$; $F,F' = (-2 \pm \sqrt{10}, 3)$; $V(-3, 3)$, $V'(-1, 3)$; $LR = 18$; $3x + y + 3 = 0$, $3x - y + 9 = 0$; $y^2 - 9x^2 - 6y - 36x - 36 = 0$

7-28: **(a)** $8x^2 - y^2 - 112x + 384 = 0$
(b) $9x^2 - 4y^2 - 18x + 16y - 151 = 0$
(c) $5x^2 - 4y^2 + 10x - 8y - 79 = 0$
(d) $3x^2 - 4y^2 - 24x - 16y + 20 = 0$

CONIC SECTIONS

THIS CHAPTER IS ABOUT

☑ The Cone and Its Sections
☑ Equations of a Conic
☑ Theorems and Locus Problems

8-1. The Cone and Its Sections

- A **right circular cone** is the surface generated when one straight line that intersects another (fixed) straight line is rotated at an oblique angle.

The fixed line of the cone is its **axis**, and the possible positions of the generating line in its rotation about the axis are its **elements**. The common intersection point of all the cone's elements is the cone's **vertex**, and the two symmetric parts of the generated surface on each side of the vertex are the cone's **nappes** (see Figure 8-1).

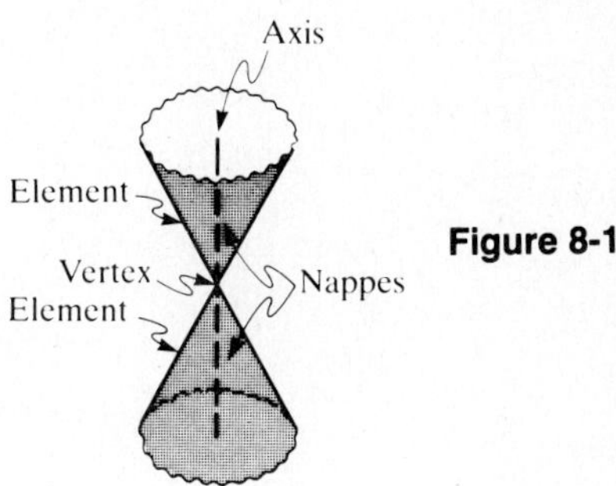

Figure 8-1

- **Conic sections** (or **conics**) are curves that can be obtained by cutting a cone with a plane.

The parabola, ellipse, circle, and hyperbola are all conics:

☑ When the intersecting plane is parallel to an element, the curve is a *parabola* (Figure 8-2):

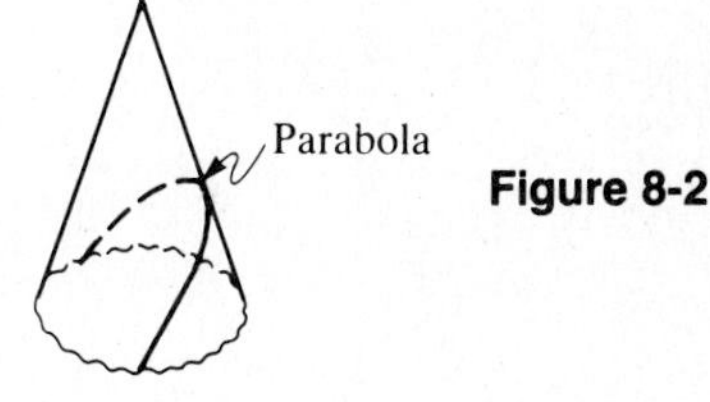

Figure 8-2

General form	Standard form ($V = (h, k)$)
$y^2 + Dx + Ey + F = 0$ **(5-5a)**	$(y - k)^2 = 4a(x - h)$ **(5-3)**
$x^2 + Dx + Ey + F = 0$ **(5-5b)**	$(x - h)^2 = 4a(y - k)$ **(5-4)**

[see Chapter 5]

☑ When the intersecting plane cuts completely across one nappe at an oblique angle to the axis, the curve is an *ellipse* (Figure 8-3):

General form	Standard form ($C = (h, k)$)
$Ax^2 + Cy^2 + Dx + Ey + F = 0$ **(6-6)** (A and C have the same sign)	$\dfrac{(x-h)^2}{a^2} + \dfrac{(y-k)^2}{b^2} = 1$ **(6-4)**
	$\dfrac{(y-k)^2}{a^2} + \dfrac{(x-h)^2}{b^2} = 1$ **(6-5)**

[see Chapter 6]

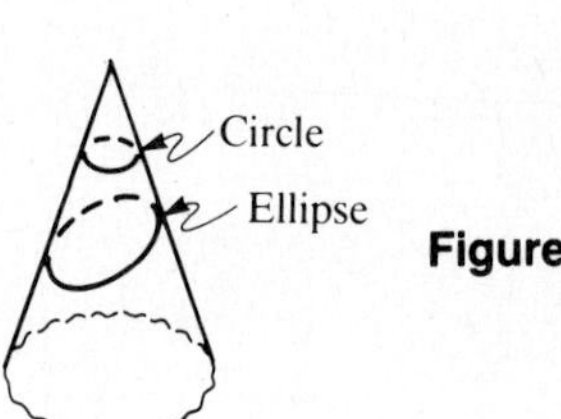

Figure 8-3

☑ When the intersecting plane cuts completely across one nappe at a right angle to the axis, the curve is a *circle*, which is a special case of the ellipse (Figure 8-3):

General form	Standard form ($C = (h, k)$)
$x^2 + y^2 + Dx + Ey + F = 0$ **(4-2)**	$(x - h)^2 + (y - k)^2 = r^2$ **(4-1)**

[see Chapter 4]

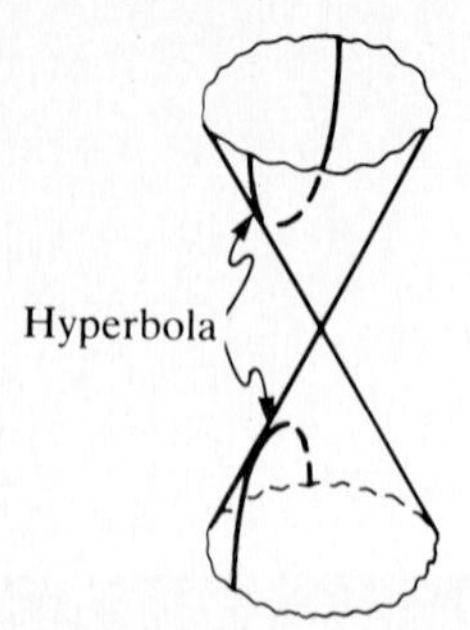

Figure 8-4

☑ When the intersecting plane cuts through both nappes, the resulting curve has two parts and is called a *hyperbola* (Figure 8-4):

General form	Standard form ($C = (h, k)$)
$Ax^2 + Cy^2 + Dx + Ey + F = 0$ **(7-5)** (A and C have different signs)	$\frac{(x-h)^2}{a^2} - \frac{(y-k)^2}{b^2} = 1$ **(7-3)**
	$\frac{(y-k)^2}{a^2} - \frac{(x-h)^2}{b^2} = 1$ **(7-4)**

[see Chapter 7]

note: **(1)** If the intersecting plane cuts across the vertex of a cone, the resulting curve is a *point circle.*

(2) If an intersecting plane fully contains the cone's axis, the resulting curve consists of two straight lines; and if an intersecting plane fully contains a single element of a cone, the resulting curve is a single straight line. These straight-line curves are called *degenerate conics.*

8-2. Equations of a Conic

A. Identification of a conic from the general equation

The general form of the equation of any conic is

CONIC SECTION (GENERAL FORM)

$$Ax^2 + Bxy + Cy^2 + Dx + Ey + F = 0 \qquad \textbf{(8-1)}$$

where A, B, C, D, E, and F are constants and A and C are not both zero; we can identify the type of curve represented by an equation in general form by looking at its second-degree variables and their coefficients:

- The parabola contains x^2 or y^2, but not both.
- The ellipse contains both x^2 and y^2, and the coefficients of x^2 and y^2 are of the same sign; the circle contains both x^2 and y^2, which have equal coefficients of the same sign.
- The hyperbola contains both x^2 and y^2, and the coefficients of x^2 and y^2 are of opposite signs.

note: The rotational effect of the Bxy term in the general second-degree equation is discussed in Chapter 10.

It's relatively easy to determine the key facts of a conic if its equation is in standard form, because the arbitrary constants in the standard form directly represent the key points and lengths that define the curve. So, given an equation in general form, we begin the process of reducing it to standard form by completing its square(s). Then, after completing the square(s), we can look at $-4AC$ in the general equation to determine which standard form we want. The curve is

- a parabola if $-4AC = 0$, since either A or C is zero and $A \neq C$
- an ellipse if $-4AC < 0$, since A and C have the same sign
- a circle if $-4AC < 0$ and $A = C$
- a hyperbola if $-4AC > 0$, since A and C have opposite signs

Finally, we perform the manipulations needed to write the equation in the standard form appropriate to the curve.

EXAMPLE 8-1: Determine which conic is represented by the equation $y^2 - 12x - 4y - 56 = 0$ and rewrite the equation in standard form

Solution: The graph of $y^2 - 12x - 4y - 56 = 0$ must be a parabola since the equation contains y^2 but not x^2, so that $-4AC = -4(0)(1) = 0$. We complete the square in y, rearrange, and factor to get

$$y^2 - 4y + 4 - 12x - 56 = 0 + 4$$
$$(y - 2)^2 = 12x + 60$$
$$(y - 2)^2 = 12(x + 5)$$

which is the standard form $(y - k)^2 = 4a(x - h)$ (eq. 5-3) of the equation of a parabola with the axis parallel to the X-axis.

EXAMPLE 8-2: Write $9x^2 + 4y^2 - 18x + 16y - 11 = 0$ in standard form.

Solution: Since x^2 and y^2 both appear in this equation and their coefficients A and C have the same sign but are not equal, the graph will be an ellipse, $(x - h)^2/a^2 + (y - k)^2/b^2 = 1$ (eq. 6-4) or $(y - k)^2/a^2 + (x - h)^2/b^2 = 1$ (eq. 6-5). So we first factor the coefficient of x^2 out of the terms in x^2 and x, and the coefficient of y^2 out of the terms in y^2 and y; then we rearrange and complete the squares:

$$9x^2 - 18x + 4y^2 + 16y - 11 = 0$$
$$9(x^2 - 2x) + 4(y^2 + 4y) - 11 = 0$$
$$9(x^2 - 2x + 1) + 4(y^2 + 4y + 4) = 11 + 9 + 16$$
$$9(x - 1)^2 + 4(y + 2)^2 = 36$$

To get this in standard form, we just have to divide each member by 36 and substitute 2^2 for 4 and 3^2 for 9:

$$\frac{(x - 1)^2}{2^2} + \frac{(y + 2)^2}{3^2} = 1$$

which is an ellipse whose major axis is parallel to the Y-axis.

EXAMPLE 8-3: Put $25x^2 + 150x - 16y^2 + 32y - 191 = 0$ in standard form.

Solution: The graph of this equation is a hyperbola since x^2 and y^2 both appear and their coefficients A and C have opposite signs. So the standard form will be $(x - h)^2/a^2 - (y - k)^2/b^2 = 1$ (eq. 7-3) or $(y - k)^2/a^2 - (x - h)^2/b^2 = 1$ (eq. 7-4). Thus

$$25x^2 + 150x - 16y^2 + 32y - 191 = 0$$
$$25(x^2 + 6x) - 16(y^2 - 2y) - 191 = 0$$
$$25(x^2 + 6x + 9) - 16(y^2 - 2y + 1) = 191 + 25(9) - 16$$
$$25(x + 3)^2 - 16(y - 1)^2 = 400$$
$$\frac{(x + 3)^2}{4^2} - \frac{(y - 1)^2}{5^2} = 1$$

is the standard form of the given hyperbola, whose transverse axis is parallel to the X-axis.

B. Identification of a conic from the eccentricity

We can also define a conic analytically:

- A **conic** is the locus of a point that moves in such a way that its distance from a fixed point is in constant ratio to its distance from a fixed straight line.

We term the fixed point the **focus**, the fixed line the **directrix**, and the constant ratio the **eccentricity** of the conic.

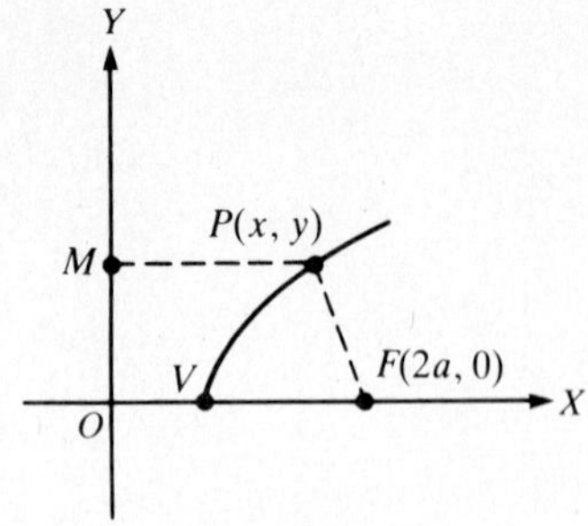

Figure 8-5

We can write an equation for a conic based on this analytic definition. Thus, taking the Y-axis as the directrix and a focus $F(2a, 0)$ on the X-axis as the fixed point (as in Figure 8-5) and designating the eccentricity by e, we can write the equation

$$FP = eMP$$

where $P(x, y)$ is any point on the curve and $e > 0$. In terms of coordinates, this equation becomes

$$\sqrt{(x - 2a)^2 + y^2} = ex$$

which may be expanded to the form

CONIC (ANALYTIC FORM): $F = (2a, 0)$

$$(1 - e^2)x^2 + y^2 - 4ax + 4a^2 = 0 \quad \textbf{(8-2)}$$

Similarly, it can be shown that when a focus is $F(0, 2a)$ and the directrix is along the X-axis, $\sqrt{(y - 2a)^2 + x^2} = ey$ and

CONIC (ANALYTIC FORM): $F = (0, 2a)$

$$(1 - e^2)y^2 + x^2 - 4ay + 4a^2 = 0 \quad \textbf{(8-3)}$$

Examining eqs. (8-2) and (8-3) in view of what we know about second-degree curves, we see that the type of conic they represent depends upon the value of e:

- If $e = 1$, then $(1 - e^2) = 0$—i.e., the coefficient of one of the squared terms is zero—so the equation represents a parabola.
- If $e < 1$, then $(1 - e^2) > 0$—i.e., the coefficients of the squared terms are both positive but of different magnitudes—so the equation represents an ellipse.
- If $e > 1$, then $(1 - e^2) < 0$—i.e., the coefficients of the squared terms are opposite in sign—so the equation represents a hyperbola.

note: The eccentricity of the ellipse and hyperbola may also be defined geometrically by the Pythagorean relationship:

(1) The eccentricity of the ellipse is the ratio c/a, where c is the distance between a focus and the center, a is the distance between a vertex and the center, and $a^2 = b^2 + c^2$ (see Section 6-2C–D).

(2) The eccentricity of the hyperbola is the ratio c/a, where c is the distance from a focus to the center, a is the distance from a vertex to the center, and $c^2 = a^2 + b^2$ (see Section 7-2B).

EXAMPLE 8-4: Find the eccentricity e and the type of conic determined by $7x^2 + 16y^2 - 128x + 256 = 0$. Also locate a focus.

Solution: Since the equation contains a linear term in x and does not contain a linear term in y, the directrix of the conic is along the Y-axis. So the equation must be compared to eq. (8-2) by reducing the coefficient of y^2 to $+1$:

$$(1 - e^2)x^2 + y^2 - 4ax + 4a^2 = 0$$

$$\frac{7x^2}{16} + y^2 - 8x + 16 = 0$$

Consequently, $1 - e^2 = 7/16$, so $e = 3/4$. And since $e = 3/4 < 1$, the conic is an ellipse. Finally, since $-4a = -8$, it follows that $a = 2$ and so a focus is at $(2a, 0) = (4, 0)$.

EXAMPLE 8-5: Determine the value of e and the type of conic represented by $x^2 - 4y^2 + 16x - 16 = 0$.

Solution: Since the equation contains a linear term in x but no linear term in y, the directrix of the conic is along the Y-axis, as in eq. (8-2). Reducing the coefficient of y^2 to $+1$, you get

$$-\frac{x^2}{4} + y^2 - 4x + 4 = 0$$

Therefore, $1 - e^2 = -1/4$, so $e = \sqrt{5/4} = \sqrt{5}/2$, which is >1. The conic is a hyperbola with transverse axis on the Y-axis.

EXAMPLE 8-6: Determine the value of e and the type of conic represented by $y^2 - 4x + 4 = 0$.

Solution: The only quadratic term here is y^2, and its coefficient is 1. Therefore, $(1 - e^2)x^2 = 0$, $e = \sqrt{1} = 1$, and the conic is a parabola with the directrix along the Y-axis.

C. Applications of conic equations

Although many of the scientific/engineering applications of the conics require a knowledge of the calculus, it's worth knowing a few of the uses of these curves for which analytic techniques are appropriate.

The parabolic curve, with its single focus, is used in the design of suspension bridges and in calculating the paths of projectiles and freely falling bodies. And devices that send or receive waves, such as searchlights and telescopes, are paraboloids, whose surfaces are traced by a parabola revolving on its axis. (See Section 5-5.) The ellipse, with its two foci, is also used in architecture and bridge design: The Colosseum is an ellipse; many stone and concrete bridges have elliptical arches; and, most interestingly, the design of whispering galleries, where a sound originating at one focus may be heard at the other focus but not at any other point, is based on the ellipse. And ellipses have applications in mechanics: Elliptical gears are used in such machines as power punches and planers, for which a slow, powerful stroke is required. Finally, the hyperbola appears in the relationships of some natural (and unnatural) laws: A hyperbola referred to its asymptotes as axes may be used to express Boyle's law of a perfect gas; this same equation is also used in economics. And range-finding (locating a source of sound) is accomplished by means of hyperbolas.

EXAMPLE 8-7: Sound-recording instruments are placed at two points, A and B, which are 300 feet apart. Sound coming from point P is heard at point B 20/100 of a second (0.20 s) earlier than at point A. Locate the possible positions of point P. [The speed of sound is ~ 1100 ft/s.]

Solution: Start with a diagram, plotting A and B on the X-axis so that the origin is the midpoint of AB and the coordinates of A and B are $(-150, 0)$ and $(150, 0)$, respectively, as shown in Figure 8-6. Since sound travels at approximately 1100 ft/s, P must be about $0.20(1100) = 220$ ft nearer to B than to A; hence $AP - BP = 220$. And if you designate the coordinates of P as (x, y), you can write this difference in coordinate form:

$$\sqrt{(x + 150)^2 + y^2} - \sqrt{(x - 150)^2 + y^2} = 220$$

Clearly, there's a constant difference between the moving point $P(x, y)$ and the fixed points $A(-150, 0)$ and $B(150, 0)$, so the locus of P must be, by definition, a

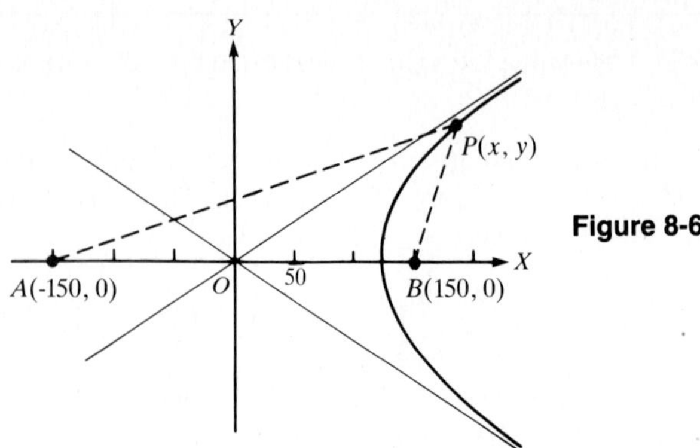

Figure 8-6

hyperbola with foci A and B on the X-axis. Now you can rewrite the difference equation as the equation of a hyperbola in any of its forms:

$$(\sqrt{(x+150)^2+y^2})^2 = [220+\sqrt{(x-150)^2+y^2}]^2$$

$$x^2+300x+(150)^2+y^2 = (220)^2+2(220)\sqrt{(x-150)^2+y^2} + x^2-300x+(150)^2+y^2$$

$$(600x-(220)^2)^2 = [2(220)\sqrt{(x-150)^2+y^2}]^2$$

$$(600x)^2-2(220)^2(600)x+(220)^4 = 4(220)^2(x^2-300x+(150)^2+y^2)$$

$$360\,000x^2+2.3426\times10^9 = 193\,600x^2+4.356\times10^9+193\,600y^2$$

$$1664x^2-1936y^2 = 2.0134\times10^7$$

$$104x^2-121y^2 = 1.2584\times10^6$$

So the general form of this hyperbola is

$$104x^2-121y^2-1\,258\,400=0$$

Therefore P is on a branch of a hyperbola represented by this equation.

note: By recording the sound at two other points, a second hyperbola could be drawn through P, thus precisely locating the point at the intersection of the two curves. This concept underlies the Loran system of navigation.

8-3. Theorems and Locus Problems

In proving general theorems—and in solving locus problems—we always choose the axes so that the work involved is reduced to a minimum.

EXAMPLE 8-8: Examine the proof of the following theorem.

THEOREM: *If the vertices V', V of an ellipse are joined at point P on the ellipse by straight lines $V'P$ and VP, and if two other lines NP and MP are drawn through P perpendicular to $V'P$ and VP, respectively, then the length of the segment MN intercepted by this second pair of lines on the axis of the ellipse is equal to the length of the latus rectum.*

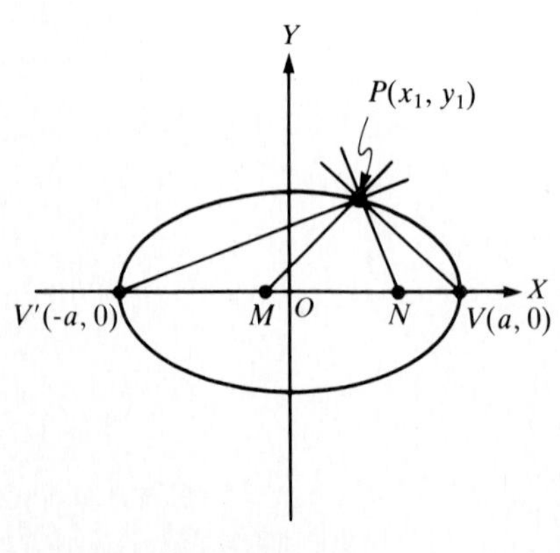

Figure 8-7

Proof: Choose the origin as the center of the ellipse, so that the major axis has length $2a$ and coincides with the X-axis, as shown in Figure 8-7. Thus the coordinates of V' and V are $(-a, 0)$ and $(a, 0)$, respectively. Then, the minor axis has length $2b$ and coincides with the Y-axis, so the equation of the ellipse is $b^2x^2+a^2y^2=a^2b^2$.

Let the coordinates of P be (x_1, y_1), so that the slope of $V'P$ is $y_1/(x_1+a)$ and the slope of VP is $y_1/(x_1-a)$. Hence NP, drawn perpendicular to $V'P$, has a slope $-(x_1+a)/y_1$ (the negative reciprocal of the slope of $V'P$) and its equation may be written in point-slope form:

$$y - y_1 = \left(-\frac{x_1 + a}{y_1}\right)(x - x_1)$$

or $$(x_1 + a)x + y_1 y - ax_1 - x_1^2 - y_1^2 = 0$$

Similarly, the equation of MP is

$$y - y_1 = \left(-\frac{x_1 - a}{y_1}\right)(x - x_1)$$

or $$(x_1 - a)x + y_1 y + ax_1 - x_1^2 - y_1^2 = 0$$

Find the X-intercepts N and M by substituting $y = 0$ in the point-slope equations for NP and MP and solving for x, thereby finding the distance ON and the distance OM, respectively:

$$(x_1 + a)x - ax_1 - x_1^2 - y_1^2 = 0$$

$$x = \frac{x_1^2 + y_1^2 + ax_1}{x_1 + a} = ON$$

$$(x_1 - a)x + ax_1 - x_1^2 - y_1^2 = 0$$

$$x = \frac{x_1^2 + y_1^2 - ax_1}{x_1 - a} = OM$$

Then, since $MN = MO + ON = ON - OM$, the length of MN can be written as

$$MN = \frac{x_1^2 + y_1^2 + ax_1}{x_1 + a} - \frac{x_1^2 + y_1^2 - ax_1}{x_1 - a} = -\frac{2ay_1^2}{x_1^2 - a^2}$$

Finally, since the point $P(x_1, y_1)$ is on the ellipse, the equation of the ellipse can be written as $b^2x_1^2 + a^2y_1^2 = a^2b^2$ so that $y_1^2 = b^2(a^2 - x_1^2)/a^2$. Substituting this value of y_1^2 into the length of MN gives

$$MN = \left(\frac{2a}{-x_1^2 + a^2}\right)\frac{b^2(a^2 - x_1^2)}{a^2} = \frac{2b^2}{a}$$

which is the length of the latus rectum ($LR = 2b^2/a$; see Section 6-2C).

SUMMARY

1. A right circular cone is the surface generated by rotating one straight line that intersects another, fixed, straight line at an oblique angle. (The fixed line is the cone's axis; the positions of the generating line in its rotation are the cone's elements; the common intersection point of the elements is the vertex; and the two symmetric parts of the generated surface on each side of the vertex are the nappes of the cone.)
2. A conic section, or conic, may be defined geometrically as the curve that results when a right circular cone is cut with a plane:
   When an intersecting plane cuts through both nappes, the resulting curve is a hyperbola, which has two parts.
   When the intersecting plane cuts through one nappe at right angles to the axis, the curve is a circle.
   When the intersecting plane cuts through one nappe at an oblique angle to the axis, the resulting curve is an ellipse.
   When the plane cuts through one nappe parallel to an element, the curve is a parabola.
3. The equation for a parabola contains x^2 or y^2 but not both.

The equation for an ellipse contains both x^2 and y^2, and the coefficients of x^2 and y^2 have the same sign but are not equal; the equation for a circle is a special case of the ellipse in which the coefficients of x^2 and y^2 are equal.
The equation for a hyperbola contains both x^2 and y^2, and the coefficients of x^2 and y^2 have opposite signs.

4. The general equation of a conic is

$$Ax^2 + Bxy + Cy^2 + Dx + Ey + F = 0$$

The graph of this equation is a parabola if $-4AC = 0$, an ellipse if $-4AC < 0$ (a circle if $-4AC < 0$ and $A = C$), a hyperbola if $-4AC > 0$.

5. A conic may be defined analytically as the locus of a point that moves in such a way that its distance from a fixed point (a focus) is in constant ratio (the eccentricity) to its distance from a fixed straight line (the directrix).

6. The equation of the conic with eccentricity e, a focus at $(2a, 0)$, and directrix along the Y-axis is

$$(1 - e^2)x^2 + y^2 - 4ax + 4a^2 = 0$$

and the equation of the conic with eccentricity e, a focus at $(0, 2a)$, and directrix along the X-axis is

$$(1 - e^2)y^2 + x^2 - 4ay + 4a^2 = 0$$

RAISE YOUR GRADES

Can you . . .?

☑ write the general equation of a conic
☑ tell, by looking at its equation in general form, whether a given curve is a parabola, a circle, an ellipse, or a hyperbola
☑ reduce the general equation of a conic to standard form
☑ write the analytic form of the equation of a conic (defined as a locus) with directrix along either coordinate axis
☑ determine the type of a conic from its eccentricity

SOLVED PROBLEMS

Equations of a Conic

Identification of a conic from the general equation

PROBLEM 8-1 Determine the type of conic represented by the equation $y^2 - 4y - 8x - 4 = 0$ and write the equation in standard form.

Solution: Since only one second-degree term (y^2) appears in the equation, it is an X-parabola. To change the equation to standard form, complete the square in y:

$$y^2 - 4y + 4 = 8x + 4 + 4$$

$$(y - 2)^2 = 8(x + 1)$$

note: From this equation you can see that the vertex (h, k) is at $(-1, 2)$ and the distance a of the focus from the center is 2 units, since $4a = 8$. [See Chapter 5.]

PROBLEM 8-2 What type of conic does the equation $4x^2 + 9y^2 - 8x - 18y = 23$ represent and what is its standard form?

Solution: Since both x^2 and y^2 are present, the equation must represent either an ellipse or a hyperbola. And since A and C (the coefficients of the two quadratic terms) have the same sign, it is an ellipse. Complete the squares in x and y to get the standard form:

$$(4x^2 - 8x + 4) + (9y^2 - 18y + 9) = 23 + 4 + 9$$

$$4(x^2 - 2x + 1) + 9(y^2 - 2y + 1) = 36$$

$$\frac{(x-1)^2}{3^2} + \frac{(y-1)^2}{2^2} = 1$$

where $a = \sqrt{3^2} = 3$, $b = \sqrt{2^2} = 2$, $c = \sqrt{a^2 - b^2} = \sqrt{5}$, $C(h, k) = (1, 1)$, and the major axis is parallel to the X-axis. [See Chapter 6.]

PROBLEM 8-3 Change $4x^2 - 9y^2 - 8x + 18y = 41$ to standard form and determine which type of conic it represents.

Solution: Both x^2 and y^2 are present in the equation, but their coefficients have different signs, so the curve is a hyperbola. Completing the squares gives the standard form of the equation

$$4(x^2 - 2x + 1) - 9(y^2 - 2y + 1) = 36$$

$$\frac{(x-1)^2}{3^2} - \frac{(y-1)^2}{2^2} = 1$$

where $a = 3, b = 2, c = \sqrt{a^2 + b^2} = \sqrt{13}, C(h, k) = (1, 1)$, and the transverse axis is parallel to the X-axis. [See Chapter 7.]

Identification of a conic from the eccentricity

PROBLEM 8-4 Determine the value of e for $2x^2 + y^2 - 4y + 2 = 0$ and the type of conic represented by the equation.

Solution: Since the equation contains a linear term in y and no linear term in x, the curve must be the locus of a conic with the directrix along the X-axis (eq. 8-3):

$$(1 - e^2)y^2 + x^2 - 4ay + 4a^2 = 0$$

So dividing through to make the coefficient of x^2 equal to $+1$, you get the analytic form:

$$\tfrac{1}{2}y^2 + x^2 - 2y + 1 = 0$$

Thus $1 - e^2 = 1/2$, so $e^2 = 1/2$ and $e = 1/\sqrt{2}$; and since $e = 1/\sqrt{2} < 1$, the curve is an ellipse with the major axis on the Y-axis.

PROBLEM 8-5 Find the value of e and the kind of conic represented by the equation $x^2 - y^2 + 2x - 1 = 0$.

Solution: Since the linear term of the equation is x, the curve must be the locus of a conic with the directrix along the Y-axis (eq. 8-2):

$$(1 - e^2)x^2 + y^2 - 4ax + 4a^2 = -(x^2 - y^2 + 2x - 1)$$

$$-x^2 + y^2 - 2x + 1 = 0$$

from which $(1 - e^2) = -1$, $e^2 = 2$, and $e = \sqrt{2}$; hence $e > 1$, and the curve is a hyperbola with the transverse axis on the X-axis.

Supplementary Exercises

PROBLEM 8-6 Determine the type of conic represented by the following equations, and write the standard form for each:

(a) $y^2 + 6y + 4x + 1 = 0$
(b) $x^2 + 4x + 12y - 32 = 0$
(c) $9x^2 + 25y^2 - 54x - 100y = 44$
(d) $16x^2 + 9y^2 - 64x + 18y = 71$

PROBLEM 8-7 Determine the value of the eccentricity e and the type of conic represented by each of the following equations:

(a) $3x^2 + 4y^2 - 16x + 16 = 0$
(b) $5x^2 + 9y^2 - 36x + 36 = 0$
(c) $9x^2 + 8y^2 - 72y + 144 = 0$
(d) $9x^2 - 7y^2 - 72y + 144 = 0$

Answers to Supplementary Exercises

8-6: **(a)** parabola; $(y + 3)^2 = -4(x - 2)$
(b) parabola; $(x + 2)^2 = -12(y - 3)$
(c) ellipse; $\dfrac{(x - 3)^2}{5^2} + \dfrac{(y - 2)^2}{3^2} = 1$
(d) ellipse; $\dfrac{(y + 1)^2}{4^2} + \dfrac{(x - 2)^2}{3^2} = 1$

8-7: **(a)** 1/2; ellipse
(b) 2/3; ellipse
(c) $1/\sqrt{3}$; ellipse
(d) 4/3; hyperbola

MIDTERM EXAM (chapters 1-8)

1. Find the distance between each of the following pairs of points:

(**a**) $(3, -5)$ and $(3, 8)$
(**b**) $(-7, -1)$ and $(-3, -1)$
(**c**) $(0, 0)$ and $(3, -4)$
(**d**) $(1, 2)$ and $(-3, 4)$

2. Given the points $A(-4, 1)$ and $B(2, 7)$, which determine a line segment AB, find (**a**) the coordinates of the midpoint of the segment and (**b**) the coordinates of the point one-third of the way from A to B.

3. Find the slope of the line segment that joins the points $(2, 3)$ and $(8, 13)$.

4. Determine whether the line segment that joins points $(-3, 4)$ and $(3, -2)$ is perpendicular, parallel, or neither to the line that joins $(6, 8)$ and $(-5, -3)$.

5. Find the tangent of the acute angle β between two lines that pass through the origin and have slopes of -1 and 2.

6. Plot the locus of the equation $y = x^2 - 2x - 1$.

7. Write the equation for (**a**) the line that is perpendicular to $x - 2y - 7 = 0$ at $(2, 1)$ and (**b**) the line that passes through $(6, -4)$ parallel to the line joining $(1, 3)$ and $(0, -2)$.

8. Find the locus of a point that moves so that the sum of its distances from $(1, 1)$ and $(2, 0)$ is 5 units.

9. Change $2x - 3y - 5 = 0$ (in general form) to two-intercept form.

10. Write the equation for the family of lines that pass through the point $(2, 3)$.

11. A triangle has vertices $A(1, 3)$, $B(-2, -1)$, and $C(4, -5)$. Find (**a**) the area and (**b**) the tangent of the angle CAB.

12. Find the distance between the parallel lines $5x + 12y = 65$ and $5x + 12y = 130$.

13. Given that $(h, k) = (-2, 2)$, write the equation of the circle that touches both axes.

14. Find the equation of the straight line joining the centers of the circles $x^2 + y^2 - 2x + 3y - 4 = 0$ and $2x^2 + 2y^2 + 4x - 8y - 5 = 0$.

15. Find the general equations for the two circles of radius $\sqrt{53}$ such that the circles intersect at $(-5, 3)$ and $(4, -2)$.

16. Write the equation of the radical axis of the two circles $x^2 + y^2 - 5x + 2y - 8 = 0$ and $x^2 + y^2 + 4x - 3y - 1 = 0$.

17. Write the equation of the parabola with vertex at $(2, -3)$ and directrix $y = 4$, and find the coordinates of the focus.

18. Which of the following equations represent parabolas?

(**a**) $x^2 - y^2 - 2x + y - 1 = 0$
(**b**) $x^2 - y - 2x + y - 1 = 0$
(**c**) $x + y^2 + 2x - y + 1 = 0$
(**d**) $x^2 + 2y^2 = 4$

19. Write the standard equation of the ellipse whose foci are at (4, 3), (8, 3) and whose eccentricity is 1/2.

20. Find the lengths of the semi-axes, the coordinates of the foci and vertices, the length of a latus rectum, and the eccentricity of the ellipse $9x^2 + 36y^2 = 324$. Sketch the curve.

21. Write the equation of the hyperbola with vertices at $(-2, 0)$, $(4, 0)$ and conjugate axis 10 units long.

22. Write the standard equation of the hyperbola for which $e = 2$, $F' = (4, 1)$, and $F = (8, 1)$. Find the equations of its asymptotes.

23. Identify the following curves and locate their centers:

(a) $x^2 + 4y^2 - 2x + 24y + 31 = 0$
(b) $4x^2 - 9y^2 + 18y + 27 = 0$
(c) $3x^2 + 6x + 3y^2 - 8y = 48$

24. Reduce the equation $3x^2 - 2y^2 + 4y - 26 = 0$ to standard form; find the coordinates of the center, the vertices, and the foci. Draw the asymptotes and sketch the graph of the equation.

25. Find the value of e for the conic $9x^2 - 4y^2 + 16y - 16 = 0$ and identify the type of curve represented by the equation.

Answers to Midterm Exam

1. (a) 13 (b) 4 (c) 5 (d) $2\sqrt{5}$

2. (a) $(-1, 4)$
(b) $(-2, 3)$

3. 5/3

4. perpendicular

5. $\tan \beta = 3$

6. See Figure MT-1.

7. (a) $2x + y - 5 = 0$
(b) $5x - y - 34 = 0$

8. $96x^2 + 8xy + 96y^2 - 292x - 108y - 329 = 0$

9. $\dfrac{x}{5/2} + \dfrac{y}{-5/3} = 1$

10. $y - 3 = m(x - 2)$

11. (a) 18 square units
(b) $\tan \angle CAB = 36/23$

12. 5

13. $x^2 + y^2 + 4x - 4y + 4 = 0$

14. $7x + 4y - 1 = 0$

15. $x^2 + y^2 - 4x - 10y - 24 = 0$
$x^2 + y^2 + 6x + 8y - 28 = 0$

16. $9x - 5y + 7 = 0$

17. $(x - 2)^2 = -28(y + 3)$; $F(2, -10)$

18. (b) and (c)

19. $\dfrac{(x - 6)^2}{16} + \dfrac{(y - 3)^2}{12} = 1$

20. $a = 6$; $b = 3$; $F,F' = (\pm 3\sqrt{3}, 0)$;
$V,V' = (\pm 6, 0)$; $LR = 3$; $e = \frac{1}{2}\sqrt{3}$
See Figure MT-2.

21. $\dfrac{(x - 1)^2}{9} - \dfrac{y^2}{25} = 1$

22. $\dfrac{(x - 6)^2}{1} - \dfrac{(y - 1)^2}{3} = 1$
$y = \sqrt{3}x - 6\sqrt{3} + 1$
$y = -\sqrt{3}x + 6\sqrt{3} + 1$

23. (**a**) ellipse; $O'(1, -3)$ (**c**) circle; $O'(-1, \frac{4}{3})$
(**b**) hyperbola; $O'(0, 1)$

24. See Figure MT-3: $\dfrac{x^2}{8} - \dfrac{(y-1)^2}{12} = 1$
$O'(0, 1)$; $V, V' = (\pm\sqrt{8}, 1)$; $F, F' = (\pm\sqrt{20}, 1)$

25. $e = \frac{1}{3}\sqrt{13}$; hyperbola

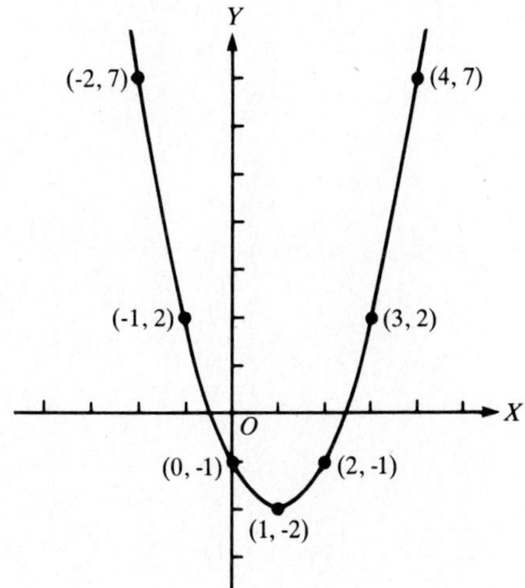

Figure MT-1

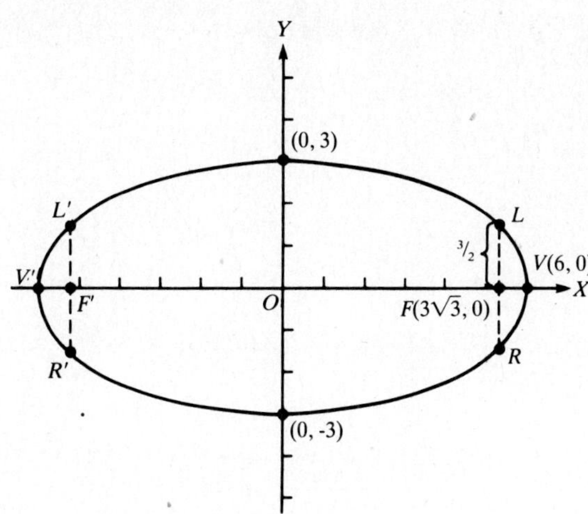

Figure MT-2

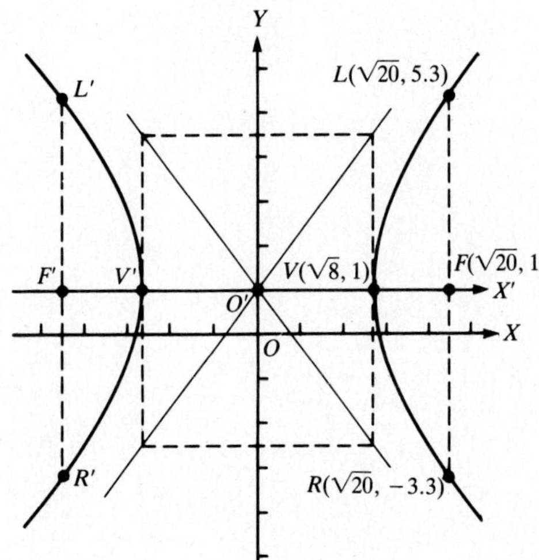

Figure MT-3

9 TANGENTS AND NORMALS OF SECOND-DEGREE CURVES

THIS CHAPTER IS ABOUT

☑ Tangents
☑ Normals

9-1. Tangents

A. General definition

Among the most important of the lines associated with second-degree curves are the *tangents*, which might be described as lines that touch—but do not cross—the curve at a common point, as shown in Figure 9-1a. Tangents can be defined generally:

- A **tangent** PT at a point P of a curve is defined as the limiting position of a secant PQ as Q approaches P along the curve.

This general definition, shown in Figure 9-1b, applies to *any* curve that has a tangent; and by its terms the methods of differential calculus are usually necessary to find the slope—and hence the equation—of PT. But if we limit our concern to curves of the second degree, we can use special analytic methods to find the equations of tangents.

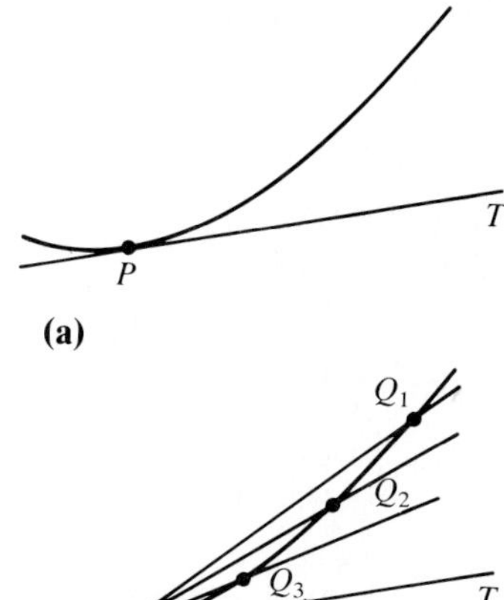

Figure 9-1

note: Before we begin, it will be useful to remember that the equation of a straight line can be written in slope-intercept form $y = mx + b$ or point-slope form $y - y_1 = m(x - x_1)$, and that the slopes m of perpendicular lines are negative reciprocals $m_2 = -1/m_1$.

B. Slope form

Assume we wish to find the equation of the line of slope m that is tangent to the X-parabola $y^2 = 4ax$. We begin with the family of straight lines $y = mx + k$ such that a member of this family crosses the parabola $y^2 = 4ax$ at the two points P and Q, as shown in Figure 9-2. Then we can find the coordinates of the intersection points P and Q by solving the equations of the line and the parabola simultaneously. Thus, if $y = mx + k$, then

$$y^2 = 4ax$$

$$m^2x^2 + 2mkx + k^2 = 4ax$$

$$m^2x^2 + 2(mk - 2a)x + k^2 = 0 \qquad \textbf{(9-1)}$$

So we can find the abscissas of P and Q by solving eq. (9-1) for x, and the ordinates by substituting these values of x back into the equation of the lines $y = mx + k$.

If the two intersection points P and Q coincide, the line is said to be tangent to the parabola. And if $P = Q$, the discriminant of eq. (9-1) must be zero.

note: The **discriminant** (from algebra) is the quantity $b^2 - 4ac$ for the general quadratic equation $ax^2 + bx + c = 0$. Thus the discriminant of eq. (9-1) has the value $4(mk - 2a)^2 - 4m^2k^2$.

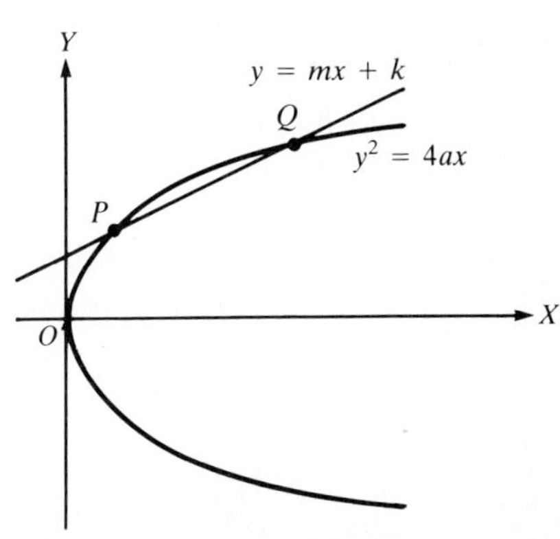

Figure 9-2

So we can set the discriminant equal to zero and find k:

$$4m^2k^2 - 16amk + 16a^2 - 4m^2k^2 = 0$$

$$16amk = 16a^2$$

$$k = a/m$$

And this value of k can be substituted into the equation of the family of lines to give the equation of the tangent to the parabola $y^2 = 4ax$:

TANGENT TO X-PARABOLA
$y^2 = 4ax$
(slope form)

$$y = mx + \frac{a}{m} \qquad \textbf{(9-2a)}$$

which is true for all finite values of m except $m = 0$.

The procedure used to find the slope form of the tangent to the X-parabola can also be used to find the slope forms of the tangents to the Y-parabola and the other second-degree curves. Thus, remembering that

- a line of the family $y = mx + k$ is tangent to a curve when the line intersects the curve at point(s) P and Q such that P and Q coincide,

we can find the slope-form tangent of a curve by the following steps:

(1) Substitute the value of y from the line $y = mx + k$ into the standard equation of the curve to get an equation for the intersection of the line and curve.
(2) Set the discriminant $(b^2 - 4ac)$ of the intersection equation equal to zero (i.e., set $P = Q$) and solve for k.
(3) Substitute the value of k found into the equation of the line.

So the tangent to the Y-parabola $x^2 = 4ax$ may be written

TANGENT TO Y-PARABOLA
$x^2 = 4ay$
(slope form)

$$y = mx - am^2 \qquad (m \neq 0) \qquad \textbf{(9-2b)}$$

And the tangents to the other second-degree curves may be written as follows:

TANGENT TO CIRCLE
$x^2 + y^2 = r^2$
(slope form)

$$y = mx \pm r\sqrt{1 + m^2} \qquad \textbf{(9-3)}$$

TANGENT TO ELLIPSE
$b^2x^2 + a^2y^2 = a^2b^2$
(slope form)

$$y = mx \pm \sqrt{a^2m^2 + b^2} \qquad \textbf{(9-4)}$$

TANGENT TO HYPERBOLA
$b^2x^2 - a^2y^2 = a^2b^2$
(slope form)

$$y = mx \pm \sqrt{a^2m^2 - b^2} \qquad (m > b/a \text{ or } m < -b/a) \qquad \textbf{(9-5)}$$

It's important to know that the circle, ellipse, and hyperbola have two tangents, each having a given slope m. Also, a line with any finite slope may be tangent to a circle or an ellipse, but this is not true for the hyperbola. For the hyperbola, $a^2m^2 - b^2$ must be positive or zero in order for the tangent to be real, so $|m| > b/a$. And when $m^2 = b^2/a^2$, so that $m = \pm b/a$, the equations become $y = \pm bx/a$, which are the equations of the asymptotes of the hyperbola.

EXAMPLE 9-1: Given the circle $x^2 + y^2 = 16$, find the equations of the tangents that have the slope $-\frac{1}{2}$.

Solution: You know that $y = -\frac{1}{2}x + k$ and $x^2 + y^2 = 16$, so you can find the intersection points of the family of lines and the circle from the quadratic equation

$$x^2 + (-\tfrac{1}{2}x + k)^2 = 16$$

$$5x^2 - 4kx + 4k^2 - 64 = 0$$

And if you set the discriminant of this equation equal to zero and solve for k,

$$16k^2 - 20(4k^2 - 64) = 0$$

$$k = \pm 2\sqrt{5}$$

you can substitute this value of k into the equation of the line to get

$$y = -\tfrac{1}{2}x \pm 2\sqrt{5}$$

which are the equations of the tangents, as shown in Figure 9-3.

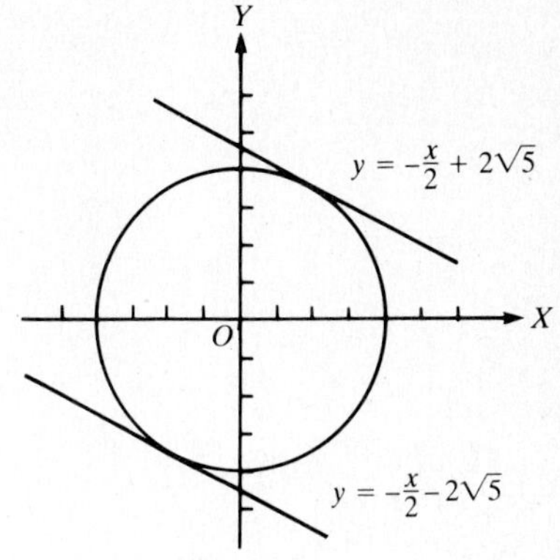

Figure 9-3

Alternative Solution: Given the circle $x^2 + y^2 = 16$ and the slope of a family of lines, you can find the members of this family that are tangent to the circle by eq. (9-3). Thus, if $m = -\frac{1}{2}$ and $r = 4$,

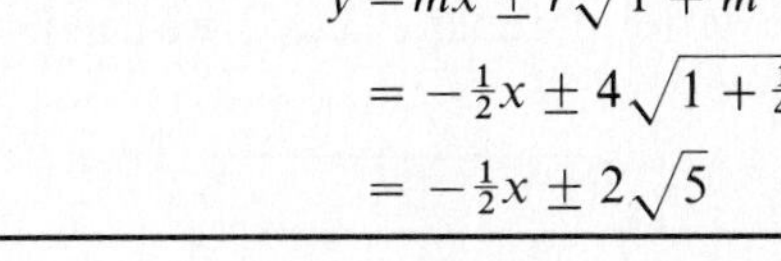

$$y = mx \pm r\sqrt{1 + m^2}$$

$$= -\tfrac{1}{2}x \pm 4\sqrt{1 + \tfrac{1}{4}}$$

$$= -\tfrac{1}{2}x \pm 2\sqrt{5}$$

C. Finding tangents from an external point

We can also find the equation(s) of the tangent(s) to a second-degree curve from an external point by solving the slope form of the desired tangent for m in terms of the given coordinates, then using the value(s) of m to find the equations.

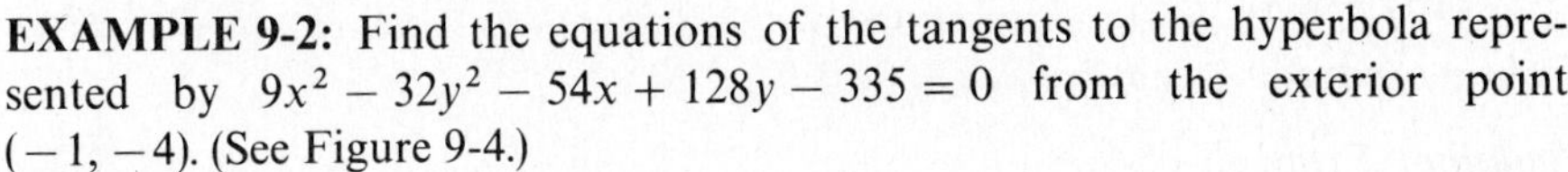

EXAMPLE 9-2: Find the equations of the tangents to the hyperbola represented by $9x^2 - 32y^2 - 54x + 128y - 335 = 0$ from the exterior point $(-1, -4)$. (See Figure 9-4.)

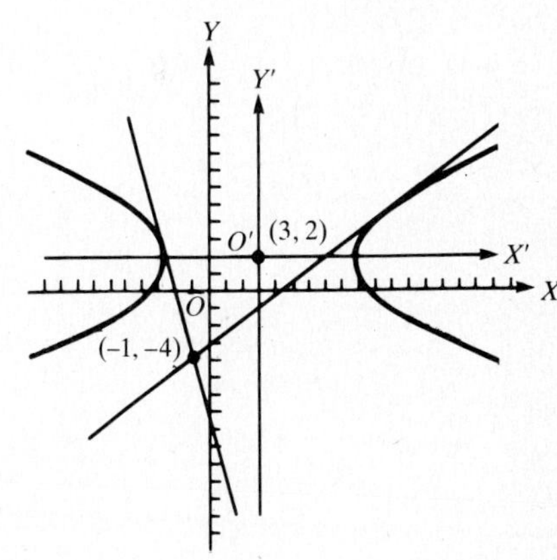

Figure 9-4

Solution: Completing the squares, we can write the standard form of the equation of the hyperbola as

$$9(x - 3)^2 - 32(y - 2)^2 = 288$$

$$\frac{(x - 3)^2}{32} - \frac{(y - 2)^2}{9} = 1$$

Or we can refer to the center of the hyperbola as the origin (O') and write

$$\frac{(x')^2}{32} - \frac{(y')^2}{9} = 1$$

which is the equation of the hyperbola referred to the X'- and Y'-axes. And if $x' = x - 3$ and $y' = y - 2$, the point $(-1, -4)$ becomes $(-4, -6)$ with respect to the X',Y'-axes. Hence the problem reduces to finding the tangents to the hyperbola $(x')^2/32 - (y')^2/9 = 1$ from the point $(x', y') = (-4, -6)$.

Since the slope form of the tangents to a hyperbola is given by $y = mx \pm \sqrt{a^2m^2 - b^2}$ (eq. 9-5), we can write

$$y' = mx' \pm \sqrt{a^2m^2 - b^2} = mx' \pm \sqrt{32m^2 - 9}$$

as the equations of the tangents to the given hyperbola referred to the X',Y'-axes. And since these tangent lines must pass through the given point, the coordinates

$(-4, -6)$ must satisfy the tangent equations. So we can use $x' = -4$ and $y' = -6$ to find the values of m:

$$-6 = -4m \pm \sqrt{32m^2 - 9} \qquad m = -\frac{15}{4} \quad \text{or} \quad \frac{3}{4}$$

then we can substitute these values of m into $y' = mx' \pm \sqrt{32m^2 - 9}$ to give

$$3x' - 4y' \pm 12 = 0 \qquad \text{and} \qquad 15x' + 4y' \pm 84 = 0$$

Two of these lines, $3x' - 4y' - 12 = 0$ and $15x' + 4y' + 84 = 0$, pass through the point $(-4, -6)$ and are the required tangents referred to the $X'Y'$-axes.

Finally, to find the equations of the tangents with respect to the X- and Y-axes, we substitute $x' = x - 3$ and $y' = y - 2$:

$$3(x - 3) - 4(y - 2) - 12 = 0 \qquad \text{and} \qquad 15(x - 3) + 4(y - 2) + 84 = 0$$

$$3x - 4y - 13 = 0 \qquad\qquad 15x + 4y + 31 = 0$$

In the case of a circle, we can take a more direct route (based on our general method). Thus if we have a circle $x^2 + y^2 = r^2$, we know that two tangents $y = mx \pm r\sqrt{1 + m^2}$ can be drawn to that circle from an exterior point. If we designate the exterior point as $P(x', y')$, we can find the slope of the line $y' = mx' \pm r\sqrt{1 + m^2}$:

$$m = \frac{x'y' \pm r\sqrt{(x')^2 + (y')^2 - r^2}}{(x')^2 - r^2}$$

Then we can rewrite the equation of the tangent in point-slope form $(y - y' = m(x - x'))$:

TANGENT TO CIRCLE (point-slope form)

$$y - y' = \left(\frac{x'y' \pm r\sqrt{(x')^2 + (y')^2 - r^2}}{(x')^2 - r^2}\right)(x - x') \qquad \textbf{(9-6)}$$

EXAMPLE 9-3: Find the equations of the tangents to the circle $x^2 + y^2 = 16$ from the exterior point $P(x', y') = (-3, 7)$.

Solution: From eq. (9-6),

$$y - 7 = \left(\frac{-21 \pm 4\sqrt{9 + 49 - 16}}{9 - 16}\right)(x + 3)$$

$$y = 10 \pm \tfrac{4}{7}\sqrt{42}(x + 3)$$

EXAMPLE 9-4: Write the equations of the tangents to the circle $x^2 + y^2 = 9$ from the exterior point $(2, -3)$.

Solution: Using eq. (9-6) and substituting $x' = 2$, $y' = -3$,

$$y + 3 = \left(\frac{-6 \pm 3\sqrt{4 + 9 - 9}}{4 - 9}\right)(x - 2)$$

$$= \left(\frac{-6 \pm 6}{-5}\right)(x - 2)$$

so $y + 3 = 0$ and $12x - 5y - 39 = 0$ are the required tangents.

D. Finding tangents at points of contact

To illustrate the method of finding the equation of a tangent to a second-degree curve in terms of the coordinates of the point of contact, we'll find such an equation for the circle $x^2 + y^2 = r^2$ at a contact point $P(x_1, y_1)$.

We know that $y = mx \pm r\sqrt{1 + m^2}$ is the equation of the tangent to the circle $x^2 + y^2 = r^2$ for all finite values of m. So if $P(x_1, y_1)$ is the point of tangency (see Figure 9-5), then (x_1, y_1) satisfies the equation of the tangent $y_1 = mx_1 \pm r\sqrt{1 + m^2}$, from which we can find the slope m. Thus

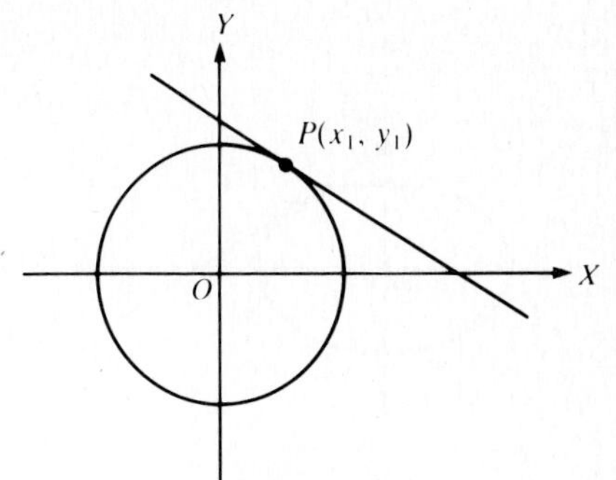

Figure 9-5

$$y_1 - mx_1 = \pm r\sqrt{1 + m^2}$$

$$y_1^2 - 2mx_1y_1 + m^2x_1^2 = r^2 + r^2m^2$$

$$(x_1^2 - r^2)m^2 - 2x_1y_1m + y_1^2 - r^2 = 0$$

and from the general quadratic

$$m = \frac{2x_1y_1 \pm \sqrt{4x_1^2y_1^2 - 4(x_1^2 - r^2)(y_1^2 - r^2)}}{2(x_1^2 - r^2)}$$

$$= \frac{x_1y_1 \pm r\sqrt{x_1^2 + y_1^2 - r^2}}{x_1^2 - r^2}$$

We also know that the point P is on the circle, so its coordinates must satisfy the equation of the circle. Therefore, we can write the circle as $x_1^2 + y_1^2 = r^2$, from which we find $x_1^2 + y_1^2 - r^2 = 0$ and $x_1^2 - r^2 = -y_1^2$. On substituting these values into the expression for m, we see that the slope of the tangent becomes

$$m = \frac{x_1y_1}{-y_1^2} = -\frac{x_1}{y_1}$$

Then, knowing the slope and the point of contact, we can use the point-slope equation of a straight line and find

$$y - y_1 = -\frac{x_1}{y_1}(x - x_1)$$

which reduces to

$$y_1y - y_1^2 = -x_1x + x_1^2 \qquad \text{or} \qquad x_1x + y_1y = x_1^2 + y_1^2$$

But $x_1^2 + y_1^2 = r^2$, and so our final equation of the tangent to the circle in terms of the coordinates of the point of contact is

TANGENT TO CIRCLE at point of contact

$$x_1x + y_1y = r^2 \qquad \textbf{(9-7)}$$

Similarly, the equations of the tangents to the other second-degree curves are found to be

TANGENT TO PARABOLA at point of contact

$$y_1y = 2a(x + x_1) \qquad \textbf{(9-8)}$$

when the curve is the parabola $y^2 = 4ax$;

TANGENT TO ELLIPSE at point of contact

$$b^2x_1x + a^2y_1y = a^2b^2 \qquad \textbf{(9-9)}$$

when the curve is the ellipse $b^2x^2 + a^2y^2 = a^2b^2$; and

TANGENT TO HYPERBOLA at point of contact

$$b^2x_1x - a^2y_1y = a^2b^2 \qquad \textbf{(9-10)}$$

when the curve is the hyperbola $b^2x^2 - a^2y^2 = a^2b^2$.

note: Each of these equations may be obtained from the equation of the corresponding curve by replacing x^2, y^2, and x by x_1x, y_1y, and $\frac{1}{2}(x + x_1)$, respectively.

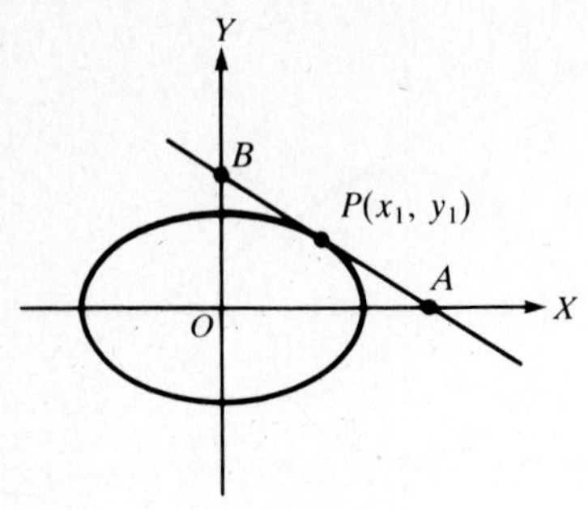

Figure 9-6

EXAMPLE 9-5: Find the coordinates of a point on the ellipse $b^2x^2 + a^2y^2 = a^2b^2$, at which the tangent makes equal angles with the coordinate axes. (See Figure 9-6.)

Solution: Let $P(x_1, y_1)$ be the desired point, and let $b^2x_1x + a^2y_1y = a^2b^2$ (eq. 9-9) be the equation of the tangent at this point. By substituting $y = 0$ into this equation, we can find the X-intercept of the tangent to be $OA = a^2/x_1$; similarly, by substituting $x = 0$, we find the Y-intercept $OB = b^2/y_1$.

We know by hypothesis that angle OAP is equal to angle OBP; that is,

$$\arctan\frac{OB}{OA} = \arctan\frac{OA}{OB}$$

so, by replacing OA and OB with their values, we get

$$\arctan\frac{b^2}{y_1}\left(\frac{x_1}{a^2}\right) = \arctan\frac{a^2}{x_1}\left(\frac{y_1}{b^2}\right)$$

Hence

$$\frac{b^2x_1}{a^2y_1} = \frac{a^2y_1}{b^2x_1}$$

$$b^4{x_1}^2 - a^4{y_1}^2 = 0$$

We also know that P is on the ellipse; hence $b^2{x_1}^2 + a^2{y_1}^2 = a^2b^2$. Therefore we can solve the two equations $b^4{x_1}^2 - a^4{y_1}^2 = 0$ and $b^2{x_1}^2 + a^2{y_1}^2 = a^2b^2$ simultaneously for x_1 and y_1 to find

$$x_1 = \frac{\pm a^2}{\sqrt{a^2 + b^2}} \qquad \text{and} \qquad y_1 = \frac{\pm b^2}{\sqrt{a^2 + b^2}}$$

which are the coordinates of the point P.

9-2. Normals

- A **normal** to a curve at any point on the curve is a straight line that is perpendicular to the tangent at that point.

In finding the equation of the normal it's usually best to find the equation of the tangent first. Then, if m is the slope of the tangent, the equation of the normal is given by

NORMAL TO A CURVE $$y - y_1 = -\frac{1}{m}(x - x_1) \qquad \textbf{(9-11)}$$

where $m \neq 0$ and (x_1, y_1) are the coordinates of the point on the curve.

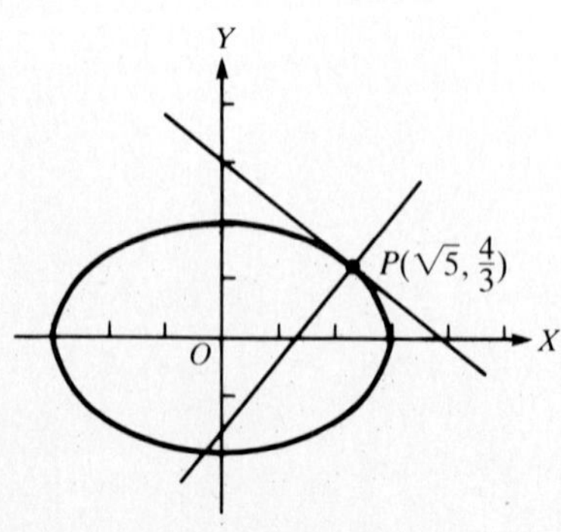

Figure 9-7

EXAMPLE 9-6: Find the equations of the tangent and the normal to the ellipse $4x^2 + 9y^2 = 36$ at the point $(\sqrt{5}, 4/3)$. (See Figure 9-7.)

Solution: Write the equation of the tangent to the curve at any point $P(x_1, y_1)$ in the form of eq. (9-9) by substituting x_1x for x^2 and y_1y for y^2 in the equation of the ellipse:

$$4x_1x + 9y_1y = 36$$

Then since $x_1 = \sqrt{5}$ and $y_1 = 4/3$, we have the equation of the tangent at this particular point:

$$4\sqrt{5}x + 12y = 36$$

Since the slope m of this line is $-\sqrt{5}/3$, we know that the slope $-1/m$ of the normal is $3/\sqrt{5}$. Hence the equation of the normal at the point $(\sqrt{5}, 4/3)$ is

$$y - y_1 = -\frac{1}{m}(x - x_1)$$

$$y - \frac{4}{3} = \left(\frac{3}{\sqrt{5}}\right)(x - \sqrt{5})$$

or

$$9x - 3\sqrt{5}y - 5\sqrt{5} = 0$$

EXAMPLE 9-7: Find the equation of the normal to the parabola $y^2 = 8x$ that is perpendicular to the line $2x - 3y + 6 = 0$.

Solution: From eq. (9-8) the equation of the tangent to the parabola at a point $P(x_1, y_1)$ on the parabola is

$$y_1 y = 4(x + x_1) \qquad \text{or} \qquad 4x - y_1 y + 4x_1 = 0$$

Its slope is $4/y_1$ and therefore the slope of the normal is $-y_1/4$. But the normal is also perpendicular to the line $2x - 3y + 6 = 0$. Thus $-y_1/4 = -3/2$, or $y_1 = 6$. Then, since P is on the curve, its coordinates satisfy the equation of the curve; i.e., ${y_1}^2 = 8x_1$. Solving the equations $y_1 = 6$ and ${y_1}^2 = 8x_1$ simultaneously, we find

$$x_1 = \frac{9}{2} \qquad \text{and} \qquad y_1 = 6$$

which are the coordinates of the point of contact (Figure 9-8). Therefore, the equation of the normal to the curve at this point is

$$y - 6 = -\frac{3}{2}\left(x - \frac{9}{2}\right)$$

or

$$6x + 4y - 51 = 0$$

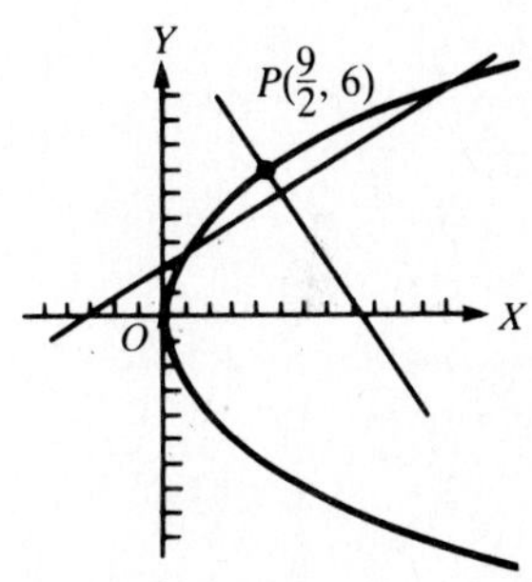

Figure 9-8

SUMMARY

1. A tangent PT at a point P of a curve is defined as the limiting position of the secant PQ as Q approaches P along the curve.
2. The equations of the tangents to the second-degree curves in slope form are

X-Parabola $y^2 = 4ax$:	$y = mx + \dfrac{a}{m}$
Circle $x^2 + y^2 = r^2$:	$y = mx \pm r\sqrt{1 + m^2}$
Ellipse $b^2x^2 + a^2y^2 = a^2b^2$:	$y = mx \pm \sqrt{a^2m^2 + b^2}$
Hyperbola $b^2x^2 - a^2y^2 = a^2b^2$:	$y = mx \pm \sqrt{a^2m^2 - b^2}$

3. To find the equations of tangents to a second-degree curve from an external point:
   (a) Write the equation of the curve in standard form.
   (b) Substitute the relevant values (a, r, or a^2 and b^2) from the standard form of the curve into the appropriate slope form of the tangent to find the slope m.
   (c) Substitute the value of m into the slope formula to obtain the equation(s) of the tangent(s) to the curve.

4. The equations of the tangents to second-degree curves at a point of contact are

Parabola $y^2 = 4ax$:	$y_1 y = 2a(x + x_1)$
Circle $x^2 + y^2 = r^2$:	$x_1 x + y_1 y = r^2$
Ellipse $b^2x^2 + a^2y^2 = a^2b^2$:	$b^2x_1x + a^2y_1y = a^2b^2$
Hyperbola $b^2x^2 - a^2y^2 = a^2b^2$:	$b^2x_1x - a^2y_1y = a^2b^2$

5. A normal to a curve at any point on the curve is a straight line that is perpendicular to the tangent at that point:

$$y - y_1 = -\frac{1}{m}(x - x_1)$$

6. To find the equation of the normal to a second-degree curve at a point:
   (a) Write the appropriate equation for the tangent to the curve at the point.
   (b) Substitute the coordinates of the point into the equation of the tangent and find the slope of the tangent.
   (c) Substitute the negative reciprocal of the tangent slope into the equation of the normal to find the desired equation.

RAISE YOUR GRADES

Can you . . .?

☑ write the equation for the intersection points of a parabola and a straight line
☑ write the slope form of the equations of the tangents to the parabola, the circle, the ellipse, and the hyperbola
☑ find the equation(s) of the tangent(s) to a given second-degree curve, given the slope of the tangent
☑ find the equation(s) of the tangent(s) to a given second-degree curve, given the coordinates of a point that is on the tangent but not on the curve
☑ find the equation(s) of the tangent(s) to a given second-degree curve, given the coordinates of the point of contact
☑ find the equations of the normals to any of the tangents to the second-degree curves

SOLVED PROBLEMS

Tangents

Slope form

PROBLEM 9-1 Write the equation of the line that has slope 4 and is tangent to the curve $y = x^2$.

Solution: The given curve is a *Y*-parabola $x^2 = y$, whose basic equation (from eq. 5-2) is $x^2 = 4ay$, so $4a = 1$ and $a = 1/4$. Substituting this value of a and the given value of m into eq. (9-2b), you get

$$y = mx - am^2$$

$$y = 4x - \left(\frac{1}{4}\right)(4)^2$$

$$y = 4x - 4$$

as the equation of the tangent.

PROBLEM 9-2 Find the equation of the tangent to the parabola $(y - 2)^2 = -3(x + 1)$ with slope 1/2.

Solution: Here you can use the slope formula $y = mx + a/m$ (eq. 9-2a) for finding the tangent to the parabola with vertex $(-1, 2)$. Thus, setting $y' = y - 2$, $x' = x + 1$, and finding $a = -3/4$, you can write

$$y' = \left(\frac{1}{2}\right)x' + \left(-\frac{3}{4}\right)\left(\frac{2}{1}\right)$$

$$2y' = x' - 3$$

so that, on substituting the values for x' and y', you get the tangent

$$2(y - 2) = (x + 1) - 3$$

$$x - 2y + 2 = 0$$

PROBLEM 9-3 Write the equations of the lines of slope 2 that are tangent to the ellipse $13x^2 + 3y^2 - 26x + 24y + 22 = 0$.

Solution: Write the equation of this ellipse in standard form:

$$13(x^2 - 2x + 1) + 3(y^2 + 8y + 16) = -22 + 13 + 48$$

$$\frac{(x - 1)^2}{3} + \frac{(y + 4)^2}{13} = 1$$

Then find a translation form of the tangent of the ellipse (in slope form) from eq. (9-4)

$$y = mx \pm \sqrt{a^2m^2 + b^2}$$

$$y - k = m(x - h) \pm \sqrt{a^2m^2 + b^2}$$

and substitute the values $h = 1$, $k = -4$, $a^2 = 3$, $b^2 = 13$, and $m = 2$ into the translation form:

$$y + 4 = 2(x - 1) \pm \sqrt{3(4) + 13}$$

$$y + 4 = 2(x - 1) \pm 5$$

Therefore the equations of the tangents are

$$2x - y - 1 = 0 \qquad \text{and} \qquad 2x - y - 11 = 0$$

PROBLEM 9-4 Write the equations of the tangents to the hyperbola $2x^2 - y^2 = 1$ with slope 2.

Solution: Here $a^2 = \frac{1}{2}$, $b^2 = 1$, and $m = 2$. Inserting these values in eq. (9-5), you get

$$y = mx \pm \sqrt{a^2m^2 - b^2}$$

$$y = 2x \pm \sqrt{\tfrac{1}{2}(4) - 1}$$

$$y = 2x \pm 1$$

as the equations of the tangents.

PROBLEM 9-5 Given the curve $(x + 1)^2 + (y - 5)^2 = 9$, find all the tangents with slope -2.

Solution: The given equation appears to be that of a circle or an ellipse. But dividing through by 9 to reduce it to the standard form of an ellipse gives you $a = 3$ and $b = 3$; and since both semi-axes are the same length (representing a radius of 3), the curve is a circle whose center is $(-1, 5)$. So you'll use eq. (9-3), letting $x' = x + 1$, $y' = y - 5$, and $r = 3$: Thus, if $y = mx \pm r\sqrt{1 + m^2}$, then

$$y' = mx' \pm r\sqrt{1 + m^2}$$
$$= -2x' \pm 3\sqrt{1 + 4}$$
$$y - 5 = -2(x + 1) \pm 3\sqrt{5}$$
$$2x + y - 3 \pm 3\sqrt{5} = 0$$

Finding tangents from an external point

PROBLEM 9-6 Find the equations of the tangents to the parabola $y^2 = 36x$ from the point $(2, 9)$.

Solution: From $y^2 = 36x$ you know that $4a = 36$, so from eq. (9-2a)

$$y = mx + a/m \qquad (a = 9)$$
$$9 = 2m + 9/m$$
$$2m^2 - 9m + 9 = 0$$
$$(2m - 3)(m - 3) = 0$$
$$m = 3,\ 3/2$$

Substituting these values of m into eq. (9-2a) gives the tangents

$$3x - y + 3 = 0 \qquad \text{and} \qquad 3x - 2y + 12 = 0$$

PROBLEM 9-7 Find the equations of the tangents to the circle $x^2 + y^2 = 4$ from the point $(1, 6)$.

Solution: This calls for eq. (9-6), with $y' = 6$, $x' = 1$, and $r = 2$: Thus, if

$$y - y' = \left(\frac{x'y' \pm r\sqrt{(x')^2 + (y')^2 - r^2}}{(x')^2 - r^2}\right)(x - x')$$

then

$$y - 6 = \left(\frac{(1)(6) \pm 2\sqrt{(1)^2 + (6)^2 - (2)^2}}{(1)^2 - 4}\right)(x - 1)$$
$$y - 6 = \left(\frac{6 \pm 2\sqrt{1 + 36 - 4}}{-3}\right)(x - 1)$$
$$y - 6 = -2 \pm \tfrac{2}{3}\sqrt{33}(x - 1)$$
$$y = 4 \pm \tfrac{2}{3}\sqrt{33}(x - 1)$$

Finding tangents at points of contact

PROBLEM 9-8 Find the equation of the tangent to the parabola $y^2 - 12x - 2y - 23 = 0$ at $(1, 7)$.

Solution: In standard form (after completing the square) the equation of the parabola becomes

$$y^2 - 2y + 1 = 12x + 24$$
$$(y - 1)^2 = 12(x + 2)$$

from which you can see that (h, k) is $(-2, 1)$ and $a = 3$ (since $(y - k)^2 = 4a(x - h)$). Then, since the vertex of this parabola is at (h, k), you can amend eq. (9-8) to get a formula for the tangent

$$y_1 y = 2a(x + x_1)$$
$$(y_1 - k)(y - k) = 2a(x - h + x_1 - h)$$
$$(y - k)(y_1 - k) = 2a(x + x_1 - 2h)$$

into which you can substitute the given values $x_1 = 1$, $y_1 = 7$ and the values $(h, k) = (-2, 1)$, $a = 3$ to get the tangent:

$$(y - 1)(7 - 1) = 2(3)(x + 1 - 2(-2))$$

$$(y - 1)(6) = 6(x + 5)$$

$$x - y + 6 = 0$$

Normals

PROBLEM 9-9 Find the normal to the parabola $y^2 - 12x - 2y - 23 = 0$ at the point $(1, 7)$.

Solution: You know from Problem 9-8 that the equation of the tangent is $x - y + 6 = 0$, which you can rewrite as $y = x + 6$ to find the slope $m = 1$. Therefore, the equation of the normal will be (from eq. 9-11)

$$y - y_1 = -\frac{1}{m}(x - x_1)$$

$$y - 7 = -(x - 1)$$

$$x + y - 8 = 0$$

PROBLEM 9-10 Write the equations of the tangent and the normal to the ellipse $16x^2 + y^2 - 16 = 0$ at $(\frac{1}{2}, -2\sqrt{3})$.

Solution: To find the tangent you can use the standard form of formula (9-9):

$$b^2x_1x + a^2y_1y = a^2b^2$$

$$\frac{xx_1}{a^2} + \frac{yy_1}{b^2} = 1$$

Thus

$$\frac{x(1/2)}{1} + \frac{y(-2\sqrt{3})}{16} = 1$$

$$4x - \sqrt{3}y - 8 = 0$$

$$y = \frac{4x}{\sqrt{3}} - \frac{8}{\sqrt{3}}$$

So $m = 4/\sqrt{3}$ for the tangent. Thus, from eq. (9-11), the equation of the normal is

$$y - y_1 = -\frac{1}{m}(x - x_1)$$

$$y + 2\sqrt{3} = -\frac{\sqrt{3}}{4}\left(x - \frac{1}{2}\right)$$

PROBLEM 9-11 Write the equations of the tangent and normal to the hyperbola $16x^2 - 9y^2 - 128x - 54y + 31 = 0$ at $(\frac{1}{4}, 0)$.

Solution: In standard form this hyperbola is

$$\frac{(x - 4)^2}{9} - \frac{(y + 3)^2}{16} = 1$$

Here you need to use the point form of the equation of the tangent to a hyperbola (9-10), namely,

$$\frac{(x - h)(x_1 - h)}{a^2} - \frac{(y - k)(y_1 - k)}{b^2} = 1$$

so the tangent to the hyperbola at $(\frac{1}{4}, 0)$ is

$$\frac{(x-4)(\frac{1}{4}-4)}{9} - \frac{(y+3)(0+3)}{16} = 1$$

$$20x + 9y - 5 = 0$$

where $m = -20/9$. Therefore $-1/m = 9/20$, and from eq. (9-11) the equation of the normal is

$$y - y_1 = -\frac{1}{m}(x - x_1)$$

$$y = \frac{9}{20}\left(x - \frac{1}{4}\right)$$

Supplementary Exercises

PROBLEM 9-12 Write the equations of the tangents to the ellipse $9x^2 + 16y^2 = 144$ that are perpendicular to the line $4x - y + 1 = 0$.

PROBLEM 9-13 Write the equations of the tangents to the hyperbola $x^2 - 4y^2 = 16$ that make equal intercepts on the coordinate axes.

PROBLEM 9-14 Write the equations of the tangents to the ellipse $5x^2 + 9y^2 - 36y - 9 = 0$ that are perpendicular to the line $3x + 4y - 13 = 0$.

PROBLEM 9-15 Find the equation of the tangent to the curve $x^2 - 4y + 7 = 0$ at the point $(2, \frac{11}{4})$.

PROBLEM 9-16 Find the tangent(s) to the curve $x^2 + 5y^2 - 3x + 2y = 0$ at $(3, 0)$.

PROBLEM 9-17 Write the equation(s) of the tangent(s) to the curve $16x^2 + 9y^2 - 32x + 54y - 47 = 0$ with slope -1.

PROBLEM 9-18 Find the equation of the tangent to the curve $(x-1)^2 - y^2 - 1 = 0$ at $(0, 0)$.

PROBLEM 9-19 Find the equation(s) of the tangents to the curve $9(x+1)^2 - 2y^2 + 9 = 0$ with slope $\frac{1}{2}$.

PROBLEM 9-20 Find the equation of the tangent to the circle $(x-1)^2 + (y+\frac{1}{2})^2 = 5$ at the point $(3, \frac{1}{2})$.

PROBLEM 9-21 Find the equation of the tangent to the parabola $y^2 = 8x$ that is parallel to the line $2x + 2y - 3 = 0$.

PROBLEM 9-22 Write the equation of the tangent to the curve $x^2 = 16y$ that is perpendicular to the line $2x + 4y + 7 = 0$.

Answers to Supplementary Exercises

9-12: $x + 4y \pm 4\sqrt{10} = 0$

9-13: $x + y \pm 2\sqrt{3} = 0$

9-14: $4x - 3y + 6 \pm 3\sqrt{21} = 0$

9-15: $4x - 4y + 3 = 0$

9-16: $3x + 2y - 9 = 0$

9-17: $x + y + 7 = 0$ and $x + y - 3 = 0$

9-18: $x = 0$

9-19: $y = \frac{1}{2}(x+1) \pm \frac{1}{2}\sqrt{17}$

9-20: $4x + 2y - 13 = 0$

9-21: $x + y + 2 = 0$

9-22: $2x - y - 16 = 0$

10 GENERAL EQUATION OF THE SECOND DEGREE

THIS CHAPTER IS ABOUT

- ☑ Rotation of Axes
- ☑ Transformation of the General Equation by Rotation
- ☑ Discriminant of the General Equation
- ☑ Locus of the General Equation

10-1. Rotation of Axes

- **Rotation** is the transformation of the coordinate axes in which the origin remains fixed and the axes are turned, or *rotated*, through some fixed angle about this point.

For a rotation through an angle θ (theta), we can derive transformation formulas that express the old coordinates in terms of θ and the new coordinates. Thus, referring to Figure 10-1, we let P be any point whose coordinates are (x, y) when referred to the original axes OX and OY, and (x', y') when referred to the new axes OX' and OY'. Then $OM = x$, $MP = y$, $OQ = x'$, $QP = y'$, and the angle of rotation XOX' is represented by θ. Now, if we draw RQ perpendicular to PM and QN perpendicular to OX, the angle $RPQ = XOX' = \theta$ (from similar triangles). So, from the figure, we have

$$x = OM = ON - MN = ON - RQ$$

$$y = MP = MR + RP = NQ + RP$$

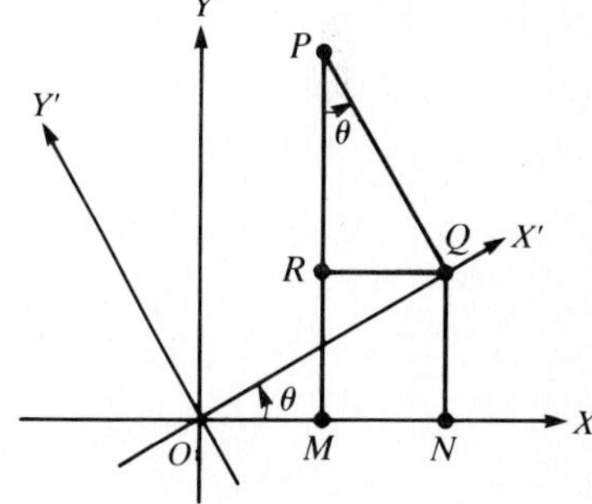

Figure 10-1.
Transformation by rotation of axes.

But $ON = OQ\cos\theta$, $RQ = PQ\sin\theta$, $NQ = OQ\sin\theta$, and $RP = PQ\cos\theta$. So, by substitution, we get

ROTATION FORMULAS

$$x = x'\cos\theta - y'\sin\theta$$
$$y = x'\sin\theta + y'\cos\theta \qquad \textbf{(10-1)}$$

These rotation formulas allow us to transform the equation of any locus referred to one pair of rectangular axes into the equation of the same locus referred to a second pair of axes that pass through the same origin and make an angle θ with the original axes.

note: See Appendix C: *Trigonometry*, for a quick review of trigonometric definitions, functions, identities, etc.

EXAMPLE 10-1: Transform the equation $x^2 - y^2 - 9 = 0$ by rotating the axes through 45°. (See Figure 10-2.)

Solution: From trigonometry, when $\theta = 45°$,

$$\sin\theta = \cos\theta = \frac{1}{\sqrt{2}}$$

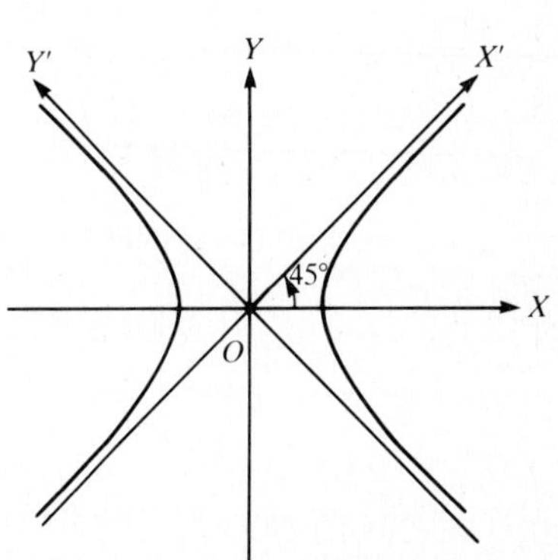

Figure 10-2

Hence the rotation formulas (eq. 10-1) become

$$x = \frac{x'}{\sqrt{2}} - \frac{y'}{\sqrt{2}} \quad \text{and} \quad y = \frac{x'}{\sqrt{2}} + \frac{y'}{\sqrt{2}}$$

Making these substitutions in the given equation and simplifying, we have

$$\left(\frac{x'}{\sqrt{2}} - \frac{y'}{\sqrt{2}}\right)^2 - \left(\frac{x'}{\sqrt{2}} + \frac{y'}{\sqrt{2}}\right)^2 - 9 = 0$$

$$\frac{(x')^2}{2} - x'y' + \frac{(y')^2}{2} - \frac{(x')^2}{2} - x'y' - \frac{(y')^2}{2} - 9 = 0$$

$$2x'y' + 9 = 0$$

as the transformed equation.

10-2. Transformation of the General Equation by Rotation

The general equation of the second degree in two variables may be written as

GENERAL EQUATION OF THE SECOND DEGREE

$$Ax^2 + Bxy + Cy^2 + Dx + Ey + F = 0 \qquad \textbf{(10-2)}$$

And this equation may be transformed into the form of the general equation of a conic, $Ax^2 + Cy^2 + Dx + Ey + F = 0$ (eq. 8-1), by proper rotation of the axes to which the locus of the equation is referred; i.e.,

- a properly chosen rotation of axes will always remove the xy-term from a second-degree equation.

To see how this choice is made, we begin by substituting the values for x and y given by the rotation formulas (10-1) into eq. (10-2):

$$\begin{aligned} A(x'\cos\theta - y'\sin\theta)^2 &+ B(x'\cos\theta - y'\sin\theta)(x'\sin\theta + y'\cos\theta) \\ &+ C(x'\sin\theta + y'\cos\theta)^2 + D(x'\cos\theta - y'\sin\theta) \\ &+ E(x'\sin\theta + y'\cos\theta) + F = 0 \end{aligned} \qquad \textbf{(10-2a)}$$

so that, after all the $x'y'$-terms are expanded and collected, the coefficient of $x'y'$ is

$$B' = -2A\sin\theta\cos\theta + B\cos^2\theta - B\sin^2\theta + 2C\sin\theta\cos\theta$$

Then we know from trigonometry that $2\sin\theta\cos\theta = \sin 2\theta$ and $\cos^2\theta - \sin^2\theta = \cos 2\theta$, so we can use these values to write the coefficient of $x'y'$ as

$$B' = -(A - C)\sin 2\theta + B\cos 2\theta$$

Now to remove the $x'y'$-term, we have to find a value of θ such that B' (the coefficient of the $x'y'$-term) will become zero; this occurs when

$$-(A - C)\sin 2\theta + B\cos 2\theta = 0$$

So we can find the **acute angle of rotation** from the trigonometric identity

$$\tan 2\theta = \frac{B}{A - C} \qquad \textbf{(10-3)}$$

where $A - C \neq 0$. And when $A - C = 0$, we have $\cos 2\theta = 0$, so $\theta = 45°$. Since there is always a value of 2θ between $0°$ and $180°$ for which eq. (10-3) is true, there is always a positive acute angle θ through which the axes may be rotated so as to remove the $x'y'$-term. If the axes are rotated through this particular angle, the general second-degree equation (10-2) will be transformed into the general form of a conic, or

TRANSFORMED GENERAL EQUATION

$$A'(x')^2 + C'(y')^2 + D'x' + E'y' + F' = 0 \qquad \textbf{(10-4)}$$

where the new coefficients, collected from the expanded form of eq. (10-2a), are as follows:

$$A' = A\cos^2\theta + B\sin\theta\cos\theta + C\sin^2\theta$$

$$C' = A\sin^2\theta - B\sin\theta\cos\theta + C\cos^2\theta$$

$$D' = D\cos\theta + E\sin\theta$$

$$E' = E\cos\theta - D\sin\theta$$

EXAMPLE 10-2: Simplify the equation

$$x^2 + 3xy + y^2 = 2$$

by rotation of axes. Draw the curve, showing the old and new axes.

Solution: Here $A - C = 0$; hence $\theta = 45°$ and eqs. (10-1) become

$$x = \left(\frac{1}{\sqrt{2}}\right)(x' - y') \quad \text{and} \quad y = \left(\frac{1}{\sqrt{2}}\right)(x' + y')$$

The transformed equation is therefore

$$\left(\frac{1}{\sqrt{2}}(x' - y')\right)^2 + 3\left(\frac{1}{\sqrt{2}}(x' - y')\frac{1}{\sqrt{2}}(x' + y')\right) + \left(\frac{1}{\sqrt{2}}(x' + y')\right)^2 = 2$$

which reduces to the equation of a hyperbola

$$5(x')^2 - (y')^2 = 4$$

as shown in Figure 10-3, where the X', Y'-axes are at a 45° angle to the X, Y-axes.

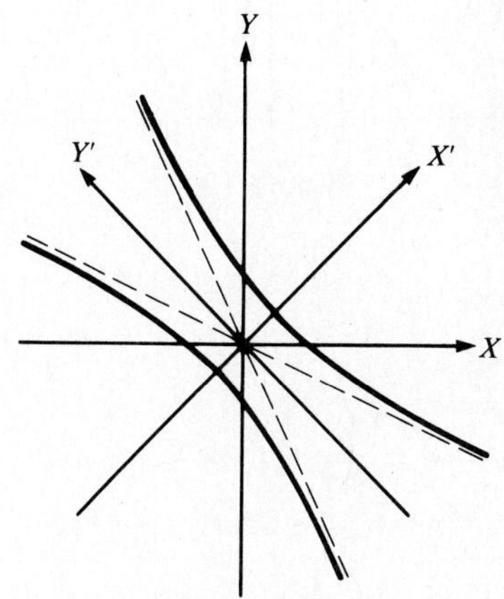

Figure 10-3

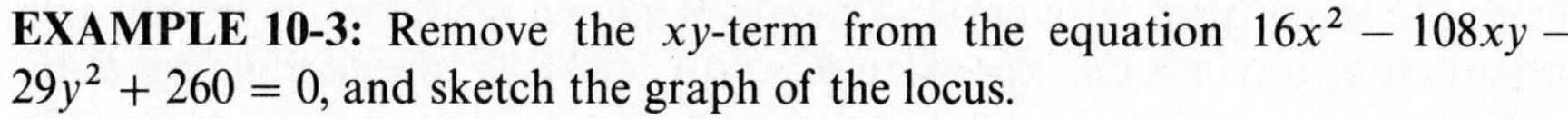

EXAMPLE 10-3: Remove the xy-term from the equation $16x^2 - 108xy - 29y^2 + 260 = 0$, and sketch the graph of the locus.

Solution: Using eq. (10-3), you have

$$\tan 2\theta = \frac{-108}{16 + 29} = \frac{-12}{5}$$

To find the functions of θ you need another identity from trigonometry:

$$\cos 2\theta = \frac{1}{\sec 2\theta} = \frac{1}{\pm\sqrt{1 + \tan^2 2\theta}} \qquad \textbf{(10-3a)}$$

which gives you

$$\cos 2\theta = \pm\frac{1}{\sqrt{1 + 144/25}} = \pm\frac{5}{13}$$

By selecting the sign of $\cos 2\theta$ to be the SAME as that of $\tan 2\theta$, so that $\cos 2\theta = -5/13$, the angle 2θ will be in the second quadrant and θ will be acute. Also from trigonometry you know that

$$\sin\theta = \sqrt{\frac{1 - \cos 2\theta}{2}} \quad \text{and} \quad \cos\theta = \sqrt{\frac{1 + \cos 2\theta}{2}} \qquad \textbf{(10-3b)}$$

so you can substitute the value of 2θ into these expressions to get

$$\sin\theta = \frac{3}{\sqrt{13}} \quad \text{and} \quad \cos\theta = \frac{2}{\sqrt{13}}$$

Therefore the formulas (10-1) for rotating the axes are

$$x = \frac{2x' - 3y'}{\sqrt{13}} \quad \text{and} \quad y = \frac{3x' + 2y'}{\sqrt{13}}$$

Substituting these values into the equation of the curve gives you

$$16\left(\frac{2x' - 3y'}{\sqrt{13}}\right)^2 - 108\left(\frac{2x' - 3y'}{\sqrt{13}}\right)\left(\frac{3x' + 2y'}{\sqrt{13}}\right) - 29\left(\frac{3x' + 2y'}{\sqrt{13}}\right)^2 + 260 = 0$$

$$845(x')^2 - 676(y')^2 = 3380$$

$$5(x')^2 - 4(y')^2 = 20$$

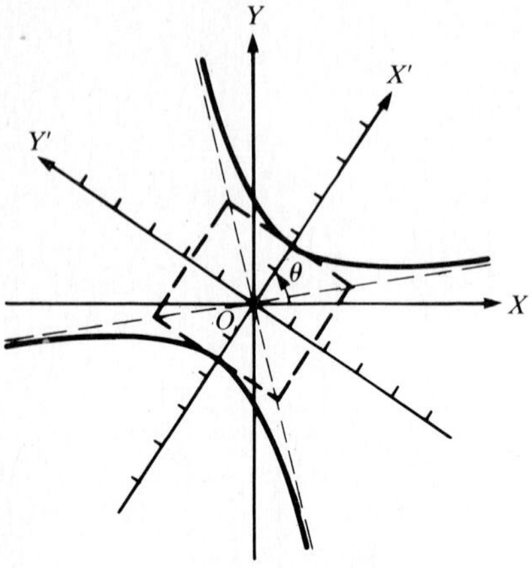

You can sketch the locus by first constructing the new axes at an angle θ with the original axes. And you can find θ by using yet another trigonometric identity:

$$\tan\theta = \frac{\sin\theta}{\cos\theta} = \frac{3/\sqrt{13}}{2/\sqrt{13}} = \frac{3}{2}$$

$$\theta = \tan^{-1}(3/2) \cong 56.3^\circ$$

Then draw the hyperbola on the OX' and OY' reference frame, as shown in Figure 10-4.

Figure 10-4

10-3. Discriminant of the General Equation

Translation (see Chapter 2) and rotation of axes are both called *transformations* of coordinates, since they change the coordinates of all points in the plane (except the origin in the case of rotation). But while translation and rotation move the axes to which a curve is referred—thereby changing the form of its equation—neither transformation changes the SHAPE of a curve described by an equation. Thus whether the equation of a curve is in its first or second (transformed) form, its graph remains the same.

In addition to this feature of the unvarying geometric representation of a curve, there are algebraic expressions whose values remain unchanged in the two forms of the equation of a curve. These expressions are called **invariants**. One important invariant is the expression $B^2 - 4AC$, which is the **discriminant** of the general equation of the second degree.

To prove that the discriminant qualifies as an invariant, we take the values for A', B', and C' (from Section 10-2)

$$A' = A\cos^2\theta + B\sin\theta\cos\theta + C\sin^2\theta$$

$$B' = 2(C - A)\sin\theta\cos\theta + B(\cos^2\theta - \sin^2\theta)$$

$$C' = A\sin^2\theta - B\sin\theta\cos\theta + C\cos^2\theta$$

and substitute them into the expression $(B')^2 - 4A'C'$:

$$\begin{aligned}(B')^2 - 4A'C' &= B^2\cos^4\theta + B^2\sin^4\theta - 8AC\sin^2\theta\cos^2\theta - 4AC\sin^4\theta \\ &\quad - 4AC\cos^4\theta + 2B^2\sin^2\theta\cos^2\theta \\ &= (B^2 - 4AC)\cos^4\theta + (B^2 - 4AC)\sin^4\theta \\ &\quad + 2(B^2 - 4AC)\sin^2\theta\cos^2\theta \\ &= (B^2 - 4AC)(\sin^2\theta + \cos^2\theta)^2 \\ &= B^2 - 4AC\end{aligned}$$

Therefore $(B')^2 - 4A'C' = B^2 - 4AC$, and

- the discriminant is invariant under the transformation of rotation.

10-4. Locus of the General Equation

So far we have considered the transformation of rotation and have shown that the equation $Ax^2 + Bxy + Cy^2 + Dx + Ey + F = 0$ may be transformed into

$A'(x')^2 + B'x'y' + C'(y')^2 + D'x' + E'y' + F = 0$ by a general rotation. Also, if we choose a value of θ such that $\tan 2\theta = B/(A - C)$ (where $A \neq C$), the $x'y'$-term will be removed and the new equation will become $A'(x')^2 + C'(y')^2 + D'x' + E'y' + F = 0$. Furthermore, in this case, $(B')^2 - 4A'C' = B^2 - 4AC$, so

$$B^2 - 4AC = -4A'C'$$

since $B' = 0$. This leaves us with three possibilities:

(1) If $B^2 - 4AC < 0$, then A' and C' have the same sign, so the locus of the equation is an ellipse when $A' \neq C'$ and a circle when $A' = C'$.
(2) If $B^2 - 4AC > 0$, then A' and C' have different signs, so the locus of the equation is a hyperbola.
(3) If $B^2 - 4AC = 0$, then either $A' = 0$ or $C' = 0$, so the locus of the equation is a parabola.

Therefore we can say that the general second-degree equation will represent a parabola, an ellipse, or a hyperbola depending upon the value of the discriminant.

note: There are cases in which a second-degree equation can be factored into two first-degree factors and is therefore graphed linearly.

EXAMPLE 10-4: Given the equation $16x^2 - 24xy + 9y^2 + 20x - 140y - 300 = 0$, **(a)** identify the conic, **(b)** simplify the equation, and **(c)** draw the curve (showing each set of axes).

Solution:

(a) To identify the conic, determine the value of the discriminant:

$$B^2 - 4AC = (-24)^2 - 4(16)(9) = 0$$

Therefore the curve is a parabola.

(b) To simplify the equation, remove the xy term by rotating the axes through the angle θ:

$$\tan 2\theta = \frac{B}{A - C} = \frac{-24}{16 - 9} = -\frac{24}{7}$$

Then from the Pythagorean theorem you can determine that the value of the hypotenuse is $\sqrt{(24)^2 + (7)^2} = 25$, so $\cos 2\theta = -7/25$. Therefore

$$\sin\theta = \sqrt{\frac{1 - \cos 2\theta}{2}} = \sqrt{\frac{1 + 7/25}{2}} = \frac{4}{5}$$

$$\cos\theta = \sqrt{\frac{1 + \cos 2\theta}{2}} = \sqrt{\frac{1 - 7/25}{2}} = \frac{3}{5}$$

The rotation formulas (eqs. 10-1) then become

$$x = \frac{3x' - 4y'}{5} \qquad \text{and} \qquad y = \frac{4x' + 3y'}{5}$$

Substituting these values into the equation, you have

$$16\left(\frac{3x' - 4y'}{5}\right)^2 - 24\left(\frac{3x' - 4y'}{5}\right)\left(\frac{4x' + 3y'}{5}\right) + 9\left(\frac{4x' + 3y'}{5}\right)^2$$
$$+ 20\left(\frac{3x' - 4y'}{5}\right) - 140\left(\frac{4x' + 3y'}{5}\right) - 300 = 0$$

Expanding, collecting like terms, and reducing, you get the equation transformed by *rotation*:

$$16[9(x')^2 + 16(y')^2] - 24[12(x')^2 - 12(y')^2] + 9[16(x')^2 + 9(y')^2]$$
$$+ 100(3x' - 4y') - 700(4x' + 3y') - 7500 = 0$$
$$625(y')^2 - 2500x' - 2500y' - 7500 = 0$$
$$(y')^2 - 4x' - 4y' - 12 = 0$$

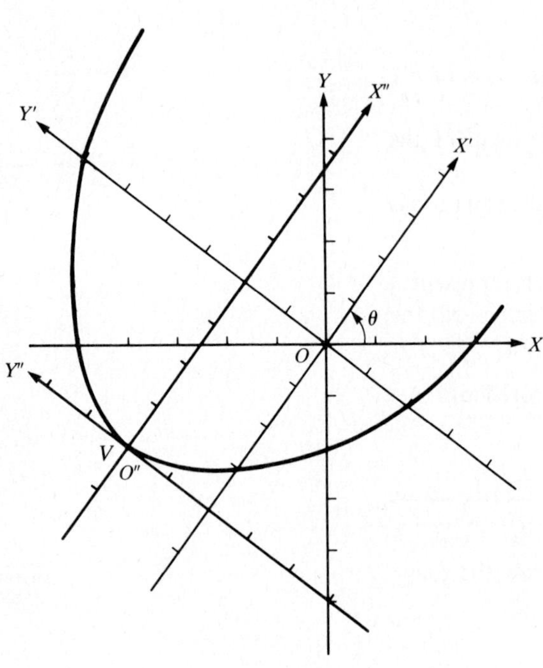

Figure 10-5

which represents a parabola with axis parallel to the OX'-axis (see Figure 10-5).

Now find the vertex of the parabola by completing the square of the y' terms, so that the transformed equation is in standard form (eq. 5-3):

$$(y' - 2)^2 = 4(x' + 4)$$

Thus the coordinates of the vertex are $(h, k) = (-4, 2)$ with reference to the OX'- and OY'-axes. So, setting $y'' = (y' - k)$ and $x'' = (x' - h)$, you can write the equation with reference to the $O''X''$- and $O''Y''$-axes drawn through this point parallel to the OX'- and OY'-axes, i.e., the equation transformed by *rotation and translation*:

$$(y'')^2 = 4x''$$

(c) Draw the graph by first constructing the OX'- and OY'-axes at an angle θ with the original axes, where $\theta = \tan^{-1}(4/3) \cong 53.1°$. Then draw $O''X''$ and $O''Y''$ parallel to OX' and OY' through the point $x' = -4$, $y' = 2$. Finally, draw the parabola on this last set of axes, as in Figure 10-5.

SUMMARY

1. Rotation is a method of transformation of coordinates in which the axes are rotated about the (fixed) origin through a fixed angle. By rotating the coordinate axes through an angle θ, we derive transformation formulas that express the old coordinates in terms of θ and the new coordinates.
2. The general form of a second-degree equation is

$$Ax^2 + Bxy + Cy^2 + Dx + Ey + F = 0$$

3. A properly chosen rotation of axes will always remove the xy-term from a second-degree equation.
4. The rotation formulas are

$$x = x' \cos\theta - y' \sin\theta$$
$$y = x' \sin\theta + y' \cos\theta$$

5. To remove the $x'y'$-term from a second-degree equation, determine a value of θ such that

$$\tan 2\theta = \frac{B}{A - C} \qquad (A - C \neq 0)$$

(If $A - C = 0$, then $\theta = 45°$.)

6. The transformed general equation is

$$A'(x')^2 + C'(y')^2 + D'x' + E'y' + F' = 0$$

7. The new coefficients of the transformed general equation are

$$A' = A\cos^2\theta + B\sin\theta\cos\theta + C\sin^2\theta$$

$$C' = A\sin^2\theta - B\sin\theta\cos\theta + C\cos^2\theta$$

$$D' = D\cos\theta + E\sin\theta$$

$$E' = E\cos\theta - D\sin\theta$$

8. Algebraic expressions whose values remain unchanged during transformation of an equation are called invariants. The discriminant of the general second-degree equation, $B^2 - 4AC$, is an invariant.

9. The value of the discriminant determines the nature of the curve:

- If $B^2 - 4AC < 0$, then A' and C' have the same sign and the equation represents an ellipse.
- If $B^2 - 4AC > 0$, then A' and C' have different signs and the equation represents a hyperbola.
- If $B^2 - 4AC = 0$, then either A' or $C' = 0$ and the equation represents a parabola.

10. If a second-degree equation can be factored into two first-degree factors, its graph is drawn linearly.

RAISE YOUR GRADES

Can you ...?

☑ write the rotation formulas
☑ transform a second-degree equation by rotating the axes through 45°
☑ simplify an equation containing an xy-term by rotating the axes through some acute angle
☑ draw the curve represented by a second-degree equation containing an xy-term
☑ determine the type of curve a second-degree equation represents by examining the discriminant

SOLVED PROBLEMS

Rotation of Axes

PROBLEM 10-1 What does the equation $x^2 - y^2 - 4 = 0$ become if the axes are rotated through an angle of 45°?

Solution: You know that the angle θ through which the axes are rotated is 45°, so you use the rotation formulas (10-1):

$$x = x'\cos 45^\circ - y'\sin 45^\circ = \frac{x' - y'}{\sqrt{2}} \qquad y = x'\sin 45^\circ + y'\cos 45^\circ = \frac{x' + y'}{\sqrt{2}}$$

since $\sin 45^\circ = \cos 45^\circ = 1/\sqrt{2}$. Then you can substitute these values into the given equation, expand, and collect like terms to get the transformed equation:

$$\left(\frac{x'-y'}{\sqrt{2}}\right)^2 - \left(\frac{x'+y'}{\sqrt{2}}\right)^2 - 4 = 0$$

$$\frac{(x')^2 - 2x'y' + (y')^2 - (x')^2 - 2x'y' - (y')^2 - 8}{2} = 0$$

$$x'y' + 2 = 0$$

PROBLEM 10-2 Transform the equation $x^2 - y^2 = 25$ by rotating the axes through the angle $\theta = 45°$.

Solution: From eqs. (10-1)

$$x = x'\cos 45° - y'\sin 45° = \frac{x'-y'}{\sqrt{2}}$$

$$y = x'\sin 45° + y'\cos 45° = \frac{x'+y'}{\sqrt{2}}$$

So substituting these values into the original equation gives

$$\left(\frac{x'-y'}{\sqrt{2}}\right)^2 - \left(\frac{x'+y'}{\sqrt{2}}\right)^2 - 25 = 0$$

$$2x'y' + 25 = 0$$

Transformation of the General Equation by Rotation

PROBLEM 10-3 Simplify $x^2 - 24xy - 6y^2 = 1$ by rotation of axes.

Solution: Find the angle of rotation θ:

From eq. (10-3): $$\tan 2\theta = \frac{B}{A-C} = \frac{-24}{1-(-6)} = -\frac{24}{7}$$

From eq. (10-3a): $$\cos 2\theta = \frac{1}{\pm\sqrt{1+\tan^2 2\theta}} = \frac{1}{-\sqrt{1+(-24/7)^2}} = -\frac{7}{25}$$

[Note that you choose the sign of $\cos 2\theta$ so it is the same as that of $\tan 2\theta$.]

From eq. (10-3b): $$\sin\theta = \sqrt{\frac{1-\cos 2\theta}{2}} = \sqrt{\frac{1-(-7/25)}{2}} = \frac{4}{5}$$

$$\cos\theta = \sqrt{\frac{1+\cos 2\theta}{2}} = \sqrt{\frac{1+(-7/25)}{2}} = \frac{3}{5}$$

Then find the values of x and y after rotation:

From eq. (10-1): $$x = x'\cos\theta - y'\sin\theta = (\tfrac{1}{5})(3x' - 4y')$$

$$y = x'\sin\theta + y'\cos\theta = (\tfrac{1}{5})(4x' + 3y')$$

Finally, substitute these values into the original equation:

$$[(\tfrac{1}{5})(3x' - 4y')]^2 - 24[(\tfrac{1}{25})(3x' - 4y')(4x' + 3y')] - 6[(\tfrac{1}{5})(4x' + 3y')]^2 = 1$$

and since the $x'y'$-products should cancel, you can write

$$(\tfrac{1}{25})[9(x')^2 + 16(y')^2] - (\tfrac{24}{25})[12(x')^2 - 12(y')^2] - \tfrac{6}{25}[16(x')^2 + 9(y')^2] = 1$$

$$9(x')^2 + 16(y')^2 - 288(x')^2 + 288(y')^2 - 96(x')^2 - 54(y')^2 = 25$$

$$-375(x')^2 + 250(y')^2 = 25$$

$$10(y')^2 - 15(x')^2 = 1$$

which is the transformed equation.

Check: Are the discriminants equal?

$$B^2 - 4AC = (B')^2 - 4A'C'$$

$$(-24)^2 - 4(1)(-6) = -4(-15)(10)$$

$$600 = 600$$

The discriminants are equal and greater than 0: The curve is a hyperbola.

PROBLEM 10-4 Find the rotation formulas that will simplify $x^2 + xy - 2y^2 + x + y = 1$.

Solution: Find the angle of rotation θ:

From eq. (10-3): $$\tan 2\theta = \frac{B}{A - C} = \frac{1}{3}$$

From eq. (10-3a): $$\cos 2\theta = \frac{1}{\pm\sqrt{1 + \tan^2 2\theta}} = \frac{1}{+\sqrt{1 + (1/3)^2}} = \frac{3}{\sqrt{10}}$$

[Notice that the signs of $\tan 2\theta$ and $\cos 2\theta$ are chosen to be the same.]

From eq. (10-3b): $$\sin\theta = \sqrt{\frac{1 - \cos 2\theta}{2}} = \sqrt{\frac{1}{2}\left(1 - \frac{3}{\sqrt{10}}\right)} = \sqrt{\frac{\sqrt{10} - 3}{2\sqrt{10}}}$$

$$\cos\theta = \sqrt{\frac{1 + \cos 2\theta}{2}} = \sqrt{\frac{1}{2}\left(1 + \frac{3}{\sqrt{10}}\right)} = \sqrt{\frac{3 + \sqrt{10}}{2\sqrt{10}}}$$

Find the transformed values of x and y:

From eqs. (10-1): $$x = x'\cos\theta - y'\sin\theta = x'\left(\sqrt{\frac{\sqrt{10} + 3}{2\sqrt{10}}}\right) - y'\left(\sqrt{\frac{\sqrt{10} - 3}{2\sqrt{10}}}\right)$$

$$y = x'\sin\theta + y'\cos\theta = x'\left(\sqrt{\frac{\sqrt{10} - 3}{2\sqrt{10}}}\right) + y'\left(\sqrt{\frac{\sqrt{10} + 3}{2\sqrt{10}}}\right)$$

Locus of the General Equation

PROBLEM 10-5 Determine the nature of the graph, if any, of the equation $2x^2 + 7xy + 3y^2 + x - 7y - 6 = 0$.

Solution: Substituting the appropriate coefficients from the equation, you find that the discriminant $B^2 - 4AC = 49 - 4(2)(3) = 25 > 0$. However, this positive result—which *does* eliminate the possibility of a parabola or an ellipse—does *not* guarantee that this is a hyperbola, as you'd normally expect. To make certain, treat the equation as a quadratic in x and apply the quadratic formula: Thus

$$2x^2 + (7y + 1)x + (3y^2 - 7y - 6) = 0$$

Therefore $$x = \frac{-(7y + 1) \pm \sqrt{(7y + 1)^2 - 8(3y^2 - 7y - 6)}}{4}$$

$$= \frac{-7y - 1 \pm \sqrt{25y^2 + 70y + 49}}{4}$$

$$= \frac{-7y - 1 \pm (5y + 7)}{4}$$

So $$x = \frac{-y + 3}{2} \quad \text{and} \quad x = -3y - 2$$

This means that the given equation may be shown in the factored form

$$(2x + y - 3)(x + 3y + 2) = 0$$

If the coordinates of a point make one of these factors equal to zero, then those coordinates also make the product zero—and therefore satisfy the original equation. [See the "note" in Section 10-4.] Thus the graph consists of the two straight lines whose equations are

$$2x + y - 3 = 0 \qquad \text{and} \qquad x + 3y + 2 = 0$$

PROBLEM 10-6 Determine the graph of the equation $y^2 - 4xy + 4x^2 - 2x + y - 12 = 0$.

Solution:
$$B^2 - 4AC = 16 - 4(1)(4) = 0$$

So the graph appears to be a parabola. But, checking for linear factors, you see that

$$y - 2x - 3 = 0 \qquad \text{and} \qquad y - 2x + 4 = 0$$

Therefore the graph of the given equation consists of two parallel lines (i.e., two straight lines whose slopes are equal).

PROBLEM 10-7 Determine the graph of $4x^2 - 12xy + 9y^2 + 20x - 30y + 25 = 0$.

Solution: Since

$$B^2 - 4AC = (-12)^2 - 4(4)(9) = 0$$

it would appear that the curve is a parabola. You could check further by solving for one variable in terms of the other; but it is evident from the equation that the left member is readily factorable:

$$(4x^2 - 12xy + 9y^2) + 10(2x - 3y) + 25 = 0$$
$$(2x - 3y)^2 + 10(2x - 3y) + 25 = 0$$
$$(2x - 3y + 5)(2x - 3y + 5) = 0$$

So the graph is the line $2x - 3y + 5 = 0$.

PROBLEM 10-8 Simplify $2x^2 + 24xy - 5y^2 - 9 = 0$ and determine its graph.

Solution: Start by finding the rotation angle θ:

From eq. (10-3): $$\tan 2\theta = \frac{B}{A - C} = \frac{24}{7}$$

From eq. (10-3a): $$\cos 2\theta = \frac{1}{\pm\sqrt{1 + \tan^2 2\theta}} = \frac{1}{+\sqrt{1 + 576/49}} = \frac{7}{25}$$

From eq. (10-3b): $$\sin\theta = \sqrt{\frac{1 - \cos 2\theta}{2}} = \sqrt{\frac{1}{2}\left(1 - \frac{7}{25}\right)} = \frac{3}{5}$$

$$\cos\theta = \sqrt{\frac{1 + \cos 2\theta}{2}} = \sqrt{\frac{1}{2}\left(1 + \frac{7}{25}\right)} = \frac{4}{5}$$

Then find the transformed values for x and y:

From eqs. (10-1): $$x = x'\cos\theta - y'\sin\theta = \tfrac{1}{5}(4x' - 3y')$$
$$y = x'\sin\theta + y'\cos\theta = \tfrac{1}{5}(3x' + 4y')$$

Now substitute these values into the original equation and simplify (dropping out the $x'y'$-products, which should cancel):

$$2[\tfrac{1}{5}(4x' - 3y')]^2 + 24(\tfrac{1}{25})(4x' - 3y')(3x' + 4y') - 5[\tfrac{1}{5}(3x' + 4y')]^2 = 9$$
$$\tfrac{2}{25}[16(x')^2 + 9(y')^2] + \tfrac{24}{25}[12(x')^2 - 12(y')^2] - \tfrac{5}{25}[9(x')^2 + 16(y')^2] = 9$$
$$32(x')^2 + 18(y')^2 + 288(x')^2 - 288(y')^2 - 45(x')^2 - 80(y')^2 = 225$$
$$275(x')^2 - 350(y')^2 = 225$$
$$11(x')^2 - 14(y')^2 = 9$$

So the graph of the equation is a hyperbola.

Check:
$$B^2 - 4AC = (B')^2 - 4A'C'$$
$$(24)^2 - 4(2)(-5) = -4(11)(-14)$$
$$616 = 616$$

The discriminants of the original and transformed equation are equal; and they are greater than zero, so the graph is a hyperbola.

PROBLEM 10-9 Determine the type of conic represented by each of the following equations:

(a) $2x^2 + 8xy + 7y^2 + x - 3y + 8 = 0$
(b) $2x^2 + 8xy + 9y^2 + x - 3y + 8 = 0$
(c) $2x^2 + 8xy + 8y^2 + x - 3y + 8 = 0$

Solution: Evaluate the discriminant of each equation:

(a) $B^2 - 4AC = 8^2 - 4(2)(7) = 8 > 0$ hyperbola
(b) $B^2 - 4AC = 8^2 - 4(2)(9) = -8 < 0$ ellipse
(c) $B^2 - 4AC = 8^2 - 4(2)(8) = 0$ parabola

PROBLEM 10-10 Identify the conic represented by
$$7x^2 - 6\sqrt{3}xy + 13y^2 - 4\sqrt{3}x - 4y - 12 = 0$$
Simplify the equation by rotation and sketch the curve referred to the new axes.

Solution: The conic is an ellipse since $B^2 - 4AC = (-6\sqrt{3})^2 - 4(7)13 = -256 < 0$.

To remove the product term, first rotate the coordinate axes through an angle θ, which you can determine by using the inverse of eq. (10-3), $\cot 2\theta = (A - C)/B$. Thus

$$\cot 2\theta = \frac{A - C}{B} = \frac{7 - 13}{-6\sqrt{3}} = \frac{1}{\sqrt{3}} \qquad \text{or} \qquad \tan 2\theta = \sqrt{3}$$

Accordingly, $2\theta = 60°$, so $\theta = 30°$. And since $\sin 30° = 1/2$ and $\cos 30° = \sqrt{3}/2$, the formulas for rotation (10-1) become

$$x = x'\cos\theta - y'\sin\theta \qquad \text{and} \qquad y = x'\sin\theta + y'\cos\theta$$
$$= x'\left(\frac{\sqrt{3}}{2}\right) - y'\left(\frac{1}{2}\right) \qquad\qquad = x'\left(\frac{1}{2}\right) + y'\left(\frac{\sqrt{3}}{2}\right)$$

Substituting these values for x and y into the given equation, you get

$$7[\tfrac{1}{2}(\sqrt{3}x' - y')]^2 - 6\sqrt{3}[\tfrac{1}{4}(\sqrt{3}x' - y')(x' + \sqrt{3}y')] + 13[\tfrac{1}{2}(x' + \sqrt{3}y')]^2$$
$$- 4\sqrt{3}[\tfrac{1}{2}(\sqrt{3}x' - y')] - 4[\tfrac{1}{2}(x' + \sqrt{3}y')] - 12 = 0$$

which can be simplified (dropping out the $x'y'$-products):

$$\frac{7[3(x')^2 + (y')^2]}{4} - \frac{6\sqrt{3}[\sqrt{3}(x')^2 - \sqrt{3}(y')^2]}{4} + \frac{13[(x')^2 + 3(y')^2]}{4}$$
$$-6x' + 2\sqrt{3}y' - 2x' - 2\sqrt{3}y' - 12 = 0$$
$$21(x')^2 + 7(y')^2 - 18(x')^2 + 18(y')^2 + 13(x')^2 + 39(y')^2 - 32x' - 48 = 0$$
$$16(x')^2 + 64(y')^2 - 32x' - 48 = 0$$
$$(x')^2 + 4(y')^2 - 2x' - 3 = 0$$

note: If you compare $B^2 - 4AC$ with $(B')^2 - 4A'C'$ at this point, you'll find that they are NOT equal. *In order to compare discriminants, you have to set the value of the constant term F equal to F'*. Here the constant term in the given equation is -12, so the transformed equation is $4(x')^2 + 16(y')^2 - 8x' - 12 = 0$.

Check:
$$B^2 - 4AC = (B')^2 - 4A'C'$$
$$-256 = -4(4)(16)$$
$$-256 = -256$$

Putting the transformed equation into standard form in order to sketch it more readily, you get

$$\frac{(x'-1)^2}{2^2}+\frac{(y')^2}{1^2}=1$$

So the center C is at $(1, 0)$, the semi-axes are $a = 2$ and $b = 1$, and the major axis is along the X'-axis. The graph is shown in Figure 10-6.

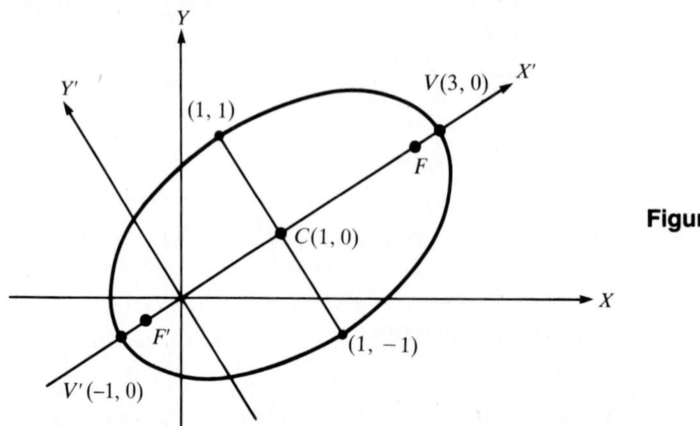

Figure 10-6

PROBLEM 10-11 Given $29x^2 + 108xy - 16y^2 - 66x - 356y - 339 = 0$, **(a)** identify the conic, **(b)** translate the axes, **(c)** rotate the axes, and **(d)** sketch the curve referred to the new axes.

Solution:

(a) Here $B^2 - 4AC = 13\,520 > 0$, so the conic is a hyperbola.

(b) To find the coordinates of its center (h, k), use the relationships

$$h=\frac{2CD-BE}{B^2-4AC} \quad \text{and} \quad k=\frac{2AE-BD}{B^2-4AC}$$

Thus

$$h=\frac{2(-16)(-66)-108(-356)}{13\,520}=3$$

$$k=\frac{2(29)(-356)-108(-66)}{13\,520}=-1$$

The equations of translation are therefore $x = x' + 3$, $y = y' - 1$. So, substituting and simplifying, you get the equation transformed by translation:

$$29(x'+3)^2+108(x'+3)(y'-1)-16(y'-1)^2-66(x'+3)-356(y'-1)-339=0$$

$$29(x')^2+108x'y'-16(y')^2=260$$

(c) For the angle of rotation,

From eq. (10-3): $\tan 2\theta=\dfrac{B}{A-C}=\dfrac{108}{29+16}=\dfrac{12}{5}$

From eq. (10-3a): $\cos 2\theta=\dfrac{1}{\pm\sqrt{1+\tan^2\theta}}=\dfrac{1}{\sqrt{1+144/25}}=\dfrac{5}{13}$

From eq. (10-3b): $\sin\theta=\sqrt{\dfrac{1-5/13}{2}}=\dfrac{2}{\sqrt{13}}$

$$\cos\theta=\sqrt{\frac{1+5/13}{2}}=\frac{3}{\sqrt{13}}$$

So the equations of the rotation are

From eqs. (10-1):
$$x' = \frac{3x''}{\sqrt{13}} - \frac{2y''}{\sqrt{13}}$$
$$y' = \frac{2x''}{\sqrt{13}} + \frac{3y''}{\sqrt{13}}$$

Substitute these values of x' and y' into the (translated) equation

$$29(x')^2 + 108x'y' - 16(y')^2 = 260$$

and simplify to get the equation transformed by rotation (*and* translation):

$$29\left(\frac{3x''}{\sqrt{13}} - \frac{2y''}{\sqrt{13}}\right)^2 + 108\left(\frac{3x''}{\sqrt{13}} - \frac{2y''}{\sqrt{13}}\right)\left(\frac{2x''}{\sqrt{13}} + \frac{3y''}{\sqrt{13}}\right) - 16\left(\frac{2x''}{\sqrt{13}} + \frac{3y''}{\sqrt{13}}\right)^2 = 260$$

$$\left(\frac{29}{13}\right)(3x'' - 2y'')^2 + \left(\frac{108}{13}\right)(3x'' - 2y'')(2x'' + 3y'') - \left(\frac{16}{13}\right)(2x'' + 3y'')^2 = 260$$

$$29[9(x'')^2 - 12x''y'' + 4(y'')^2] + 108[6(x'')^2 + 5x''y'' - 6(y'')^2]$$
$$- 16[4(x'')^2 + 12x''y'' + 9(y'')^2] = 13(260)$$

$$261(x'')^2 - 348x''y'' + 116(y'')^2 + 648(x'')^2 + 540x''y'' - 648(y'')^2$$
$$- 64(x'')^2 - 192x''y'' - 144(y'')^2 = 3380$$
$$845(x'')^2 - 676(y'')^2 = 3380$$
$$5(x'')^2 - 4(y'')^2 = 20$$

(d) To draw the graph, rewrite the transformed equation in standard form

$$\frac{(x'')^2}{4} - \frac{(y'')^2}{5} = 1$$

so you have $a = 2$, $b = \sqrt{5}$, and $c = 3$. Then, using the angle $\theta \cong 33.7°$, draw the $X''Y''$ axes through the center $(h, k) = O'(3, -1)$ and construct the hyperbola on these axes, as shown in Figure 10-7.

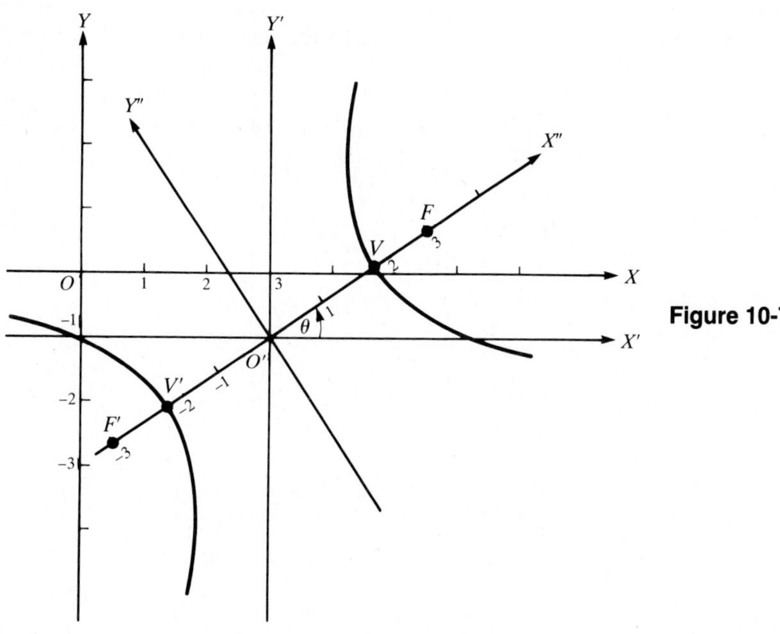

Figure 10-7

Supplementary Exercises

PROBLEM 10-12 Simplify the following equations by rotating the axes through the indicated angles:

(a) $6xy = 7$; $45°$
(b) $x^2 - 2xy + y^2 = 2$; $45°$
(c) $2x^2 + xy + 2y^2 = 1$; $45°$
(d) $3x^2 - 2\sqrt{3}xy + 5y^2 = 12$; $30°$
(e) $x^2 + \sqrt{3}xy + 2y^2 = 2$; $60°$
(f) $6x^2 - 2\sqrt{3}xy + 8y^2 = 5$; $30°$

PROBLEM 10-13 Find the equations of rotation that will transform the following into equations that lack the xy-term:

(a) $8x^2 + 24xy + y^2 = 1$
(b) $6x^2 - 12xy + y^2 = 2$
(c) $3x^2 - 3xy - y^2 = 3$
(d) $x^2 - 5xy - 11y^2 = 2$

PROBLEM 10-14 Simplify the following equations by rotating the axes through the proper angle:

(a) $6x^2 + 4xy + 3y^2 = 2$
(b) $7x^2 - 3xy + 3y^2 = 1$
(c) $8x^2 - 8xy - 7y^2 = 3$
(d) $9x^2 + 20xy - 12y^2 = 1$
(e) $15x^2 + 7xy - 9y^2 = 1$
(f) $9x^2 - 21xy - 11y^2 = 2$

PROBLEM 10-15 Identify the following conics and simplify the equations by translating and rotating the axes:

(a) $5x^2 + 2xy + 5y^2 - 12x - 12y = 0$
(b) $x^2 - 2xy + y^2 - 8x + 16 = 0$
(c) $12xy - 5y^2 + 48y - 36 = 0$
(d) $x^2 + 3xy + y^2 + x - y - 1 = 0$

Answers to Supplementary Exercises

10-12: **(a)** $3(x')^2 - 3(y')^2 = 7$
(b) $(y')^2 = 1$
(c) $5(x')^2 + 3(y')^2 = 2$
(d) $(x')^2 + 3(y')^2 = 6$
(e) $5(x')^2 + (y')^2 = 4$
(f) $5(x')^2 + 9(y')^2 = 5$

10-13: **(a)** $x = \dfrac{4x' - 3y'}{5}$; $y = \dfrac{3x' + 4y'}{5}$
(b) $x = \dfrac{2x' - 3y'}{\sqrt{13}}$; $y = \dfrac{3x' + 2y'}{\sqrt{13}}$
(c) $x = \dfrac{x' - 3y'}{\sqrt{10}}$; $y = \dfrac{3x' + y'}{\sqrt{10}}$
(d) $x = \dfrac{x' - 5y'}{\sqrt{26}}$; $y = \dfrac{5x' + y'}{\sqrt{26}}$

10-14: **(a)** $7(x')^2 + 2(y')^2 = 2$
(b) $5(x')^2 + 15(y')^2 = 2$
(c) $8(x')^2 - 9(y')^2 = -3$
(d) $13(x')^2 - 16(y')^2 = 1$
(e) $31(x')^2 - 19(y')^2 = 2$
(f) $31(x')^2 - 27(y')^2 = -4$

10-15: **(a)** ellipse: $3(x'')^2 + 2(y'')^2 = 6$
(b) parabola: $(y'')^2 = 2\sqrt{2}x''$
(c) hyperbola: $4(x'')^2 - 9(y'')^2 = 36$
(d) straight lines: $5(x'')^2 - (y'')^2 = 0$

EXAM 3 (chapters 9 and 10)

1. Given the circle $x^2 + y^2 - 2x - 4y - 4 = 0$, write the equations of the tangents making an angle of $135°$ with the X-axis.

2. Find the equations of the tangents to the parabola $y^2 = -8x$ at the ends of the latus rectum.

3. Find the equations of the tangent and normal at the point (1, 1) on the ellipse $x^2 + 4y^2 + 4x - 24y + 15 = 0$.

4. Find the equations of the tangents to the hyperbola

$$-\frac{(x+8)^2}{4} + \frac{(y+3)^2}{25} = 1$$

that have the slope $m = 2$.

5. Write the equations of the tangents to the parabola $y^2 - 4y - 9x - 5 = 0$ from the point $(-5, 2)$.

6. Find the equations of the tangent and normal to the parabola $x^2 - 4y = 0$ at the point (2, 1).

7. Transform each of the following equations by means of rotation of axes through the indicated acute angle:

   (a) $x + y - 5 = 0, \qquad \theta = 45°$
   (b) $x^2 + 4xy + y^2 = 4, \qquad \theta = 45°$

8. Identify the following conics and simplify the equations:

   (a) $16x^2 - 24xy + 9y^2 - 60x - 80y + 400 = 0$
   (b) $x^2 - 5xy + y^2 + 8x - 20y + 15 = 0$

Answers to Exam 3

1. $x + y - 3 \pm 3\sqrt{2} = 0$

2. $x + y - 2 = 0, \quad x - y - 2 = 0$

3. $3x - 8y + 5 = 0; \quad 8x + 3y - 11 = 0$

4. $2x - y + 16 = 0, \quad 2x - y + 10 = 0$

5. $3x + 4y + 7 = 0, \quad 3x - 4y + 23 = 0$

6. $x - y - 1 = 0; \quad x + y - 3 = 0$

7. **(a)** $2x' - 5\sqrt{2} = 0$
   (b) $3(x')^2 - (y')^2 = 4$

8. **(a)** parabola: $(y'')^2 = 4x''$
   $(x'' = x' - 4)$
   (b) hyperbola: $7(y'')^2 - 3(x'')^2 = 2$
   $\left(y'' = y' - \frac{4\sqrt{2}}{2}; x'' = x' + \frac{4\sqrt{2}}{2}\right)$

11 POLAR COORDINATES

THIS CHAPTER IS ABOUT

☑ The Polar Coordinate System
☑ Relating Polar and Rectangular Coordinates
☑ Polar Equations

11-1. The Polar Coordinate System

In the system of rectangular (Cartesian) coordinates, a point is located on a plane by means of two distances, x and y, each of which is measured in either of two directions, $+$ or $-$. In the *polar coordinate system* the location is effected by means of an angle and a distance:

- In the **polar coordinate system** the position of a point is determined by a *direction* (θ) and a *distance* (r), and the frame of reference in the plane consists of a fixed point (O) and a directed line.

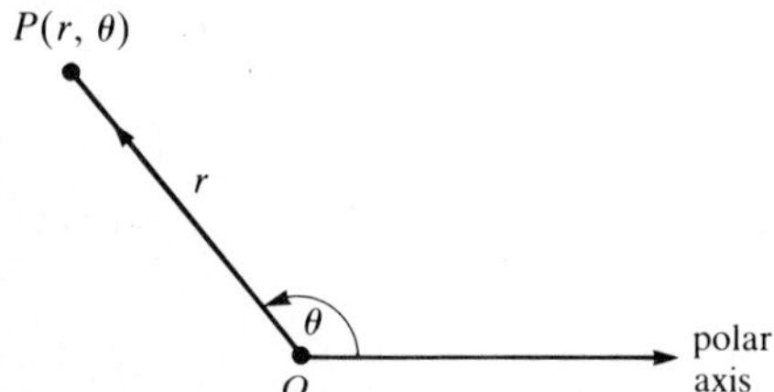

Figure 11-1. The polar coordinate system.

Thus, as shown in Figure 11-1, we begin with a fixed point O, called the **origin** or **pole**, and a fixed directed (to the right) line, called the **polar axis**. Then the position of any point P is determined by two numbers, the distance r, called the **radius vector**, and the angle θ, called the **vectorial angle**.

note: The usual convention of signs applies to the vectorial angle; that is, as in trigonometry, a positive angle is generated by a counterclockwise rotation and a negative angle by a clockwise rotation of the initial side.

The radius vector is positive ($r > 0$) when it is measured from the pole along the terminal side of the angle, and negative ($r < 0$) when measured in the opposite direction. When $r = 0$, the angle θ is arbitrary and the point P is the pole.

A. Plotting points on the polar plane

To plot a point (r, θ) on the polar plane, we first draw the angle θ in the proper direction, thus locating the terminal side. Then the distance r is measured—either along the terminal side, if $r > 0$, or along the reflection of the terminal side through the pole, if $r < 0$. Thus, for example, the point $Q(2, 120°)$ is plotted 2 units along the terminal side of the 120° angle, drawn counterclockwise from the polar axis (Figure 11-2a); and the point $Q(-2, 300°)$ is plotted 2 units along the *reflection* of the terminal side of the 300° angle, drawn counterclockwise from the polar axis (Figure 11-2b).

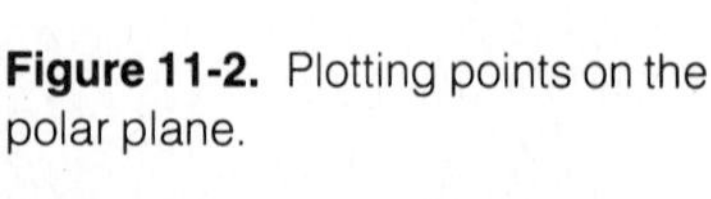

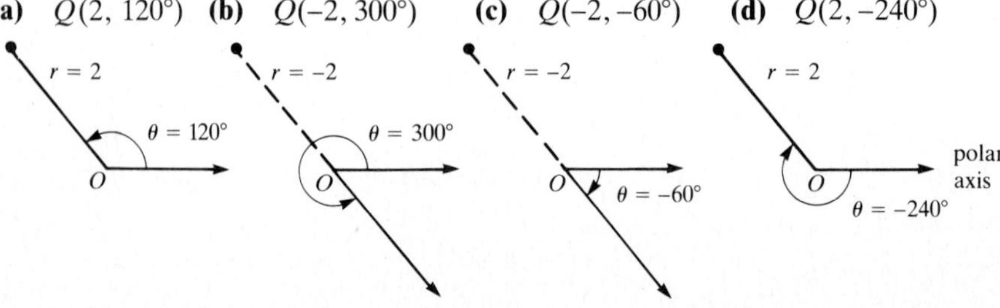

Figure 11-2. Plotting points on the polar plane.

note: One pair of polar coordinates will determine one, and only one, point in the plane; but any given point may have an unlimited number of polar coordinates. *If the angle is restricted to values between 0° and 360°, any given point may be designated by four different pairs of polar coordinates.* In Figure 11-2, for example, the points $(2, 120°)$, $(-2, 300°)$, $(-2, -60°)$, and $(2, -240°)$ all determine the same point Q.

EXAMPLE 11-1: Plot the following points:

(**a**) $A(5, 30°) = (5, \pi/6)$
$B(-3, 15°) = (-3, \pi/12)$
$C(8, -60°) = (8, -\pi/3)$

(**b**) $D(2, 90°) = (2, \pi/2)$
$E(6, -180°) = (6, -\pi)$
$F(-5, 45°) = (-5, \pi/4)$

note: (**1**) We'll use both degrees and radian measure for angles in this chapter. See Appendix C: *Geometry*, for a quick review of radian measure.
(**2**) Polar coordinate paper is supplied at the back of this book.

Solution: See Figure 11-3.

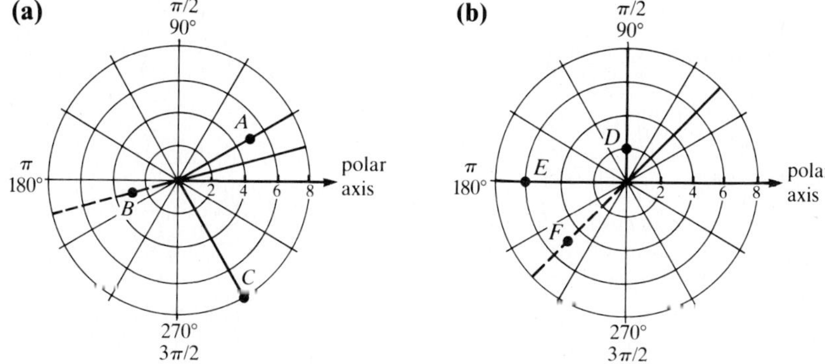

Figure 11-3

B. Sketching polar equations

If r and θ are related by an equation, values may be assigned to θ and the corresponding values for r calculated, so that we have a table of values for points. These points may then be plotted and joined by a curve, thus describing the locus of the equation. And when plotting polar equations, we should be aware of the *symmetry* of the curve:

- If θ can be replaced by $-\theta$ without changing the value of r, then the locus is symmetric with respect to the polar axis.
- If r can be replaced by $-r$ without changing the value of θ, then the curve is symmetric with respect to the pole.

EXAMPLE 11-2: Plot the curve $r = 2(1 - \cos\theta)$.

Solution: Compute a table of values for the equation. Because the cosine function is an even function $[\cos(-\theta) = \cos\theta]$, you only have to compute the values of θ from 0 to 180°, or from 0 to π, since the curve is symmetric with respect to the polar axis. Now, with the aid of a sheet of polar coordinate paper (nearly indispensable for plotting polar coordinates), plot the r values for the selected angles and obtain the curve shown in Figure 11-4. (The resulting curve is a *cardiod.*)

Figure 11-4

θ (radians)	θ (deg.)	$\cos\theta$	$1-\cos\theta$	r
0	0°	1.000	0.000	0.00
$\frac{\pi}{6}$	30°	0.866	0.134	0.27
$\frac{\pi}{3}$	60°	0.500	0.500	1.00
$\frac{\pi}{2}$	90°	0.000	1.000	2.00
$\frac{2\pi}{3}$	120°	−0.500	1.500	3.00
$\frac{5\pi}{6}$	150°	−0.866	1.866	3.73
π	180°	−1.000	2.000	4.00

EXAMPLE 11-3: Plot the curve $r = 3\cos\theta$.

Solution: Generate a table of values by assigning values to θ and calculating the corresponding values of r:

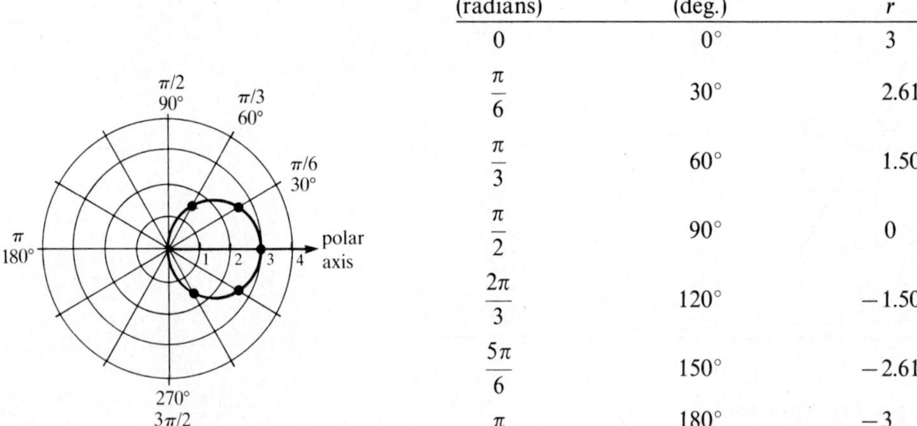

θ (radians)	θ (deg.)	r
0	0°	3
$\frac{\pi}{6}$	30°	2.61
$\frac{\pi}{3}$	60°	1.50
$\frac{\pi}{2}$	90°	0
$\frac{2\pi}{3}$	120°	−1.50
$\frac{5\pi}{6}$	150°	−2.61
π	180°	−3

Figure 11-5

The curve, which is symmetric with respect to the polar axis, is shown in Figure 11-5.

note: Examples 11-2 and 11-3 represent the simplest problem of tracing polar curves—the case in which there is only one value of r for each value of θ. Such curves are called **single-valued functions.** On the other hand, there is a more complex case, in which r^2 is expressed as a function of θ, yielding two values of r for each value of θ, as in $r^2 = 25\sin 2\theta$. Such a case is called a **double-valued function.**

11-2. Relating Polar and Rectangular Coordinates

If the pole in the polar coordinate system coincides with the origin in the Cartesian system and the polar axis overlays the positive X-axis (as shown in Figure 11-6), then any point P has both rectangular coordinates (x, y) and polar coordinates (r, θ). The relations between these two systems, which can be taken directly from Figure 11-6, are

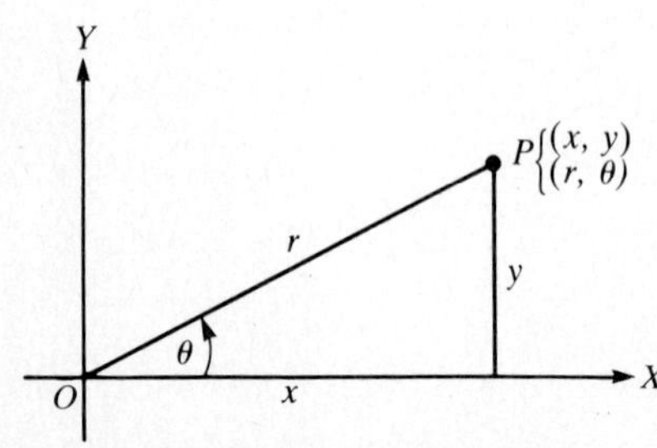

Figure 11-6. Relating polar to rectangular coordinates.

POLAR/RECTANGULAR TRANSFORMATION EQUATIONS

$$x = r\cos\theta, \qquad y = r\sin\theta$$
$$r^2 = x^2 + y^2, \qquad \theta = \tan^{-1}(y/x) \tag{11-1}$$

These relations allow us to transform an equation in polar coordinates to one in rectangular coordinates, and vice versa.

EXAMPLE 11-4: Transform the equation $r = 5\cos\theta$ into an equation in rectangular coordinates.

Solution: Substituting (from eqs. 11-1) $r = \sqrt{x^2 + y^2}$ and $\cos\theta = x/r$ into the given equation, you get

$$r = 5\cos\theta$$

$$\sqrt{x^2 + y^2} = \frac{5x}{\sqrt{x^2 + y^2}}$$

$$x^2 + y^2 - 5x = 0$$

EXAMPLE 11-5: Change $(3 - 2\cos\theta)r = 2$ into Cartesian form.

Solution: Performing the indicated multiplication in the left-hand side, you can write the equation as

$$3r - 2r\cos\theta = 2$$

Then by substituting $r = \sqrt{x^2 + y^2}$ and $r\cos\theta = x$ and simplifying, you get

$$3\sqrt{x^2 + y^2} - 2x = 2$$

$$9x^2 + 9y^2 = 4x^2 + 8x + 4$$

$$5x^2 + 9y^2 - 8x - 4 = 0$$

EXAMPLE 11-6: Transform $x^2 + 2y^2 = 8$ into polar form.

Solution: Since $x = r\cos\theta$ and $y = r\sin\theta$

Substitute: $$r^2\cos^2\theta + 2r^2\sin^2\theta = 8$$

Factor: $$r^2(\cos^2\theta + \sin^2\theta + \sin^2\theta) = 8$$

Use $\sin^2\theta + \cos^2\theta = 1$: $$r^2(1 + \sin^2\theta) = 8$$

11-3. Polar Equations

A. The straight line

To derive the equation of a line in polar coordinates, consider Figure 11-7 in which l is any line in the plane that does not pass through the pole. Then let $ON = p$ be the perpendicular distance from O to N on l, so that the polar coordinates of N are (p, ω); and let $P(r, \theta)$ be any point on line l. Therefore, angle $NOP = \theta - \omega$, and from right triangle ONP we have $OP\cos(\theta - \omega) = ON$, or

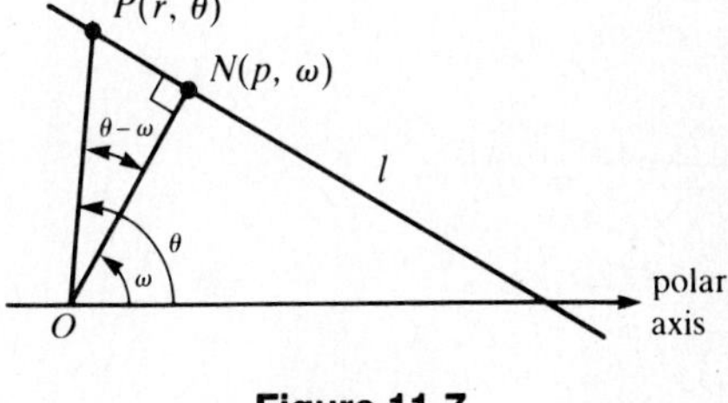

Figure 11-7

POLAR EQUATION OF A LINE
$$r\cos(\theta - \omega) = p \tag{11-2}$$

Since this formula is true for any point P on the line, it is the equation of the line. However, the following special cases should be considered:

(1) If the line l is perpendicular to the polar axis, then either $\omega = 0° = 0$ or $\omega = 180° = \pi$ and eq. (11-2) may be written

LINE PERPENDICULAR TO POLAR AXIS
$$r\cos\theta = \pm p \tag{11-3}$$

(2) If the line l is parallel to the polar axis, then either $\omega = 90° = \pi/2$ or $\omega = 270° = 3\pi/2$ and the equation becomes

LINE PARALLEL TO POLAR AXIS
$$r\sin\theta = \pm p \tag{11-4}$$

(3) If the line passes through the pole, the vectorial angle is the same for every point on the line and the equation may be written $\theta = \alpha$, where α is a constant angle.

B. The circle

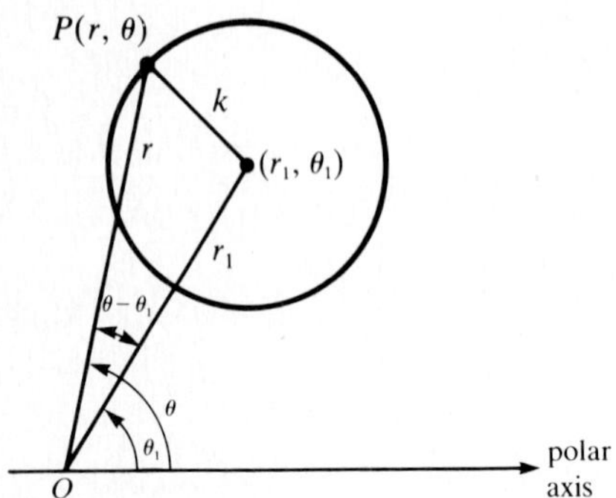

Figure 11-8. Polar equations of circles.

Consider Figure 11-8. Let (r_1, θ_1) be the coordinates of the center of a circle of radius k, and let $P(r, \theta)$ be a point on the circumference of the circle. Then by the law of cosines we have the equation of a circle:

POLAR EQUATION OF A CIRCLE $O \neq (r_1, \theta_1)$

$$k^2 = r^2 + r_1{}^2 - 2rr_1\cos(\theta - \theta_1) \qquad \textbf{(11-5)}$$

If (r_1, θ_1) is at the pole O, then $r_1 = 0$ and eq. (11-5) becomes

POLAR EQUATION OF A CIRCLE $O = (r_1, \theta_1)$

$$r = \pm k \qquad \textbf{(11-6)}$$

which is the equation of a circle of radius k with center at the pole.

Then there are some special cases:

(1) If $\theta_1 = 0$ and $k = \pm r_1$, eq. (11-5) reduces to

CIRCLES PASSING THROUGH POLE (centers on polar axis)

$$r = \pm 2k\cos\theta \qquad \textbf{(11-7)}$$

which are equations of circles passing through the pole and having centers on the polar axis $(+)$ or on the reflection of the polar axis $(-)$.

(2) If $\theta_1 = 90° = \pi/2$ and $k = \pm r_1$, eq. (11-5) reduces to

CIRCLES PASSING THROUGH POLE (centers on 90° axis)

$$r = \pm 2k\sin\theta \qquad \textbf{(11-8)}$$

which are equations of circles passing through the pole and having centers on the $\pi/2$ (90°) axis $(+)$ or the $3\pi/2$ (270°) axis $(-)$.

(3) If $r_1 = k$, eq. (11-5) reduces to

CIRCLE THROUGH POLE (polar intercept *a*; 90° intercept *b*)

$$r = a\cos\theta + b\sin\theta \qquad \textbf{(11-9)}$$

which is the equation of a circle passing through the pole and having intercepts a on the polar axis and b on the $\pi/2$ (90°) axis.

EXAMPLE 11-7: Find the equation of the circle with center (r_1, θ_1) at $(5, \pi/3)$ and radius $k = 3$.

Solution: Substituting in eq. (11-5), you have

$$k^2 = r^2 + r_1{}^2 - 2rr_1\cos(\theta - \theta_1)$$

$$3^2 = r^2 + 5^2 - 2[5r\cos(\theta - \pi/3)]$$

$$r^2 - 10r\cos(\theta - \pi/3) + 16 = 0$$

C. Conics

Figure 11-9. Polar equations of conics.

Since a conic is the locus of a point that moves in such a way that its distance from a fixed point is proportional to its distance from a fixed line, we can derive its equation in polar coordinates as follows.

Referring to Figure 11-9, we let ABC be the fixed line and O the fixed point. Then, letting $P(r, \theta)$ be the variable point, we have

$$\frac{OP}{MP} = e \qquad \text{or} \qquad OP = eMP$$

where e (the *eccentricity*) is the proportionality constant. To express this equation in polar form, we let O be the pole and OD be the polar axis. Thus $OP = r$ and

$$MP = BO + ON = p + r\cos\theta$$

Therefore $$r = e(p + r\cos\theta)$$

or, solving for r,

POLAR EQUATION OF A CONIC (principal axis is polar axis)

$$r = \frac{ep}{1 - e\cos\theta} \qquad \textbf{(11-10)}$$

The value of e will determine which of the three conics (parabola, ellipse, or hyperbola) we may have in any special case:

- If $e = 1$, the equation is the polar form of a parabola.
- If $e < 1$, the equation is the polar form of an ellipse.
- If $e > 1$, the equation is the polar form of a hyperbola.

In the derivation of eq. (11-10) we took the polar axis as the principal axis of the conic. If the $\pi/2$ (90°) axis is the principal axis, $\cos\theta$ is replaced by $\sin\theta$ and we get

POLAR EQUATION OF A CONIC (principal axis is $\pi/2$)

$$r = \frac{ep}{1 - e\sin\theta} \qquad \textbf{(11-11)}$$

EXAMPLE 11-8: Sketch the conic whose equation is $r = 6/(3 + 2\cos\theta)$.

Solution: Dividing the numerator and denominator by 3, we have

$$r = \frac{2}{1 + \frac{2}{3}\cos\theta}$$

which is the equation of an ellipse since $e = 2/3 < 1$. The polar axis is the principal axis. To sketch the curve, all you need to do is find the intercepts:

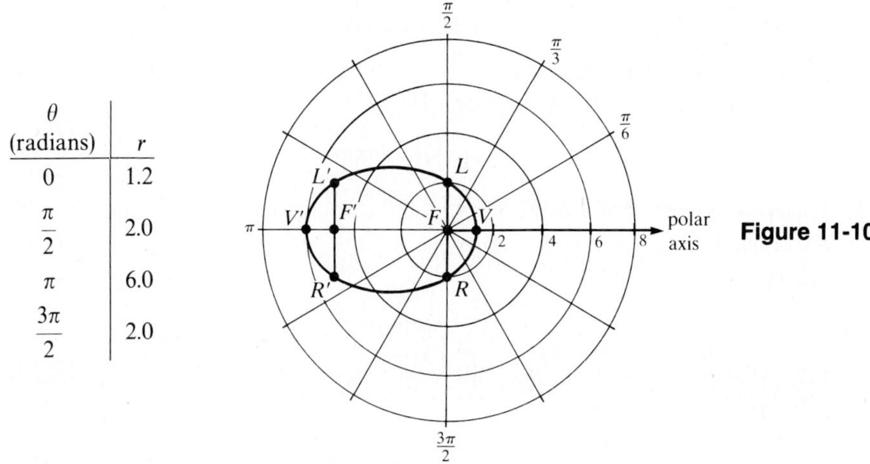

θ (radians)	r
0	1.2
$\frac{\pi}{2}$	2.0
π	6.0
$\frac{3\pi}{2}$	2.0

Figure 11-10

These are shown in Figure 11-10, together with the sketch. Since one focus is at the pole, the other is at $(4.8, \pi)$; and you can find the rest of the curve by symmetry.

SUMMARY

1. In the polar coordinate system the position of a point is determined by a direction θ, called the vectorial angle, and a distance r, called the radius vector; and the frame of reference consists of a fixed point O, called the pole, and a directed line, called the polar axis.
2. To plot a point on the polar plane, the angle θ is first drawn in the proper direction, thus locating the terminal side; then the distance r is measured either along the terminal side, if $r > 0$, or along the terminal side reflected (extended) through the pole if $r < 0$.
3. One pair of polar coordinates will determine one, and only one, point in the plane, but a point may have an unlimited number of polar coordinates.
4. If r and θ are related by an equation, values may be assigned to θ and corresponding values for r calculated, thus defining points that can be plotted (on polar coordinate paper) to describe the locus of the equation.
5. Equations in polar form may be transformed into equations in rectangular (Cartesian) form, and vice versa, by means of the relationships

$$x = r\cos\theta, \qquad y = r\sin\theta$$
$$r^2 = x^2 + y^2, \qquad \theta = \tan^{-1}(y/x)$$

6. The polar equation of a straight line is $r\cos(\theta - \omega) = p$.
   The equation of a line perpendicular to the polar axis is $r\cos\theta = \pm p$.
   The equation of a line parallel to the polar axis is $r\sin\theta = \pm p$.
7. The polar equation of a circle not centered at the pole is

$$k^2 = r^2 + r_1{}^2 - 2rr_1\cos(\theta - \theta_1)$$

the equation of a circle centered at the pole is

$$r = \pm k$$

The equations of circles passing through the pole and having centers on the polar axis are

$$r = \pm 2k\cos\theta$$

The equations of circles passing through the pole and having centers on the $\pi/2$ (90°) axis are

$$r = \pm 2k\sin\theta$$

The equation of a circle passing through the pole and having polar and $\pi/2$ (90°) intercepts of a and b, respectively, is

$$r = a\cos\theta + b\sin\theta$$

8. The polar equation of a conic, for which the polar axis is the principal axis of the conic, is

$$r = \frac{ep}{1 - e\cos\theta}$$

The polar equation of a conic, for which the $\pi/2$ (90°) axis is the principal axis, is

$$r = \frac{ep}{1 - e\sin\theta}$$

9. For polar equations of the conics, if $e = 1$, the equation represents a parabola; if $e < 1$ the equation represents an ellipse; if $e > 1$, the equation represents a hyperbola.

RAISE YOUR GRADES

Can you...?

☑ construct a table of values for, and plot, the locus of a polar equation

☑ transform a polar equation into an equation in rectangular coordinates, and vice versa

☑ find the polar equation of a circle, given its radius and the polar coordinates of its center

☑ determine the type of curve represented by, and sketch the locus of, the polar equation of a conic

SOLVED PROBLEMS

The Polar Coordinate System

PROBLEM 11-1 Using degree measure, construct the graph of $r = 3 + \sin\theta$.

Solution: By assigning selected values of θ from $0°$ to $360°$ you can calculate the corresponding values for r:

θ:	0°	30°	45°	60°	90°	120°	150°	180°	210°	240°	270°	300°	330°	360°
r:	3	3.5	3.7	3.9	4	3.9	3.5	3	2.5	2.1	2	2.1	2.5	3

(The fractional values of r are rounded off to one decimal place from your calculator.) By plotting these points and drawing a curve through them, you obtain the curve shown in Figure 11-11.

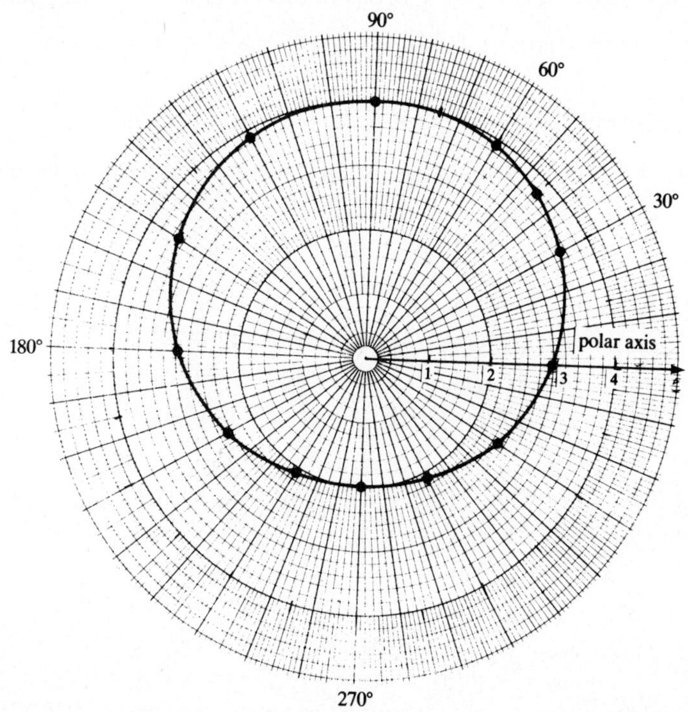

Figure 11-11

PROBLEM 11-2 Draw the graph of $r = 4\cos\theta$. (Use radian measure.)

Solution: Prepare a table of corresponding values of r and θ for $0 < \theta < \pi$ and plot these to obtain the curve shown in Figure 11-12:

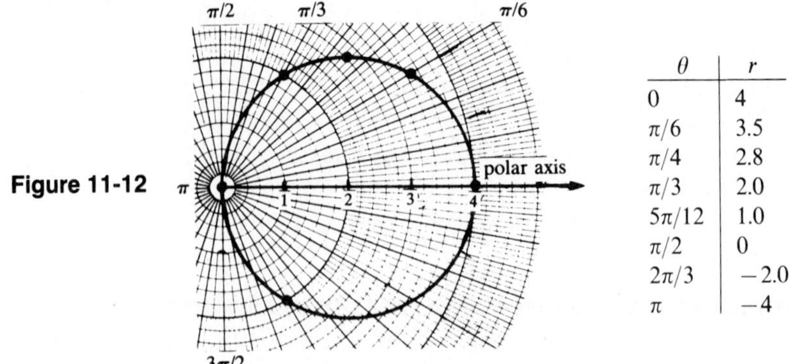

Figure 11-12

θ	r
0	4
$\pi/6$	3.5
$\pi/4$	2.8
$\pi/3$	2.0
$5\pi/12$	1.0
$\pi/2$	0
$2\pi/3$	-2.0
π	-4

There is no need to extend the table to include values of θ in the interval π to 2π, since values of θ in this range would merely repeat the graph already obtained: For example, point $(-3.5, 7\pi/6)$ is on the graph, but this point is also defined by the coordinates $(3.5, \pi/6)$.

The graph appears to be a circle. You can confirm this by transforming the equation to rectangular coordinates (using eqs. 11-1). Thus, since $r = \sqrt{x^2 + y^2}$ and $\cos\theta = x/r$, the given polar equation becomes

$$r = 4\cos\theta = \sqrt{x^2 + y^2} = \frac{4x}{\sqrt{x^2 + y^2}}$$

$$x^2 + y^2 = 4x$$

$$(x^2 - 4x + 4) + y^2 = 4$$

$$(x - 2)^2 + y^2 = 4$$

which is the rectangular of the equation of a circle with radius $\sqrt{4} = 2$ and center at $(2, 0°)$.

Check: Use eq. (11-9), where $b = 0$ (the $\pi/2$ axis intercept) and $a = 4$ (the polar axis intercept):

$$r = a\cos\theta + b\sin\theta = 4\cos\theta + 0\sin\theta = 4\cos\theta$$

PROBLEM 11-3 Draw the graph of the equation $r = 1/(1 + \sin\theta)$.

Solution: Construct a table of corresponding values of r and θ, and draw the curve as shown in Figure 11-13.

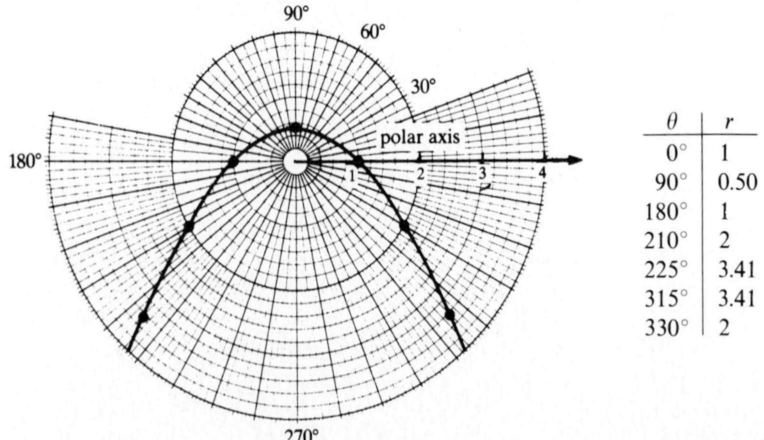

θ	r
0°	1
90°	0.50
180°	1
210°	2
225°	3.41
315°	3.41
330°	2

Figure 11-13

Alternatively, from $r = ep/(1 - e\sin\theta)$ (eq. 11-11), you can quickly see that $e = 1$, so the curve is a parabola whose axis is the 90° axis. Its vertex is at $(\frac{1}{2}, 90°)$, and the curve opens downward.

Relating Polar and Rectangular Coordinates

PROBLEM 11-4 Change $3x + 4y = 6$ to polar form.

Solution: By eqs. (11-1) $x = r\cos\theta$ and $y = r\sin\theta$, so the given equation becomes

$$3(r\cos\theta) + 4(r\sin\theta) = 6$$

Or, in the form most convenient for plotting,

$$r = \frac{6}{3\cos\theta + 4\sin\theta}$$

PROBLEM 11-5 Change $r = 1/(1 - \sin\theta)$ to rectangular form.

Solution:

$$r = \frac{1}{1 - \sin\theta}$$

Clear fractions: $\quad r - r\sin\theta = 1$

Use $y = r\sin\theta$ from eqs. (11-1): $\quad r = y + 1$

Square both sides: $\quad r^2 = (y + 1)^2$

Use $r^2 = x^2 + y^2$ from eqs. (11-1): $\quad x^2 + y^2 = y^2 + 2y + 1$

$$x^2 = 2(y + \tfrac{1}{2})$$

This is the equation of a parabola.

PROBLEM 11-6 Change $r = 1 + \cos\theta$ to an equation in rectangular form and find its degree.

Solution:

$$r = 1 + \cos\theta$$

Multiply both sides by r: $\quad r^2 = r + r\cos\theta$

Use eqs. (11-1): $\quad x^2 + y^2 = r + x$

$$r = x^2 + y^2 - x$$

Square both sides and use eqs. (11-1): $\quad x^2 + y^2 = (x^2 + y^2 - x)^2$

The original equation in r and θ therefore becomes a rather cumbersome fourth-degree equation in x and y.

PROBLEM 11-7 Transform $r = 4\sin 2\theta$ into rectangular form.

Solution:

$$r = 4\sin 2\theta$$

Use $\sin 2\theta = 2\sin\theta\cos\theta$ (from trigonometry): $\quad r = 8\sin\theta\cos\theta$

Use $\cos\theta = x/r$ and $\sin\theta = y/r$ from eq. (11-1): $\quad r = 8\left(\frac{y}{r}\right)\left(\frac{x}{r}\right)$

$$r^3 = 8xy$$

Use $r = \sqrt{x^2 + y^2}$: $\quad (x^2 + y^2)^{3/2} = 8xy$

$$(x^2 + y^2)^3 = 64x^2y^2$$

Polar Equations

PROBLEM 11-8 Find the polar equation of the circle with center at $(4, 0°)$ in polar coordinates and radius 4.

Solution: Use eq. (11-5), with $r_1 = 4$, $\theta_1 = 0$, and radius $k = 4$:

$$r^2 + r_1{}^2 - 2rr_1\cos(\theta - \theta_1) = k^2$$

$$r^2 + 4^2 - 2(4r)\cos(\theta - 0) = 4^2$$

$$r^2 + 16 - 8r\cos\theta = 16$$

$$r^2 = 8r\cos\theta$$

$$r = 8\cos\theta$$

which is the polar form of the equation of a circle with center on the polar axis ($k = r_1$).

PROBLEM 11-9 A circle has its center at $(3, 2\pi/3)$ and a radius of 2. What is its polar equation?

Solution: Again, use eq. (11-5), with radius $k = 2$, $r_1 = 3$, and $\theta_1 = 2\pi/3$, so

$$r^2 + 9 - 6r\cos\left(\theta - \frac{2\pi}{3}\right) = 4$$

$$r^2 - 6r\cos\left(\theta - \frac{2\pi}{3}\right) + 5 = 0$$

PROBLEM 11-10 Identify and sketch the graph of $r = 4/(3 - \cos\theta)$.

Solution: The constant term in the denominator must be 1 for standard polar form, so divide the numerator and denominator by 3 to get

$$r = \frac{\frac{4}{3}}{1 - \frac{1}{3}\cos\theta}$$

Then from $r = ep/(1 - e\cos\theta)$ (eq. 11-10) you see that $e = \frac{1}{3} < 1$; hence the curve is an ellipse with a focus at the pole and corresponding directrix 4 units to the left of the pole. Using these facts, together with symmetry with respect to the polar axis and a table of values, you can sketch the graph shown in Figure 11-14.

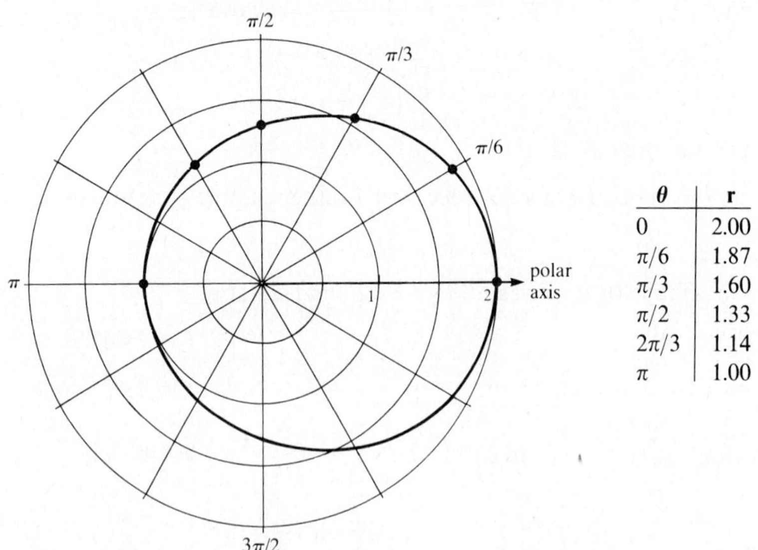

θ	r
0	2.00
$\pi/6$	1.87
$\pi/3$	1.60
$\pi/2$	1.33
$2\pi/3$	1.14
π	1.00

Figure 11-14

PROBLEM 11-11 Sketch the conic whose equation is $r = 4/(1 - \sin\theta)$.

Solution: Compare eq. (11-11) with the given equation:

$$r = \frac{ep}{1 - e\sin\theta} \quad \text{vs.} \quad r = \frac{4}{1 - \sin\theta}$$

Since the equation is in the form of eq. (11-11), the coefficient of $\sin\theta$ is $e = 1$; therefore the curve is a parabola with the $\pi/2$ axis as the principal axis. The numerator of the fraction in the equation is 4, so $ep = 4$ or $p = 4/1 = 4$. Thus the distance from the focus to the directrix is 4 units, as shown in Figure 11-15. (On the figure, the line $D'D$ is the directrix.)

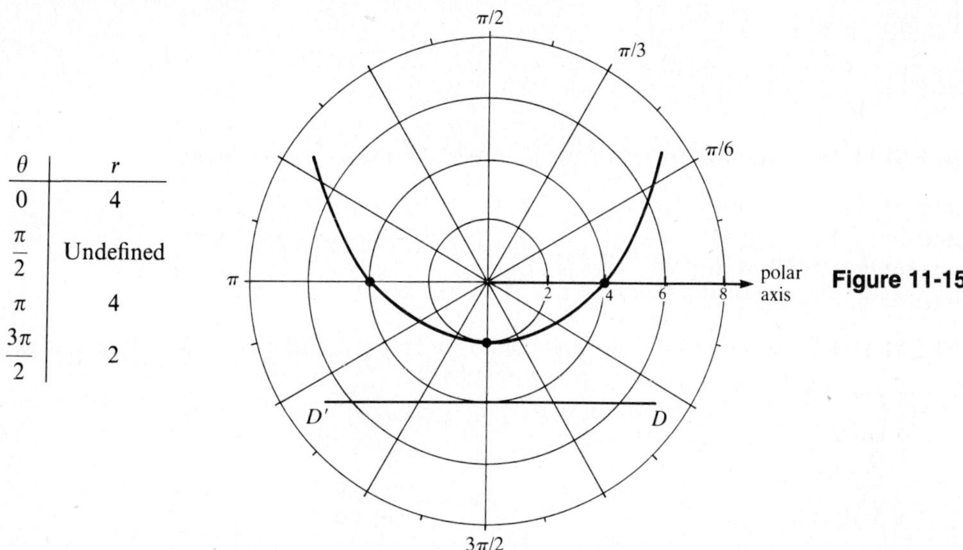

θ	r
0	4
$\frac{\pi}{2}$	Undefined
π	4
$\frac{3\pi}{2}$	2

Figure 11-15

Supplementary Exercises

PROBLEM 11-12 Plot the points whose polar coordinates are

(a) $A(2, 30°)$; $B(-2, 30°)$; $C(5, -30°)$; $D(-5, -30°)$; $E(1, 45°)$; $F(-1, 45°)$; $G(3, -45°)$; $H(-3, -65°)$

(b) $P(-1, \pi)$; $Q(-3, 4\pi/3)$; $R(5, -5\pi/3)$; $S(4, 3\pi/2)$; $T(2, 5\pi/4)$; $U(2, \pi/6)$; $V(4, -3\pi/2)$; $W(5, 7\pi/4)$

PROBLEM 11-13 In each of the following problems, find three other pairs of polar coordinates with $|\theta| < 360°$ that represent the same point:

(a) $(3, 25°)$
(b) $(4, -10°)$
(c) $(-2, 50°)$
(d) $(6, 7\pi/6)$
(e) $(4, -4\pi/3)$
(f) $(3, -\pi/6)$

PROBLEM 11-14 Sketch the following curves:

(a) $\theta = 0$
(b) $\theta = \pi/6$
(c) $r = 6$
(d) $r = 3(1 + \sin\theta)$
(e) $r^2 = 9\cos 2\theta$
(f) $r = 4\cos 2\theta$

PROBLEM 11-15 Change the following equations to polar form and isolate r when possible:

(a) $2x + 3y = 2$
(b) $y = 4x$
(c) $3x - 7y = 5$
(d) $y^2 = 9x$
(e) $x^2 - y^2 = 1$
(f) $x^2 + 4xy + y^2 = 7$

PROBLEM 11-16 Change the following equations to rectangular form:

(a) $r = 3$
(b) $r = 2\sin\theta$
(c) $r = 4\cos\theta$
(d) $r^2 = \dfrac{1}{\sin 2\theta}$
(e) $r^2 = \dfrac{9}{\cos 2\theta}$
(f) $r^2 = \tan 2\theta$

PROBLEM 11-17 Change the equations in the following problems to polar coordinate form and simplify, eliminating any radicals:

(a) $\dfrac{(x-3)^2}{25} + \dfrac{y^2}{16} = 1$

(b) $x^2 = 3(2y + 3)$

(c) $\dfrac{(x+5)}{9} - \dfrac{y^2}{16} = 1$

PROBLEM 11-18 Find the polar equations of each of the following circles:

(a) center at $(5, 0°)$ and radius 5
(b) center at $(-4, 0°)$ and radius 4
(c) center at $(5, 0°)$ and radius 4
(d) center at $(5, \pi/4)$ and radius 4

PROBLEM 11-19 Describe the following conics (i.e., type of curve and values of e and p):

(a) $r = \dfrac{3}{2 + \cos\theta}$

(b) $r = \dfrac{12}{2 + 3\cos\theta}$

(c) $r = \dfrac{5}{1 - \cos\theta}$

(d) $r = \dfrac{24}{3 - 4\cos\theta}$

(e) $r = \dfrac{7}{1 + \cos\theta}$

(f) $r = \dfrac{12}{3 + 2\sin\theta}$

Answers to Supplementary Exercises

11-12: **(a)** See Figure 11-16a;
(b) see Figure 11-16b.

11-13: **(a)** $(-3, 205°); (3, -335°); (-3, -155°)$
(b) $(-4, 170°); (4, 350°); (-4, -190°)$
(c) $(2, 230°); (2, -130°); (-2, -310°)$
(d) $(-6, \pi/6); (6, -5\pi/6); (-6, -11\pi/6)$
(e) $(4, 2\pi/3); (-4, 5\pi/3); (-4, -\pi/3)$
(f) $(3, 11\pi/6); (-3, 5\pi/6); (-3, -7\pi/6)$

11-14: See Figure 11-17.

11-15: **(a)** $r = \dfrac{2}{2\cos\theta + 3\sin\theta}$

(b) $\theta = \tan^{-1} 4$

(c) $r = \dfrac{5}{3\cos\theta - 7\sin\theta}$

(d) $r = 9\cot\theta\csc\theta$

(e) $r^2 = \sec 2\theta$

(f) $r^2 = \dfrac{7}{1 + 2\sin 2\theta}$

11-16: **(a)** $x^2 + y^2 = 9$
(b) $x^2 + y^2 = 2y$
(c) $x^2 + y^2 = 4x$
(d) $2xy = 1$
(e) $x^2 - y^2 = 9$
(f) $x^4 - y^4 = 2xy$

11-17: **(a)** $r = \dfrac{-16}{5 + 3\cos\theta}$ or $\dfrac{16}{5 - 3\cos\theta}$

(b) $r = \dfrac{-3}{1 + \sin\theta}$ or $\dfrac{3}{1 - \sin\theta}$

(c) $r = \dfrac{-16}{5\cos\theta + 3}$ or $\dfrac{-16}{5\cos\theta - 3}$

11-18: **(a)** $r = 10\cos\theta$
(b) $r + 8\cos\theta = 0$
(c) $r^2 - 10r\cos\theta + 9 = 0$
(d) $r^2 - 10r\cos(\theta - 45°) + 9 = 0$

11-19: **(a)** X-ellipse; $e = 1/2, p = 3$
(b) X-hyperbola; $e = 3/2, p = 4$
(c) X-parabola; $e = 1, p = 5$
(d) X-hyperbola; $e = 4/3, p = 6$
(e) X-parabola; $e = 1, p = 7$
(f) Y-ellipse; $e = 2/3, p = 6$

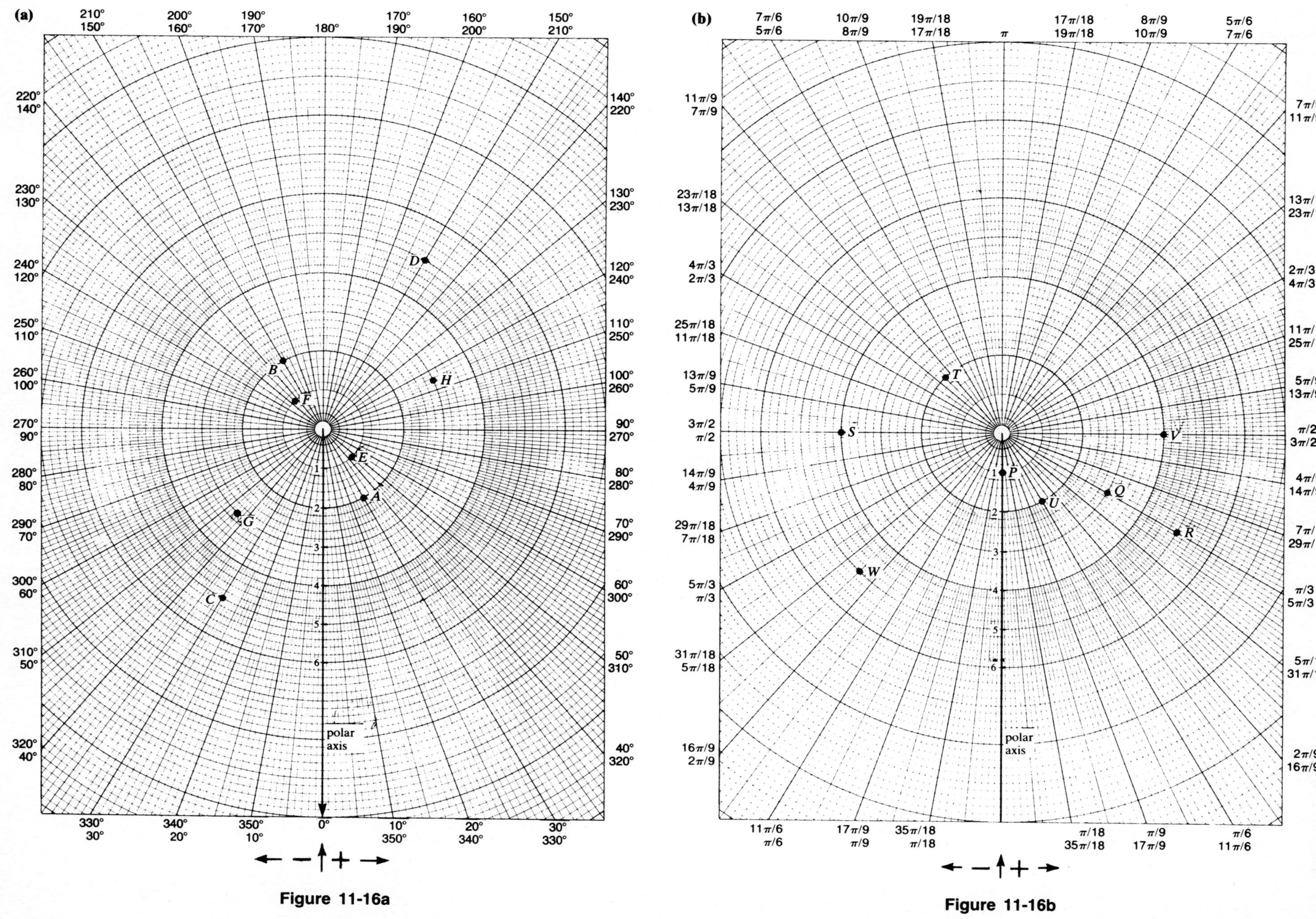

Figure 11-16a

Figure 11-16b

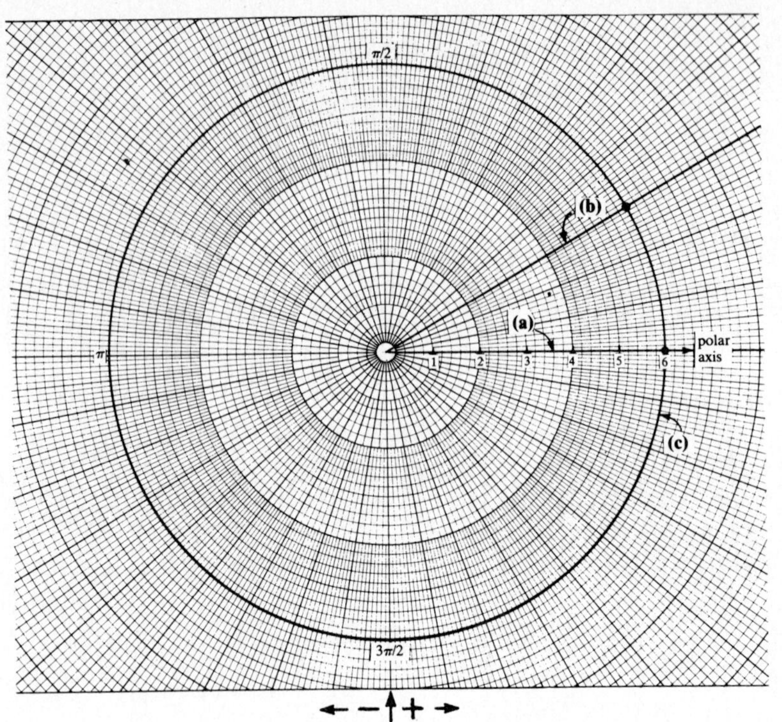

Figure 11-17a, b, c

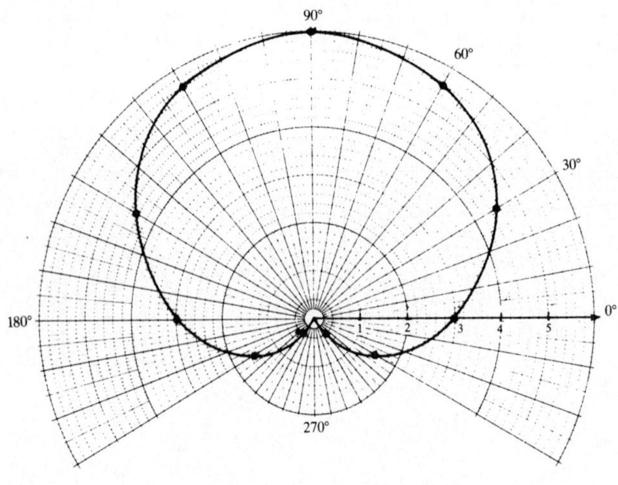

Figure 11-17d. Cardiod.

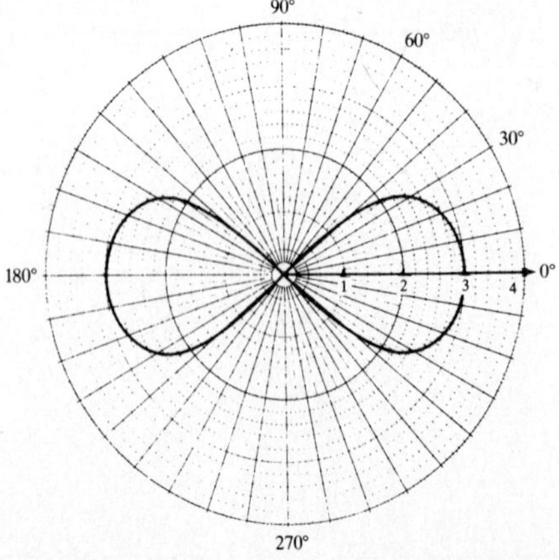

Figure 11-17e. Lemniscate of Bernoulli.

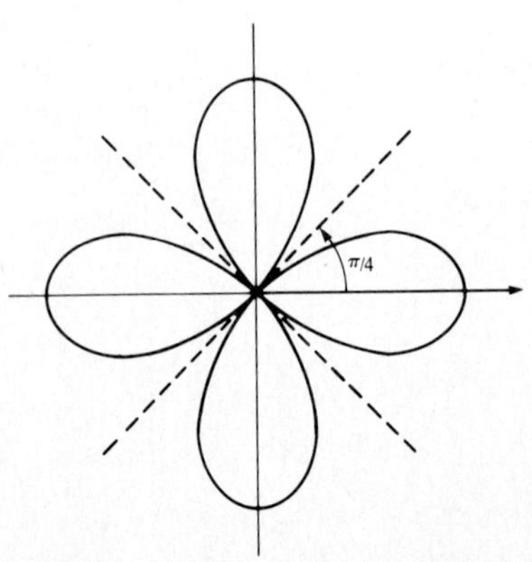

Figure 11-17f. Four-petal rose.

12 PARAMETRIC AND TRANSCENDENTAL EQUATIONS

THIS CHAPTER IS ABOUT

☑ Parametric Equations
☑ Transcendental Equations
☑ Graphing by Composition of Ordinates

12-1. Parametric Equations

A. Parametric representation (definition)

In addition to graphing equations in Cartesian (rectangular) form in terms of the two variables (x, y) and in polar form in terms of the polar variables (r, θ), there is another way of defining a graph. We can express x and y separately in terms of a third variable in a *parametric equation*. Parametric equations facilitate the treatment of many problems—in some cases they represent the ONLY practical way to approach the solution of certain problems.

As an applied approach to the use of parametric equations, consider Example 12-1.

EXAMPLE 12-1: A stone is thrown outward from the top of a building at a speed of 100 feet per second. Neglecting air resistance, what course will the stone follow? Sketch the graph of its course.

Solution: In solving a problem of this type, it is convenient to express the coordinates of the moving point separately in terms of the time t. Let the initial point of the stone's descent—the release point—be at the origin at the instant of throwing, so that at this point $t = 0$. We then have

$$x = 100t \quad \text{(feet)} \tag{a}$$

where t is in seconds. And, since the stone falls downward because of the acceleration of gravity, which is ~ 32 feet per second per second, we also have

$$y = -\frac{1}{2}gt^2 = -16t^2 \tag{b}$$

We now have a choice of two methods for plotting the path of the stone:

(1) We may assign values to t in our equations and obtain the corresponding values of x and y:

t	0	1	2	3	4	5
$x = 100t$	0	100	200	300	400	500
$y = -16t^2$	0	-16	-64	-144	-256	-400

Note that the values of t are used only as aids in finding the coordinates of x and y and are disregarded when the graph (Figure 12-1) is drawn.

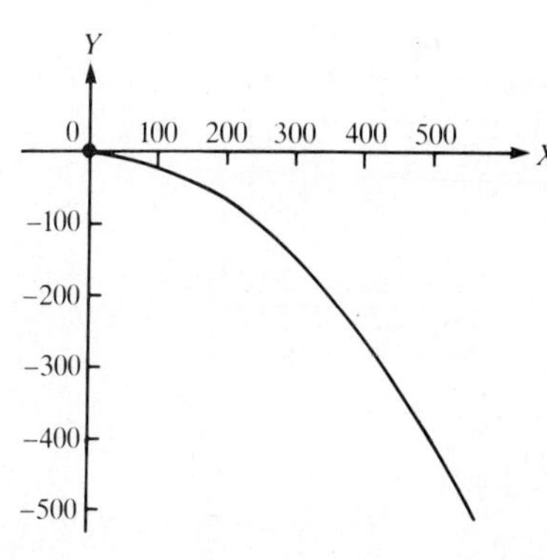

Figure 12-1

(2) We may eliminate the variable t by solving the equations for x and y simultaneously:

$$y = -16\left(\frac{x}{100}\right)^2 = \frac{-x^2}{625}$$

which is evidently the equation of a parabola opening downward (see Chapter 5).

warning: The locus of the parametric equations may represent only a portion of the points whose coordinates satisfy the Cartesian equation obtained by eliminating the parameter. Here, we are only interested in $t \geq 0$, and the desired curve is only the right-hand side of the Cartesian parabola, $y = -x^2/625$.

Equations (a) and (b), considered together, illustrate the following definition:

- The equation of a curve in two dimensions is said to be in **parametric form** if each of the coordinates of the general point $P(x, y)$ is expressed in terms of a *third variable* (represented by a letter) called the **parameter.**

B. Eliminating the parameter

It is sometimes desirable to eliminate the parameter from a parametric representation and thereby obtain the rectangular or polar form of the equation. Unfortunately, there is no ONE algebraic or trigonometric method of elimination that is applicable in all cases. ANY method used in algebra or trigonometry for eliminating a variable between two equations may prove helpful at times. The following examples represent three possible procedures.

EXAMPLE 12-2: Eliminate the parameter from

$$x = t^2/4 \qquad \text{and} \qquad y = t + 1$$

and identify the Cartesian curve.

Solution: If we solve the second equation for t, we get $t = y - 1$. Substituting this expression for t in the first equation and simplifying, we get

$$x = \frac{(y-1)^2}{4}$$

$$(y-1)^2 = 4x$$

which represents a parabola with vertex at (0, 1), axis parallel to the X-axis, and focus at (1, 1).

EXAMPLE 12-3: Eliminate the parameter from

$$x = \sin t \qquad \text{and} \qquad y = 2\cos t$$

Solution: If we multiply each member of the first equation by 2, square each new member, and add to the squares the corresponding members of the second equation, we get

$$\begin{aligned}(2x)^2 + y^2 &= (2\sin t)^2 + (2\cos t)^2 \\ &= 4\sin^2 t + 4\cos^2 t = 4(\sin^2 t + \cos^2 t) \\ &= 4 \qquad (\text{since } \sin^2 t + \cos^2 t = 1)\end{aligned}$$

Therefore, $4x^2 + y^2 = 4$ is the equation found by eliminating the parameter from the given equations. (You should recognize this equation as that of an ellipse with center at the origin, major axis of length 4 along the Y-axis, and minor axis of length 2; see Chapter 6.)

EXAMPLE 12-4: Eliminate the parameter from

$$x = \frac{1}{2+t} \quad \text{and} \quad y = \frac{t}{2+t}$$

Solution: If we divide y by x, we find that $y/x = t$. Substituting this value for t in the first of the parametric equations and simplifying, we have

$$x = \frac{1}{2 + y/x} = \frac{x}{2x + y}$$

$$2x + y = 1$$

C. Graphing parametric equations

Before actually sketching any parametric equations, you may find it helpful to analyze a few of the questions that arise when you're deciding what approach to take.

EXAMPLE 12-5: How would you prepare to sketch the equations $x = t - 1$ and $y = 2t + 3$?

Solution: THINK—These are parametric equations and t is the parameter. The equations define a graph. If t is assigned a value, corresponding values can be determined for x and y. The pair of (x, y) values constitutes the coordinates of a point of the graph. The complete graph consists of the set of all points determined in this way as t varies through all suitable values.

Alternatively, you can eliminate t between the two equations and obtain a single equation in x and y. Thus, solving either equation for t and substituting the value obtained into the other, you get the equation $2x - y + 5 = 0$. The graph of this equation, which is also the graph of the parametric equations, is a straight line.

Although the parameter can often be eliminated to obtain an equation in x and y, there are times when the process is not easy (or even *possible*) because the parameter is included in a complicated way, as in the case of the equations $x = t^5 + \log t$ and $y = t^3 + \tan t$. *Now* what?! When we have complications like these (among others), the method we use depends on the problem—we use what *works.* Examples 12-6, 12-7, and 12-8 illustrate various methods that can be used to deal with certain types of problems.

It is sometimes helpful in solving a problem to change an equation in x and y to parametric form, as Example 12-6 shows.

EXAMPLE 12-6: How would you analyze, and prepare to sketch, the equation $x^2 + 2x + y = 4$?

Solution: THINK—Because of the quadratic term in x and the linear terms in x and y the equation must be that of a parabola. If you substitute $2t$ for x and solve the resulting equation for y, you get $y = 4 - 4t - 4t^2$. Therefore the parametric equations $x = 2t$ and $y = 4 - 4t - 4t^2$ must also represent a parabola. It is evident that other representations could be obtained by equating x to other expressions in t.

But the procedure that worked in Example 12-6 may be inconvenient or impossible in equations that contain both variables in a complicated relationship. Example 12-7 illustrates yet another method.

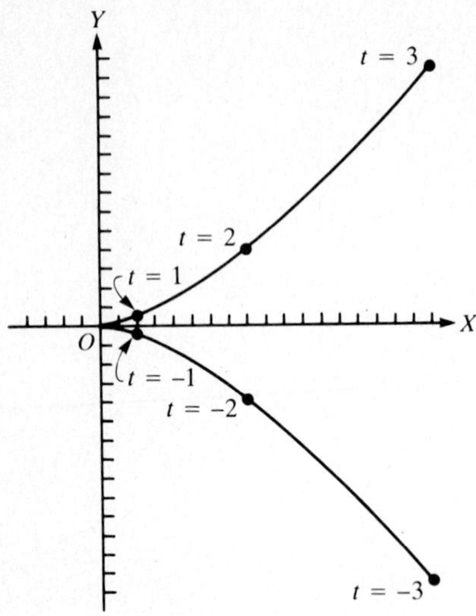

Figure 12-2

EXAMPLE 12-7: Sketch the curve represented by the parametric equations $x = 2t^2$ and $y = \frac{1}{2}t^3$.

Solution: Construct a table of values and, from these (x, y) values, plot the curve shown in Figure 12-2.

t	x	y
0	0	0
1	2	0.5
2	8	4.0
3	18	13.5
−1	2	−0.5
−2	8	−4.0
−3	18	−13.5

Note that the parameter does not appear on the axes, although the plotted points may be marked by the corresponding values of t.

The equation of a curve may be changed from parametric form to rectangular form by eliminating the parameter. The method used depends upon the example: Here, you could solve the first equation for t, getting $t = (x/2)^{1/2}$, substitute this value for t in the second equation, and simplify:

$$y = \frac{1}{2}\left(\frac{x}{2}\right)^{3/2}$$

$$32y^2 = x^3$$

EXAMPLE 12-8: Find the rectangular equation of the curve $x = a\cos\phi$ and $y = b\sin\phi$.

Solution: Here the parameter is the variable angle ϕ. To eliminate the parameter in this case, use the trigonometric identity $\sin^2\phi + \cos^2\phi = 1$. Divide the first equation by a, the second by b, square both equations, and add: This will give

$$\frac{x}{a} = \cos\phi \qquad \frac{x^2}{a^2} = \cos^2\phi$$

$$\frac{y}{b} = \sin\phi \qquad \frac{y^2}{b^2} = \sin^2\phi$$

$$\frac{x^2}{a^2} + \frac{y^2}{b^2} = \cos^2\phi + \sin^2\phi = 1$$

which is the rectangular equation of an ellipse.

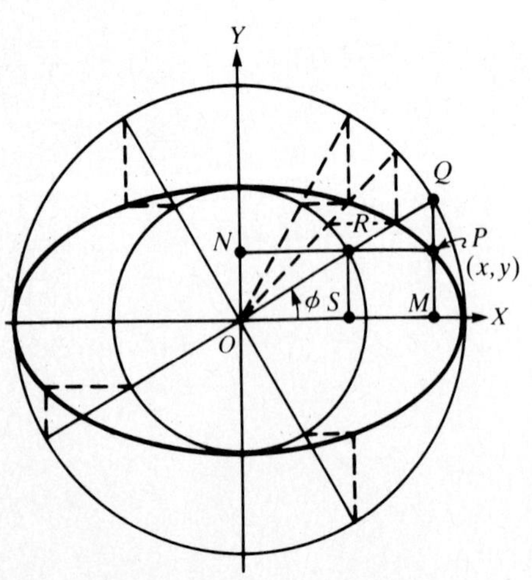

Figure 12-3. Auxiliary circles.

Digression: The parametric equations of an ellipse $x = a\cos\phi$, $y = b\sin\phi$ are associated with another method of constructing such a curve. This method makes use of auxiliary circles and is shown in Figure 12-3.

Construct two concentric circles with centers at the origin O with radii a and b, where $a > b$. Through O draw any line making an angle ϕ with the X-axis and intersecting the circles at points R and Q. Through R draw NR parallel to OX, and through Q draw QM parallel to OY. Let these lines intersect at the point $P(x, y)$. Finally, draw RS perpendicular to OX. Then, from the figure, you have

$$\frac{OM}{OQ} = \cos\phi \qquad \text{and} \qquad \frac{RS}{OR} = \sin\phi$$

But $OM = x$, $OQ = a$, $RS = y$, and $OR = b$. Therefore

$$\frac{x}{a} = \cos\phi \qquad \text{and} \qquad \frac{y}{b} = \sin\phi$$

These, then, are the parametric equations of an ellipse, and the point P lies on this curve. The two circles have as their diameters the major and minor axes of the ellipse and are called the **auxiliary circles** of the ellipse. By choosing different values of ϕ—i.e., by drawing OQ at different angles with the X-axis—you can construct as many points as necessary to draw the ellipse. The angle ϕ is called the **eccentric angle** of the point P.

12-2. Transcendental Equations

An algebraic curve is one that can be represented by a polynomial in x and y set equal to zero. Curves whose equations cannot be so represented are called **transcendental curves**. Examples of these are exponential, logarithmic, and trigonometric functions.

A. Exponential and logarithmic functions

An exponential curve has an equation of the form $y = a^x$, where x and y are variables and a is a constant such that $a > 0$. Since, by the definition of a logarithm, this equation may be written $x = \log_a y$, the locus may also be called a logarithmic curve.

note: Logarithms to the base 10 ($\log_{10}$) are designated simply by "log," and logarithms to the base e are designated "ln"; logarithms to other bases, say a, are designated by "$\log_a$."

EXAMPLE 12-9: Plot (**a**) the curve $y = \log x$ and (**b**) the curve $y = 10^x$.

Solution:

(**a**) To draw the curve $y = \log x$, construct a table of (x, y) values (using any table of common logarithms or your calculator)

x	y	x	y
0.1	−1.000	5	0.699
0.5	−0.301	6	0.778
1	0.000	7	0.845
2	0.301	8	0.903
3	0.477	9	0.954
4	0.602	10	1.000

and plot as shown in Figure 12-4a.

(**b**) Now, you know from algebra that $y = \log x$ may also be written $10^y = x$, so if you interchange the variables, you have $y = 10^x$, which represents the same curve as the one shown in Figure 12-4a but with the axes as indicated in Figure 12-4b.

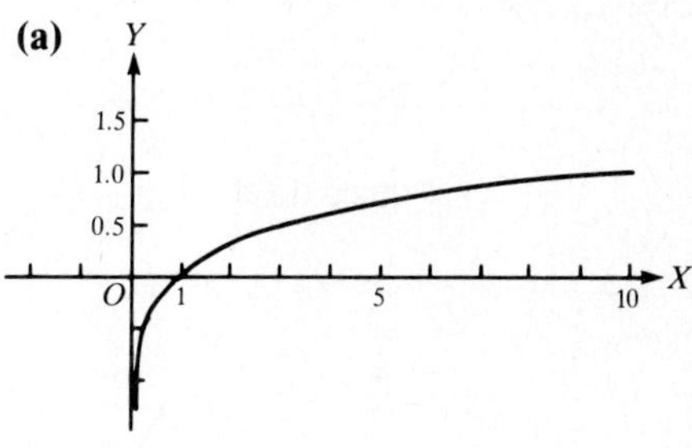

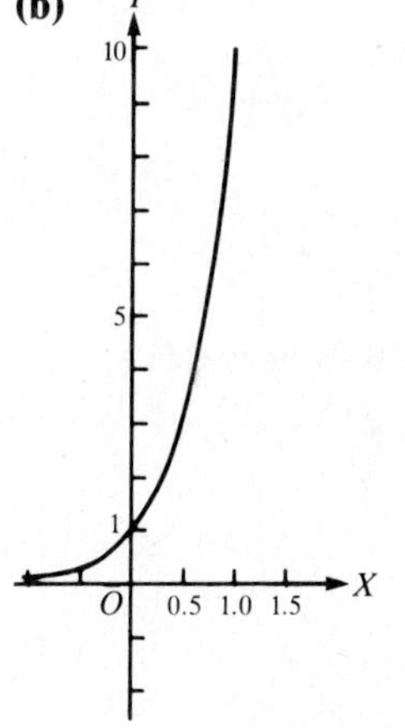

Figure 12-4

EXAMPLE 12-10: Change $y = \log_3 x$ to its equivalent form with base-10 logs.

Solution: Write the equation in the form $3^y = x$ and then take the common (base 10) logarithms of both sides to get

$$\log 3^y = \log x \qquad \text{or} \qquad y \log 3 = \log x$$

Therefore

$$y = \left(\frac{1}{\log 3}\right)(\log x) = \left(\frac{1}{0.477}\right)\log x = 2.096 \log x$$

B. Trigonometric functions

Corresponding to every trigonometric *function* there is a trigonometric *curve*. The method of drawing trigonometric curves is essentially the same as that used in plotting graphs of algebraic functions.

Consider, for example, the sine function $y = \sin x$. Even before drawing the graph by means of plotted points, we can observe some important characteristics of the sine curve. For instance, the Y-intercept is $y = 0$ and the X-intercepts are $x = n\pi$, where n is any positive or negative integer, or zero. Since the sine function is *odd*—i.e., $-y = \sin(-x) = -\sin x$—the curve is symmetric with respect to the origin. And since, by definition, y cannot exceed 1 in numerical value, the curve must lie entirely between the lines $y = 1$ and $y = -1$. The maximum value of y is called the **amplitude** of the curve. Finally, the curve is **periodic**; i.e., the sine function *repeats* its values at regular intervals. When the angle is increased by 360° or 2π radians, $\sin(x + 2\pi) = \sin x$; so the period is 2π. Therefore we only have to plot values of x such that $0 \le x \le 2\pi$.

To plot the sine curve, we can compute a table of (x, y) values

x: 0	$\frac{\pi}{6}$	$\frac{\pi}{3}$	$\frac{\pi}{2}$	$\frac{2\pi}{3}$	$\frac{5\pi}{6}$	π	$\frac{7\pi}{6}$	$\frac{4\pi}{3}$	$\frac{3\pi}{2}$	$\frac{5\pi}{3}$	$\frac{11\pi}{6}$	2π
y: 0	0.5	0.87	1.0	0.87	0.5	0	-0.5	-0.87	-1	-0.87	-0.5	0

then, using the general characteristics just observed, we can draw the curve shown in Figure 12-5.

Figure 12-5

Although sine curves may have different periods and amplitudes, they all have the same general appearance. It is important to note that the maximum numerical value of y occurs at the first and third quarter periods and that the curve may be repeated by sliding it along the X-axis one period.

EXAMPLE 12-11: Find the amplitude and period of $y = 1.5 \sin 2x$ and sketch the curve.

Solution: The maximum value of y occurs when $\sin 2x = 1$, so the amplitude is 1.5. To find the period, note that $\sin(2x + 2\pi) = \sin 2(x + \pi) = \sin 2x$, so the period is π radians. To sketch the curve, first lay off the total period of π radians on the X-axis and divide it into quarter-periods, as shown in Figure 12-6; then measure the amplitude at the odd quarter-periods. Additional points may be calculated and plotted if you want a more accurate figure.

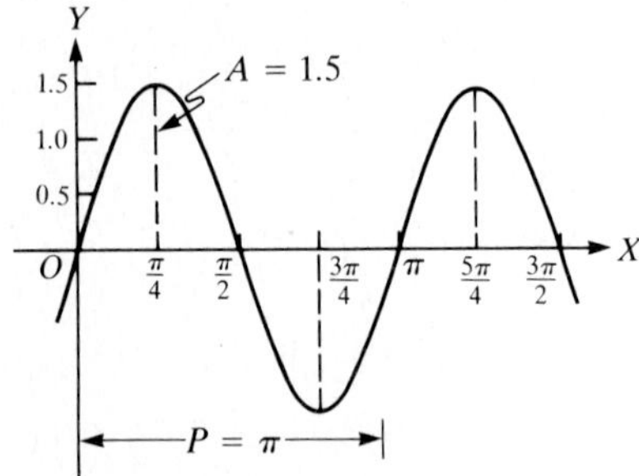

Figure 12-6. Sine function.

The other trigonometric curves—which are all periodic—are plotted similarly to the sine curve.

note: Although you can use degrees as units on the horizontal axis if you want only the general shape of the curve, you MUST use radian measure when the equation of a curve contains both algebraic and trigonometric terms.

12-3. Graphing by Composition of Ordinates

When the equation of a curve consists of several terms, it is sometimes convenient to consider each term as representing a simple curve and to obtain the complete curve by **composing** (i.e., *adding*) the ordinates of these simpler curves. When graphing by the composition of ordinates, the curves must be plotted on the same axes and to the same scale.

EXAMPLE 12-12: Plot the graph of the equation

$$y = x + \frac{1}{x}$$

Solution: Consider the graphs of the two equations

$$y_1 = x \quad \text{and} \quad y_2 = \frac{1}{x}$$

Evidently, an ordinate of the given curve corresponding to any given abscissa is the sum of the ordinates y_1 and y_2, since $y = y_1 + y_2 = x + 1/x$. To obtain the points of the given curve, select any value of x and add the corresponding ordinates. For example, if you set $x = 1$, then $y_1 = 1$ and $y_2 = \frac{1}{1}$; therefore, $y = 1 + \frac{1}{1}$, or 1 unit is added graphically to the ordinate of the line $y_1 = x$, as indicated in Figure 12-7.

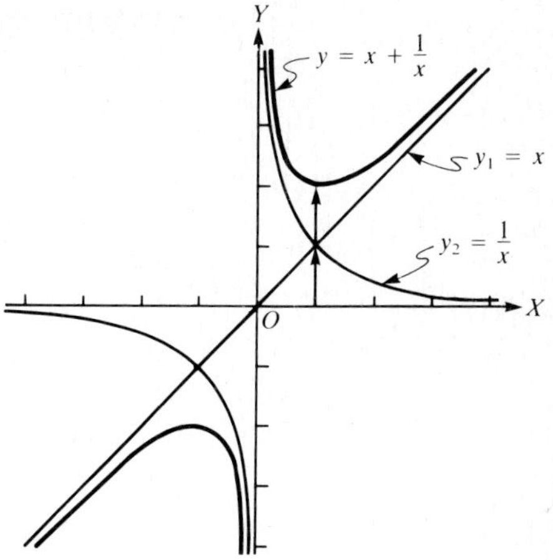

Figure 12-7

SUMMARY

1. The equation of a curve in two dimensions is said to be in parametric form if each of the coordinates of the general point $P(x, y)$ is expressed in terms of a third variable called the parameter.
2. Although there is no one, set way of eliminating the parameter from a pair of equations, the most common way—where it will work—is to solve one equation in terms of the parameter and then substitute this value of the parameter into the other equation.
3. To graph parametric equations, prepare a table of assigned values of the parameter and the resulting values of x and y; then plot the pairs of (x, y) coordinates to obtain the curve.
4. Transcendental curves are curves whose equations cannot be represented in the form of a polynomial in x and y set equal to zero, such as exponential, logarithmic, and trigonometric functions.
5. An exponential curve is one that is in the form $y = a^x$, where x and y are variables and a is a constant such that $a > 0$. ($y = a^x$ may also be written $x = \log_a y$, so the locus of an exponential curve may also be called a logarithmic curve.)
6. The trigonometric curves are simply graphs of the trigonometric functions, whose distinguishing characteristic is periodicity.
7. When the equation of a curve consists of several terms, it is sometimes convenient to consider each term as representing a simpler curve and to obtain the complete curve by composing [adding] the ordinates of the simpler curves.

RAISE YOUR GRADES

Can you . . .?

☑ eliminate the parameter from a parametric representation to obtain the rectangular or polar form of the equation
☑ prepare a table of (x, y) values and plot the resulting graph, given a set of parametric equations
☑ change an equation in x and y to parametric form
☑ find the rectangular equation of a curve whose parametric equations contain the variable angle ϕ
☑ plot the curve of an exponential or logarithmic equation
☑ plot the equation of a curve consisting of several terms by composition of ordinates

SOLVED PROBLEMS

Parametric Equations

PROBLEM 12-1 Sketch the graph of $x = 2\sin\theta$ and $y = 2\cos\theta$.

Solution: By assigning values to θ, you can compute the rectangular coordinates of the corresponding points and draw the smooth curve through these points, as shown in Figure 12-8.

θ	0°	30°	60°	90°	120°	150°	180°	210°	240°	270°	300°	330°
x	0	1	$\sqrt{3}$	2	$\sqrt{3}$	1	0	-1	$-\sqrt{3}$	-2	$-\sqrt{3}$	-1
y	2	$\sqrt{3}$	1	0	-1	$-\sqrt{3}$	-2	$-\sqrt{3}$	-1	0	1	$\sqrt{3}$

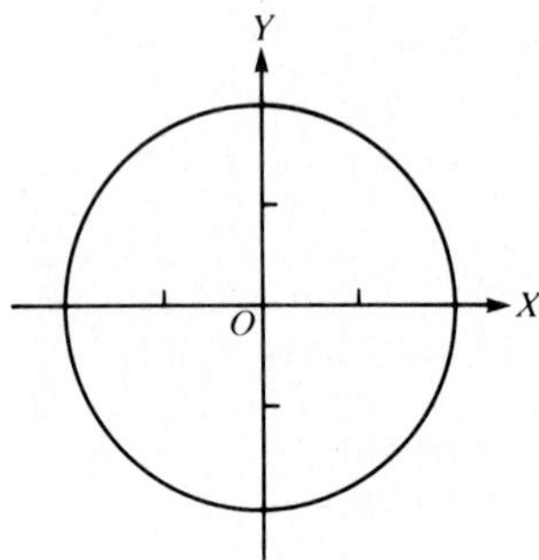

Figure 12-8

Alternative Solution: Use the trigonometric identity $\sin^2\theta + \cos^2\theta = 1$ to eliminate the parameter. Thus, squaring both equations, adding, and simplifying, you get

$$x^2 = 4\sin^2\theta \qquad y^2 = 4\cos^2\theta$$

$$x^2 + y^2 = 4(\sin^2\theta + \cos^2\theta)$$

$$= 4(1) = 2^2$$

So you have $x^2 + y^2 = 2^2$, which is the Cartesian equation of a circle [see Chapter 4] of radius 2. Since there are no restrictions on the parameter, the circle is the full locus of the parametric equation.

PROBLEM 12-2 Sketch the graph of the parametric equations

$$x = 2 + t \qquad \text{and} \qquad y = 3 - t^2$$

Solution: Inspecting the equations, you'll see that x may have any real value and that y may have any real value not exceeding 3. Preparing a table of values for $-3 \le t \le 3$,

t	-3	-2	-1	0	1	2	3
x	-1	0	1	2	3	4	5
y	-6	-1	2	3	2	-1	-6

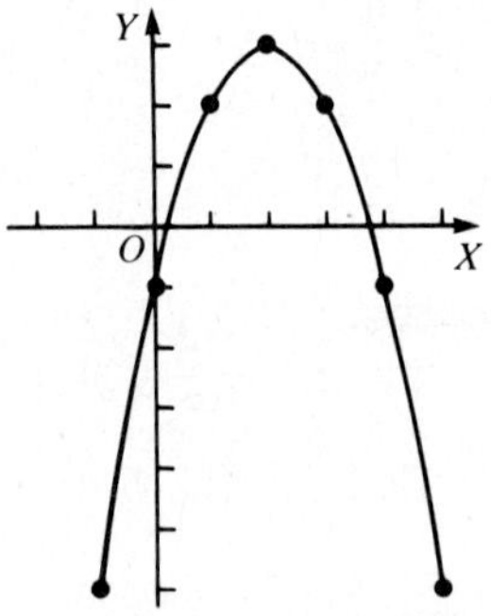

you can sketch the part of the graph shown in Figure 12-9. (Actually, the graph extends indefinitely far into the third and fourth quadrants.)

Figure 12-9

PROBLEM 12-3 Sketch the graph of $x = \sec^2\theta$ and $y = -\tan^2\theta$. Eliminate the parameter between the two equations and compare the graph of the resulting Cartesian equation with that of the parametric form.

Solution: Since $x = \sec^2\theta$ is always greater than or equal to 1 (by definition) and $y = -\tan^2\theta$ is always negative or zero for real angles, it follows that the graph obtained for the parametric form of the equation lies entirely in the fourth quadrant to the right of the point (1,0) on the X-axis. Substituting values of θ from 0° to 90° in the parametric equations, you can get a table of values and plot the graph shown in Figure 12-10.

θ	$0°$	$30°$	$60°$	$90°$
$x = \sec^2\theta$	1	$\frac{4}{3}$	4	∞
$y = -\tan^2\theta$	0	$-\frac{1}{3}$	-3	$-\infty$

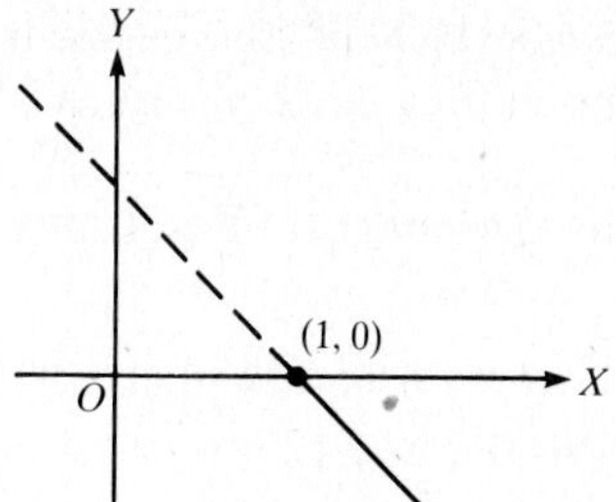

Figure 12-10

(The table is not continued further because assigning additional values of θ will merely give points (x, y) that have already been determined.) The part of the graph obtained from the parametric form is shown as a solid line in the graph.

If you eliminate the parameter by adding x and y, you will get $x + y = 1$, since $\sec^2\theta - \tan^2\theta = 1$ (a trigonometric identity). Thus the graph of the equation obtained by eliminating the parameter is the entire line shown in Figure 12-10.

note: This example illustrates the necessity of being careful not to impose unintended restrictions on the range of x and y in choosing a parametric form of the equation.

PROBLEM 12-4 Sketch the graph of the equations $x = \cos^2\theta$ and $y = 2\sin\theta$.

Solution: Start by eliminating the parameter from these equations. Thus, square the second equation, add it to the first, and simplify:

Given: $\cos^2\theta = x \qquad \sin\theta = \dfrac{y}{2}$

Squaring: $\sin^2\theta = \dfrac{y^2}{4}$

Adding: $\cos^2\theta + \sin^2\theta = \dfrac{y^2}{4} + x$

And since (from trigonometry) $\sin^2\theta + \cos^2\theta = 1$,

$$1 = \frac{y^2}{4} + x$$

$$y^2 = -4(x - 1)$$

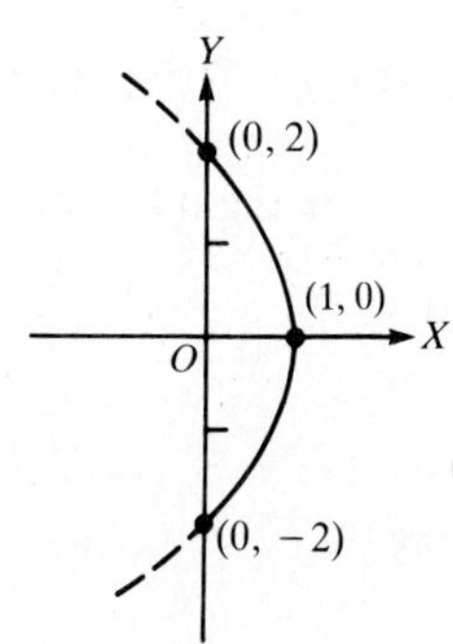

Figure 12-11

The graph of this equation is therefore the parabola shown in Figure 12-11. Notice, however, that the graph of the parametric equations does not include the part of the parabola to the left of the Y-axis. This results from the fact that $x = \cos^2\theta$, which is never negative.

PROBLEM 12-5 Find a parametric representation of the equation $y^{2/3} + x^{2/3} = a^{2/3}$ and sketch the graph.

Solution: This is an instance in which the equation in its original form is difficult to plot—but you can represent it by more manageable equations in parametric form.

Solving the equation for $y^{2/3}$, you get

$$y^{2/3} = a^{2/3} - x^{2/3}$$

$$= a^{2/3}\left[1 - \left(\frac{x}{a}\right)^{2/3}\right]$$

Figure 12-12

The bracketed expression can be simplified by setting $(x/a)^{2/3} = \sin^2\theta$ or $x = a\sin^3\theta$. When x has this value, you find that $y = a\cos^3\theta$, and thus the given equation is represented in parametric form by the equations

$$x = a\sin^3\theta \qquad \text{and} \qquad y = a\cos^3\theta$$

You can visualize the graph by letting θ increase, in $90°$ steps, from $0°$ to $360°$. In the first step, x increases from 0 to a and y decreases from a to 0. The graph, shown in Figure 12-12, is called a

hypocycloid of four cusps. It can be shown that this curve represents the path traced by a given point on a circle of radius $a/4$ as it rolls inside and along a circle of radius a.

Transcendental Equations

Exponential and logarithmic functions

PROBLEM 12-6 Draw, on the same coordinate axes, the graphs of the functions determined by the equations $y = \log_2 x$ and $y = \log_3 x$.

Solution: In order to sketch the graphs, you'll need to prepare a table of corresponding values, using the equivalent equations $x = 2^y$ and $x = 3^y$. For convenience, it will be best to assign integral values to y and compute the values for 2^y and 3^y:

y	-2	-1	0	1	2
$x = 2^y$	$\frac{1}{4}$	$\frac{1}{2}$	1	2	4
$x = 3^y$	$\frac{1}{9}$	$\frac{1}{3}$	1	3	9

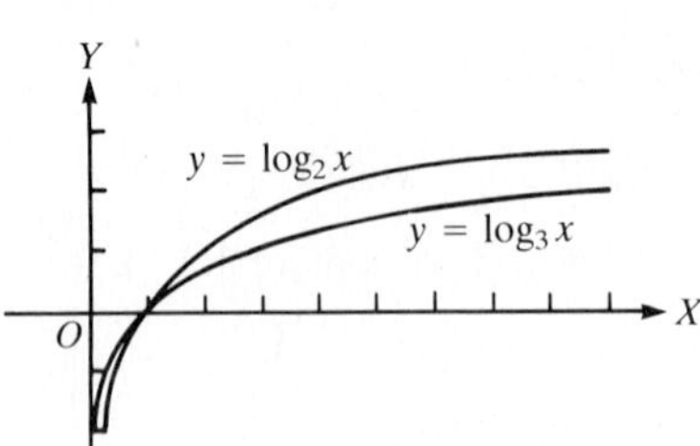

Figure 12-13

Using the points determined by the table, construct the graphs on the same axes. Your results should correspond to those shown in Figure 12-13. Both graphs cross the X-axis at $x = 1$. For all other values of x, the graph obtained with the larger base of logarithms is closer to the X-axis.

PROBLEM 12-7 Sketch the graphs of the functions defined by the equations $y = 2^x$ and $y = \log_2 x$.

Solution: These functions are inverses of each other, so you can draw the graph of $y = 2^x$ and then get the graph of $y = \log_2 x$ (across the line $y = x$) by the property of symmetry. Accordingly, prepare the table of values of x and the corresponding values of y

x	-2	-1	0	1	2	3
y	$\frac{1}{4}$	$\frac{1}{2}$	1	2	4	8

and draw the graph as shown in Figure 12-14. The tabulated values of x and y allow you to draw the graph of $y = 2^x$. The graph of $y = \log_2 x$ is symmetric with respect to the line $y = x$.

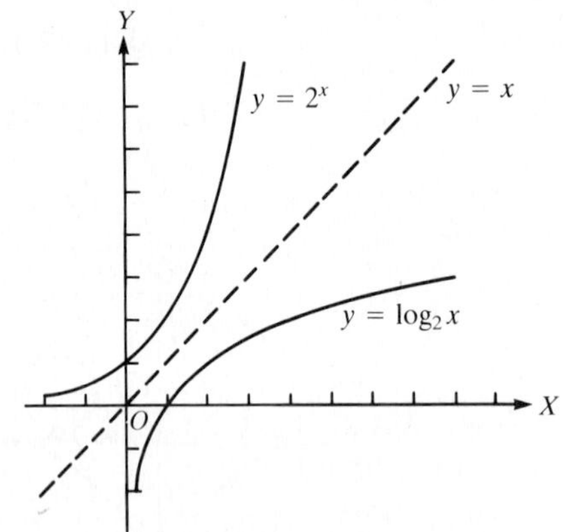

Figure 12-14

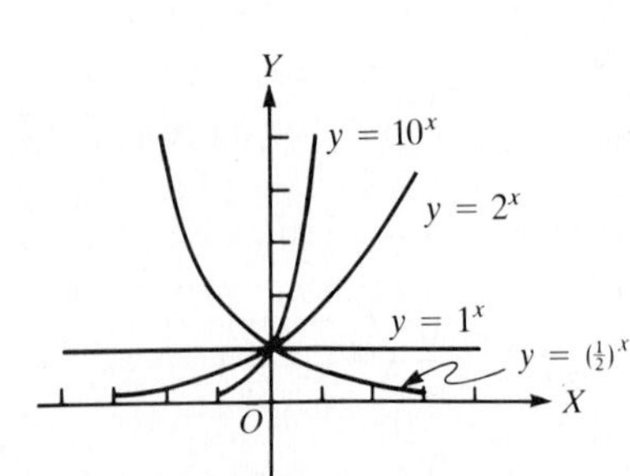

Figure 12-15

PROBLEM 12-8 Graph the equation $y = a^x$, for $a = \frac{1}{2}$, 1, 2, and 10.

Solution: The graph of the equation $y = 2^x$ was obtained in Problem 12-7. The other members of this family are shown in Figure 12-15.

PROBLEM 12-9 Sketch the graph of the function defined by the equation $y = \log(x + 1)$.

Solution: Substituting values of x ranging from 0 to 9, you will get (with the aid of your calculator) the values for y shown in the table

x	0	1	2	3	4	5	6	7	8	9
y	0	0.30	0.47	0.60	0.70	0.78	0.85	0.90	0.95	1.00

When these coordinate points are plotted, the resulting curve is the nearly flat curve, with y values ranging from 0 to 1, shown in Figure 12-16.

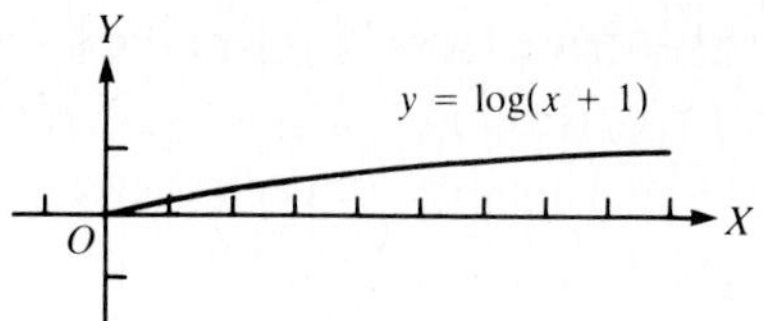

Figure 12-16

Graphing by Composition of Ordinates

PROBLEM 12-10 Plot the graph of the equation

$$y = \frac{x}{2} + \frac{3}{2}\sin\frac{\pi x}{5}$$

Solution: On the same axes and to the same scale, plot the graphs of

$$y_1 = \frac{x}{2} \quad \text{and} \quad y_2 = \frac{3}{2}\sin\frac{\pi x}{5}$$

The ordinates of the two curves are added to give the graph of the original equation, as indicated in Figure 12-17. In plotting the graph of the second curve, you should note that it is a sine curve with amplitude 3/2 and period $2\pi \div \pi/5 = 10$ units. (Pay particular attention to the algebraic sign of the ordinates in adding.)

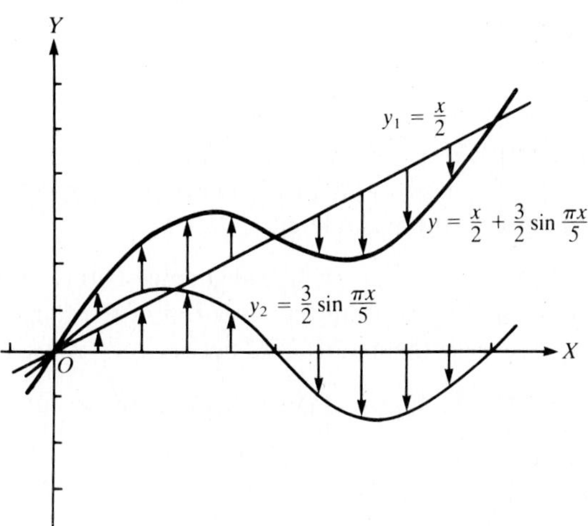

Figure 12-17

PROBLEM 12-11 Draw the graph of the equation

$$2x^2 - 2xy + y^2 + 8x - 12y + 36 = 0$$

Solution: To express y as the sum of two quantities, treat the equation as a quadratic in y:

$$y^2 + (-2x - 12)y + (2x^2 + 8x + 36) = 0$$

Solving for y gives

$$y = \frac{2x + 12 \pm \sqrt{(-2x - 12)^2 - 4(2x^2 + 8x + 36)}}{2}$$

$$= x + 6 \pm \sqrt{4x - x^2}$$

Now you can draw the graphs of the equations

$$y_1 = x + 6 \quad \text{and} \quad y_2 = \pm\sqrt{4x - x^2}$$

The graph of the first equation is a line. By squaring and then completing the square in the x terms, you can reduce the second equation to $(x - 2)^2 + {y_2}^2 = 4$, whose graph is a circle of radius 2 and with center at (2, 0). The line and the circle are shown in Figure 12-18. The point D on the graph of the original equation is found by adding the ordinates AB and AC, i.e., AC extended by a length equal to AB. The addition of ordinates for this purpose must be algebraic. Thus MN is negative, and the point Q is found by measuring downward from P so that $PQ = MN$. By plotting a sufficient number of points in this manner, you can construct the desired graph.

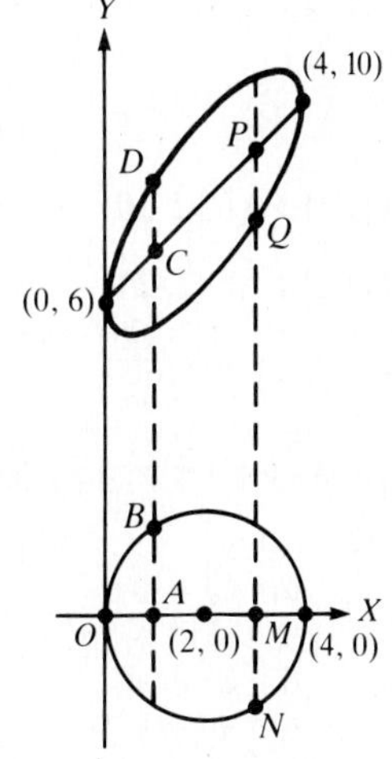

Figure 12-18

Supplementary Exercises

PROBLEM 12-12 Sketch the following curves using the parametric equations. Also find the Cartesian equation for each curve.

(a) $x = t,\quad y = t + 2$
(b) $x = 3t,\quad y = 3/t$
(c) $x = 3\cos\theta,\quad y = 4\sin\theta$
(d) $x = t^3,\quad y = t^2$
(e) $x = \frac{1}{2}t - 4,\quad y = t^2$
(f) $x = 2\sec\theta,\quad y = 2\tan\theta$

PROBLEM 12-13 Express the following equations in parametric form, making use of the indicated relation between x or y and the parameter:

(a) $x^2 = 25y + 5,\quad y = t^2 - \frac{1}{5}$
(b) $2x - xy = 1,\quad y = 2 + t$
(c) $xy = x - y - 1,\quad x = t + 1$
(d) $9x^2 - y^2 = k^2,\quad y = k\tan\theta$
(e) $x^2 + y^2 + 6x - 2y = -6,\quad y = 1 - 2\sin\theta$
(f) $x^{1/2} + y^{1/2} = a^{1/2},\quad y = a\cos^4\theta$

PROBLEM 12-14 A point is moving in a plane with horizontal and vertical velocities equal to r feet per second and s feet per second, respectively. Find the equation of the path of the point, using time as a parameter.

PROBLEM 12-15 A line segment 12 units long moves with its end points in contact with the coordinate axes. Find the equation of the locus of a point 2 units from the end that touches the X-axis. (Use the acute angle between the X-axis and the line as a parameter.)

PROBLEM 12-16 Plot the graphs of the following equations:

(a) $y = \log_{1.5}x$
(b) $y = \log_2 x$
(c) $y = \log_e x$
(d) $y = \log 3x$
(e) $y = \log x$

PROBLEM 12-17 Give the logarithmic form of each of the following exponential equations:

(a) $3^3 = 27$
(b) $2^4 = 16$
(c) $8^1 = 8$
(d) $15^0 = 1$

PROBLEM 12-18 Give the exponential form of each of the following logarithmic equations:

(a) $\log_3 1 = 0$
(b) $\log_6 6 = 1$
(c) $\log_9 1 = 0$
(d) $\log_2 \frac{1}{16} = -4$

PROBLEM 12-19 Plot the following curves:

(a) $y = 2\sin x$
(b) $y = \sin x$
(c) $y = \sin(3x + 2)$
(d) $y = \sin 3x$

PROBLEM 12-20 Sketch the curve $y = \cos x$ after finding its period and amplitude.

PROBLEM 12-21 Draw the curve $y = \sin x + \frac{1}{2}\sin 2x$ by the composition of ordinates. [*Hint:* Use 0°, 30°, 45°, 60°, and 90° for your values of x from which to compute, separately, the values of $\sin x$ and $\sin 2x$.]

Answers to Supplementary Exercises

12-12: (a) $x - y + 2 = 0$
(b) $xy = 9$
(c) $16x^2 + 9y^2 = 144$
(d) $x^2 = y^3$
(e) $y = 4x^2 + 32x + 64$
(f) $x^2 - y^2 = 4$

12-13: (a) $x = 5t;\quad y = t^2 - \frac{1}{5}$
(b) $x = -1/t;\quad y = t + 2$
(c) $x = t + 1;\quad y = t/(t + 2)$
(d) $x = (k\sec\theta)/3;\quad y = k\tan\theta$
(e) $x = -3 \pm 2\cos\theta;\quad y = 1 - 2\sin\theta$
(f) $x = a\sin^4\theta;\quad y = a\cos^4\theta$

12-14: $x = rt;\quad y = st$

12-15: $x = 10\cos\theta;\quad y = 2\sin\theta$

12-16: See Figure 12-19.

12-17: (a) $\log_3 27 = 3$
(b) $\log_2 16 = 4$
(c) $\log_8 8 = 1$
(d) $\log_{15} 1 = 0$

12-18: **(a)** $3^0 = 1$ **(c)** $9^0 = 1$
(b) $6^1 = 6$ **(d)** $2^{-4} = \frac{1}{16}$

12-19: See Figure 12-20.

12-20: $P = 2\pi$; $A = 1$
See Figure 12-21.

12-21: See Figure 12-22.

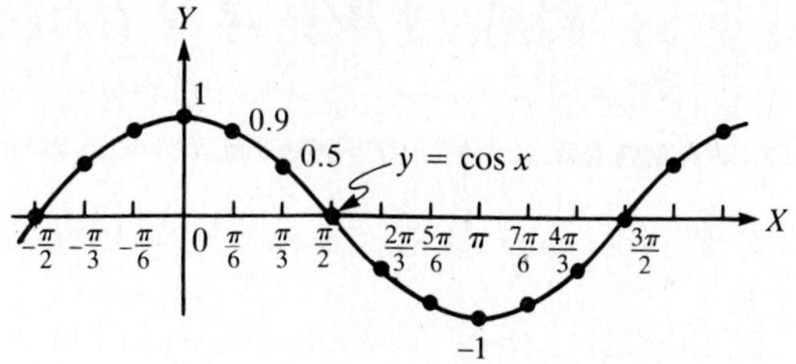

Figure 12-21

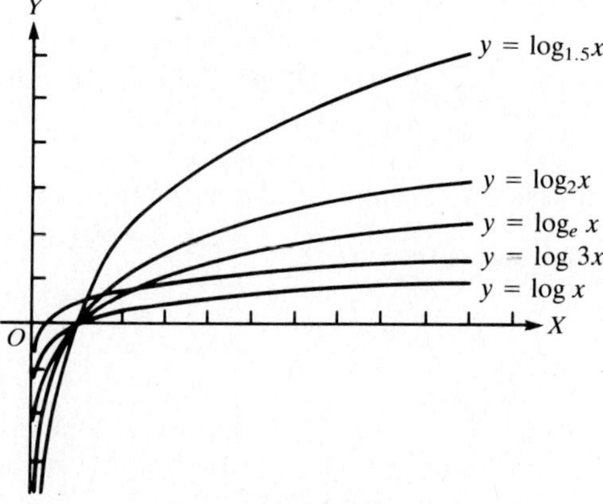

Figure 12-19

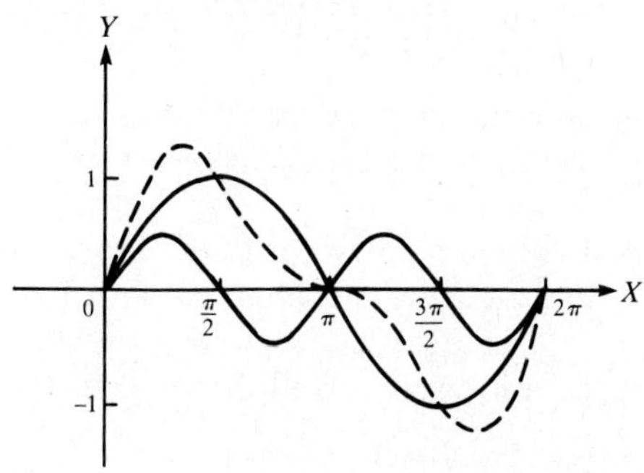

Figure 12-22

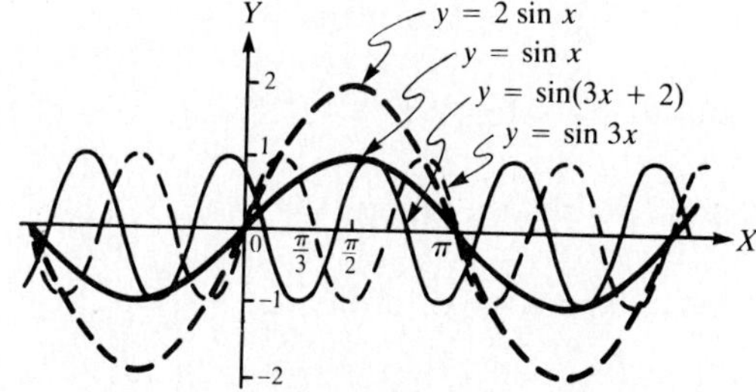

Figure 12-20

EXAM 4 (chapters 11 and 12)

1. Express each of the following equations in terms of polar coordinates: (a) $y = 4$; (b) $x = 2$.

2. Express each of the following equations in terms of rectangular coordinates:

$$\text{(a) } r = \frac{3}{2\cos\theta - \sin\theta} \qquad \text{(b) } r = \frac{6}{3\cos\theta + 2\sin\theta}$$

3. (a) Find the polar equation of the circle with center at $(2, \pi/6)$ and radius 2; (b) change the equation to rectangular form.

4. Find the equation of the line that is (a) parallel to the $\pi/2$ axis and 3 units to the right of it; (b) parallel to the polar axis and 4 units below it.

5. Identify each of the following curves:

   (a) $r\cos\theta = 2$ (c) $r = \dfrac{4}{1 - \cos\theta}$

   (b) $r^2 + 9 - 6r\cos(\theta - 45°) = 4$

6. Find the rectangular form of the equation of the curve described by the parametric equations $x = t^2 - 1$ and $y = t^2$.

7. Express the equation $x^2 + y^2 = 16$ in parametric form with $x = 4\sin\theta$ and $y = 4 - t$.

8. Sketch the graph of the function defined by the equation $y = \log_e x$. ($e = 2.718\ldots.$)

9. Find the period and amplitude of the function determined by the equation $y = \cos 3x$.

10. Draw the curve defined by $y = \sin x + \sin 2x$ by the composition of ordinates.

Answers to Exam 4

1. (a) $r\sin\theta = 4$ (b) $r\cos\theta = 2$

2. (a) $2x - y = 3$ (b) $3x + 2y = 6$

3. (a) $r^2 = 4r\cos(\theta - \pi/6)$
   (b) $(x - \sqrt{3})^2 + (y - 1)^2 = 4$

4. (a) $r\cos\theta = 3$ (b) $r\sin\theta = -4$

5. (a) line: 2 units to the right of the $\pi/2$ axis
   (b) circle: radius 2; center at $(3, 45°)$
   (c) parabola: focus at pole; directrix perpendicular to polar axis and 4 units to the left of the pole

6. $x - y + 1 = 0$

7. $y = \pm 4\cos\theta$; $x = \pm\sqrt{8t - t^2}$

8. See Figure E4-1

9. $P = 2\pi/3$, $A = 1$

10. See Figure E4-2

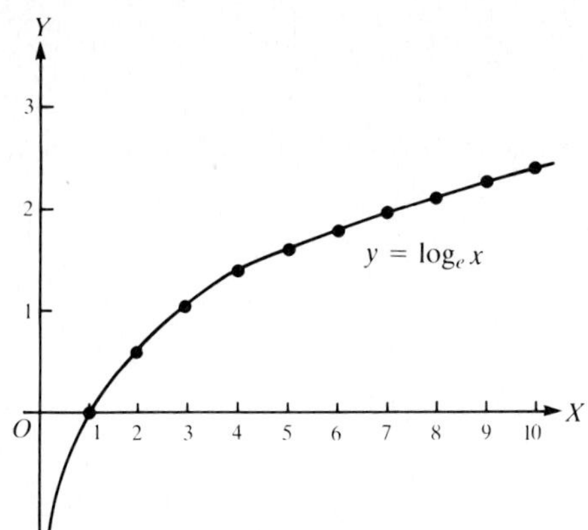

Figure E4-1

x	1	2	3	4	5	6	7	8	9	10
y	0	0.69	1.1	1.4	1.6	1.8	1.9	2.1	2.2	2.3

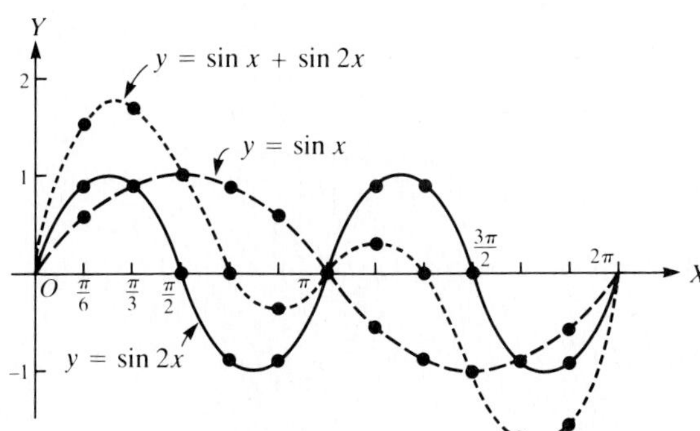

Figure E4-2

x	0	$\frac{\pi}{6}$	$\frac{\pi}{3}$	$\frac{\pi}{2}$	$\frac{2\pi}{3}$	$\frac{5\pi}{6}$	π	$\frac{7\pi}{6}$	$\frac{4\pi}{3}$	$\frac{3\pi}{2}$	$\frac{5\pi}{3}$	$\frac{11\pi}{6}$	2π
$y = \sin x$	0	0.50	0.87	1	0.87	0.50	0	−0.5	−0.87	−1	−0.87	−0.50	0
$y = \sin 2x$	0	0.87	0.87	0	−0.87	−0.87	0	0.87	0.87	0	−0.87	−0.87	0
$y = \sin x + \sin 2x$	0	1.37	1.74	1	0	−0.37	0	0.37	0	−1	−1.74	−1.37	0

PART II

Solid Analytic Geometry

13 THE POINT IN THREE-DIMENSIONAL SPACE

THIS CHAPTER IS ABOUT

- ☑ Three-Dimensional Rectangular Coordinates
- ☑ Distance between Two Points
- ☑ Direction Cosines of a Line
- ☑ Angle between Two Lines

13-1. Three-Dimensional Rectangular Coordinates

In solid analytic geometry we locate a point in space (i.e., in three dimensions) by describing its perpendicular distance from three mutually perpendicular planes, which can be represented by the following procedure:

Through a fixed point O in space, draw three mutually perpendicular lines, $X'OX$, $Y'OY$, and $Z'OZ$. Call these lines the X-, Y-, and Z-axes, respectively; call their point of intersection O the origin; and indicate positive direction along an axis by means of an arrowhead (just as in the Cartesian plane). Each pair of axes determines a plane—the XY-plane, the YZ-plane, or the ZX-plane—as shown in Figure 13-1.

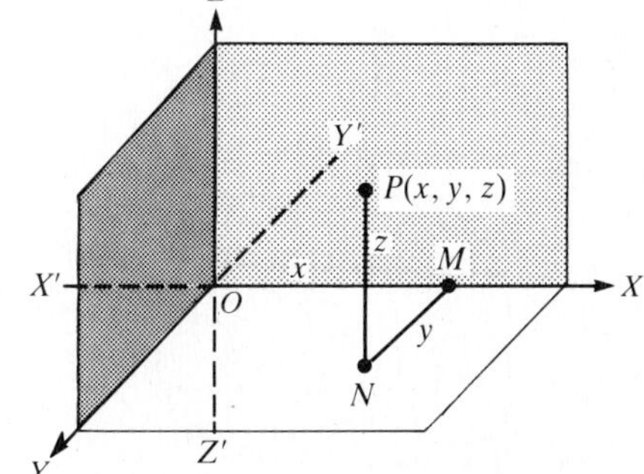

Figure 13-1. Three-dimensional rectangular coordinate system.

The three planes, which divide the space into **octants**, are called **coordinate planes** and are used in determining the position of a point in space. Thus, to every point P there correspond three directed distances x, y, and z, measured along lines perpendicular to the YZ-, the ZX-, and the XY-planes, respectively. Conversely, any three directed numbers x, y, and z, measured as indicated, will determine the position of a point P. These numbers, written (x, y, z), are called the *coordinates* of the point P.

note: When plotting points, it is customary to measure the directed distance $OM = x$ along the X-axis, the directed distance $MN = y$ parallel to the Y-axis, and the directed distance $NP = z$ parallel to the Z-axis.

To visualize the system, we can sketch a rectangular room, as in Figure 13-2a. If we let the point in the corner at which two side walls and the floor come together be the origin, then the intersection of the right-hand wall with the floor is the X-axis, the intersection of the left-hand wall with the floor is the Y-axis, and the intersection of the two walls is the Z-axis. So the floor is the XY-plane, the right-hand wall is the ZX-plane, and the left-hand wall is the YZ-plane.

Now we can imagine that the walls and the floor extend through the axes to create eight such rooms, all coming together at the origin O as if in a two-story, eight-room "house," shown schematically in Figure 13-2b. *Our* room, on the second story at the right, is then the FIRST OCTANT, where x, y, and z are POSITIVE. Going around the Z-axis in a counterclockwise direction, we come to octants II, III, and IV on the same level as octant I. The room directly below us is octant V, the one below octant II is octant VI, and so on.

note: Octant I is defined (by everyone, everywhere) as the octant for which x, y, and z are all positive. There is no absolute rule defining the other octants.

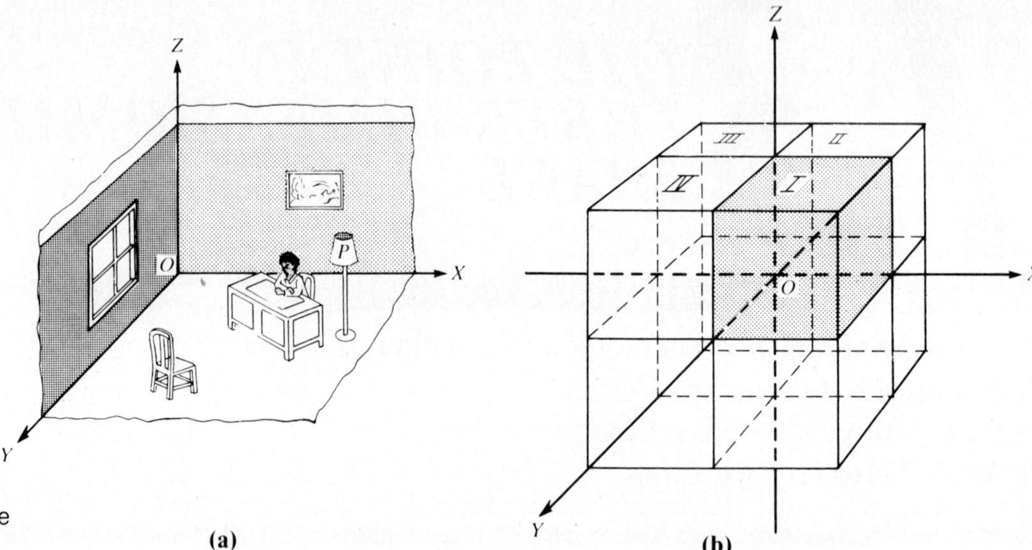

Figure 13-2. Visualizing the three-dimensional system. (**a**) Rectangular-room paradigm; (**b**) the octants.

To locate the position of an object/point in a room/octant, say the shade on a floor lamp, we measure its perpendicular distances x, y, and z from the two walls and the floor.

13-2. Distance between Two Points

To find the distance between two points in space, such as $P_1(x_1, y_1, z_1)$ and $P_2(x_2, y_2, z_2)$ in Figure 13-3, we make use of the Pythagorean theorem. Thus, in the right triangle P_1MN,

$$MN = x_2 - x_1 \quad \text{and} \quad P_1M = y_2 - y_1$$

therefore

$$d = \sqrt{(x_2 - x_1)^2 + (y_2 - y_1)^2}$$

But d and the distance $NP_2 = z_2 - z_1$ are sides of the right triangle P_1NP_2, and so the distance between points P_1 and P_2 is expressed in terms of the coordinates of the two points by the equation

Figure 13-3

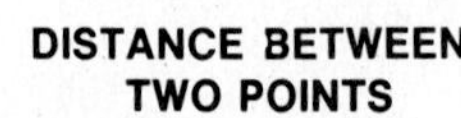

DISTANCE BETWEEN TWO POINTS

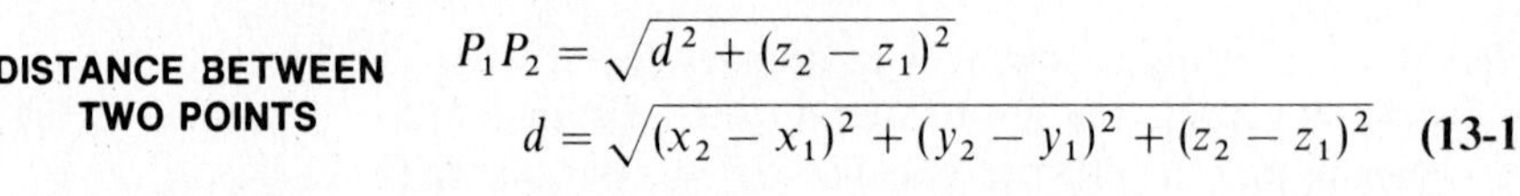

$$P_1P_2 = \sqrt{d^2 + (z_2 - z_1)^2}$$

$$d = \sqrt{(x_2 - x_1)^2 + (y_2 - y_1)^2 + (z_2 - z_1)^2} \quad \textbf{(13-1)}$$

EXAMPLE 13-1: Plot the points $(-5, 2, -4)$, $(3, 2, 5)$, and $(3, 2, -4)$ and use the distance formula to show that the lines joining them form a right triangle.

Solution: Referring to Figure 13-4, let P_1, P_2, and P_3 represent the points. Then

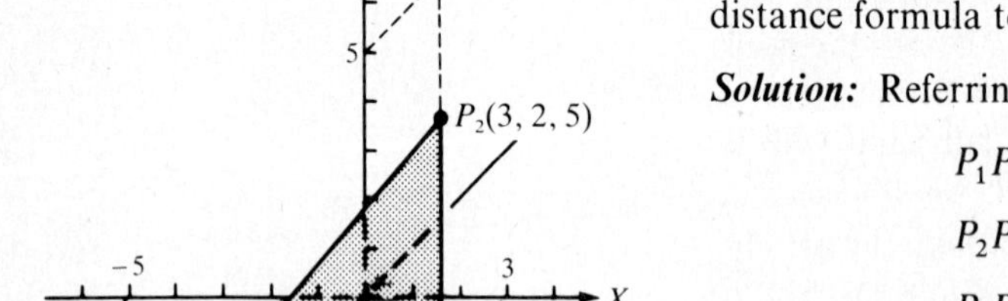

$$P_1P_2 = \sqrt{(3 + 5)^2 + (2 - 2)^2 + (5 + 4)^2} = \sqrt{145}$$

$$P_2P_3 = \sqrt{(3 - 3)^2 + (2 - 2)^2 + (5 + 4)^2} = 9$$

$$P_1P_3 = \sqrt{(3 + 5)^2 + (2 - 2)^2 + (-4 + 4)^2} = 8$$

Therefore, since $\sqrt{9^2 + 8^2} = \sqrt{145}$, $(P_1P_2)^2 = (P_2P_3)^2 + (P_1P_3)^2$ and the triangle $P_1P_2P_3$ has a right angle at P_3.

Figure 13-4

13-3. Direction Cosines of a Line

The angles that a directed line makes with the positive directions of the coordinate axes are called the **direction angles** of the line. And the cosines of these angles are known as the **direction cosines** of the line.

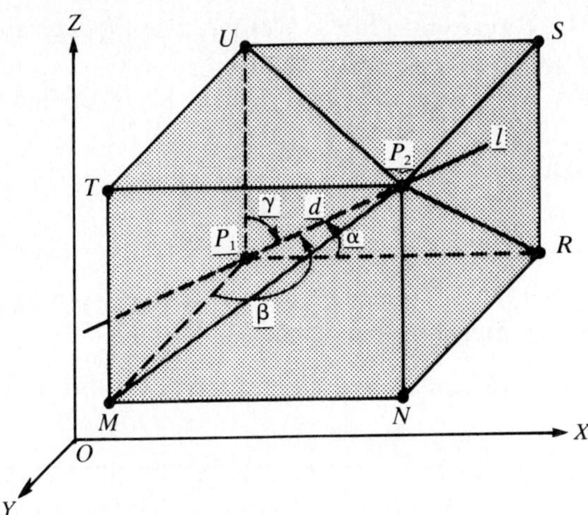

Figure 13-5. Direction cosines of a line.

Thus, in Figure 13-5, if P_1R, P_1M, and P_1U have the same directions as the X-, Y-, and Z-axes, respectively, and if a directed line l passing through $P_1(x_1, y_1, z_1)$ and $P_2(x_2, y_2, z_2)$ makes angles α, β, and γ with these lines as shown in the figure, then these angles are the direction angles of l and the cosines of these angles are the direction cosines of l.

note: Angles α, β, and γ are always positive and $\leq 180°$ $(=\pi)$, since they always correspond to one direction along l. The angles $180° - \alpha$, $180° - \beta$, and $180° - \gamma$ correspond to the opposite direction.

Triangles P_1RP_2, P_1MP_2, and P_1UP_2 in Figure 13-5 are right triangles; therefore we may write

$$\cos\alpha = \frac{P_1R}{P_1P_2} = \frac{x_2 - x_1}{P_1P_2}$$

$$\cos\beta = \frac{P_1M}{P_1P_2} = \frac{RN}{P_1P_2} = \frac{y_2 - y_1}{P_1P_2}$$

$$\cos\gamma = \frac{P_1U}{P_1P_2} = \frac{NP_2}{P_1P_2} = \frac{z_2 - z_1}{P_1P_2}$$

or

$$x_2 - x_1 = d\cos\alpha, \qquad y_2 - y_1 = d\cos\beta, \qquad z_2 - z_1 = d\cos\gamma \qquad \textbf{(13-2)}$$

where $d = P_1P_2$. By squaring these expressions and taking their sum, we have

$$(x_2 - x_1)^2 + (y_2 - y_1)^2 + (z_2 - z_1)^2 = d^2(\cos^2\alpha + \cos^2\beta + \cos^2\gamma)$$

But, by the distance formula (13-1), the left side of this equation is equal to d^2, so

SUM OF SQUARES OF DIRECTION COSINES

$$\cos^2\alpha + \cos^2\beta + \cos^2\gamma = 1 \qquad \textbf{(13-3)}$$

• The sum of the squares of the direction cosines of a line is equal to unity.

If P_1 of Figure 13-5 is at the origin, so that $d = \sqrt{x^2 + y^2 + z^2}$ is the distance from this point to any point $P(x, y, z)$, then eqs. (13-2) become

DIRECTION COSINES

$$x = d\cos\alpha, \qquad y = d\cos\beta, \qquad z = d\cos\gamma \qquad \textbf{(13-4)}$$

If, as in Figure 13-6, the coordinates of a point P are (a, b, c), the direction cosines of the line OP may be obtained from eq. (13-4):

$$\cos\alpha = \frac{a}{r}, \qquad \cos\beta = \frac{b}{r}, \qquad \cos\gamma = \frac{c}{r} \qquad \textbf{(13-5)}$$

where $r = \pm\sqrt{a^2 + b^2 + c^2}$. [The sign of the radical depends upon the direction

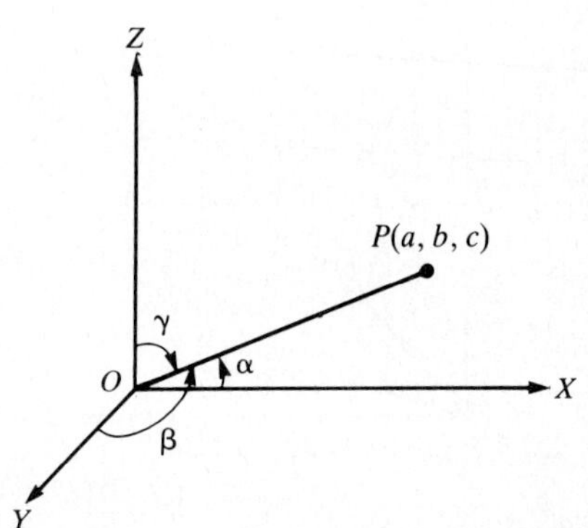

Figure 13-6

of the line: If the direction from O to P is positive, then the radical is positive and the opposite direction, from P to O, is negative.]

By solving eqs. (13-5) for r and equating like values, we find that

DIRECTION NUMBERS
$$\frac{\cos\alpha}{a} = \frac{\cos\beta}{b} = \frac{\cos\gamma}{c} \tag{13-6}$$

This relation is very useful because it tells us that

- The direction cosines of a line OP—or of a line PARALLEL to OP—are proportional to the three **direction numbers** a, b, and c.

Direction numbers of a line may be used in place of the direction cosines.

EXAMPLE 13-2: Find the direction cosines of a line that extends from $(-6, 1, -3)$ to $(2, -3, 5)$.

Solution: The distance between the points is calculated from eq. (13-1)

$$d = \sqrt{(x_2 - x_1)^2 + (y_2 - y_1)^2 + (z_2 - z_1)^2}$$
$$= \sqrt{(2 + 6)^2 + (-3 - 1)^2 + (5 + 3)^2} = 12$$

and the direction cosines are found from eqs. (13-2):

$$\cos\alpha = \frac{x_2 - x_1}{d} = \frac{2 + 6}{12} = \frac{2}{3}, \qquad \cos\beta = \frac{-3 - 1}{12} = -\frac{1}{3}, \qquad \cos\gamma = \frac{5 + 3}{12} = \frac{2}{3}$$

EXAMPLE 13-3: A line directed upward has direction numbers $\frac{1}{2}$, $\frac{1}{3}$, and $\frac{1}{5}$. What are the direction cosines of the line?

Solution: From eqs. (13-5)

$$r = \pm\sqrt{a^2 + b^2 + c^2} = \sqrt{\frac{1}{4} + \frac{1}{9} + \frac{1}{25}} = \frac{19}{30}$$

then

$$\cos\alpha = \frac{1}{2}\left(\frac{30}{19}\right) = \frac{15}{19}, \qquad \cos\beta = \frac{1}{3}\left(\frac{30}{19}\right) = \frac{10}{19}, \qquad \cos\gamma = \frac{1}{5}\left(\frac{30}{19}\right) = \frac{6}{19}$$

13-4. Angle between Two Lines

The angle θ between two (given) directed lines in space may be defined as the angle between two other lines that pass through the origin with the same direction cosines as the given lines.

To find an expression for angle θ, we proceed as follows: As in Figure 13-7, draw two lines l and m through O parallel to the given lines, letting the direction angles of l be α_1, β_1, γ_1 and those of m be α_2, β_2, γ_2. Then let $P_1(x_1, y_1, z_1)$ be a point on l and $P_2(x_2, y_2, z_2)$ be a point on m. Now, from a form of the law of cosines

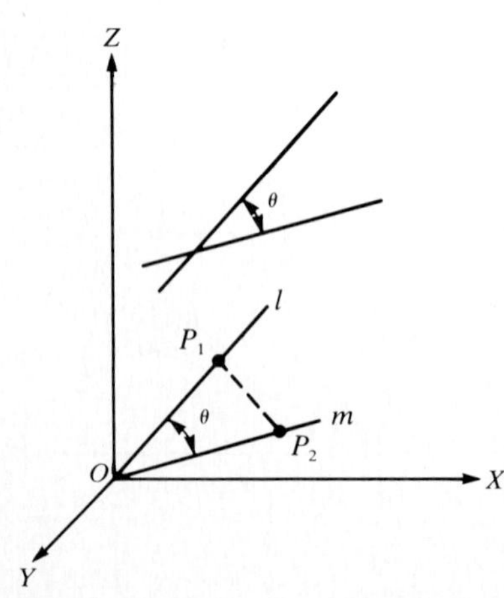

Figure 13-7. Angle between two lines.

$$\cos\theta = \frac{a^2 + b^2 - c^2}{2ab}$$

we may write

$$\cos\theta = \frac{(OP_1)^2 + (OP_2)^2 - (P_1P_2)^2}{2(OP_1)(OP_2)}$$

But since $(OP_1)^2 = x_1{}^2 + y_1{}^2 + z_1{}^2$ and $(OP_2)^2 = x_2{}^2 + y_2{}^2 + z_2{}^2$, by eq. (13-1)

$$(P_1P_2)^2 = (x_2 - x_1)^2 + (y_2 - y_1)^2 + (z_2 - z_1)^2$$

Therefore

$$\cos\theta = \frac{x_1x_2 + y_1y_2 + z_1z_2}{\sqrt{x_1^2 + y_1^2 + z_1^2}\sqrt{x_2^2 + y_2^2 + z_2^2}} = \frac{x_1x_2}{r_1r_2} + \frac{y_1y_2}{r_1r_2} + \frac{z_1z_2}{r_1r_2} \qquad \textbf{(13-7)}$$

where $r_1 = \sqrt{x_1^2 + y_1^2 + z_1^2}$ and $r_2 = \sqrt{x_2^2 + y_2^2 + z_2^2}$. But

$$\cos\alpha_1 = \frac{x_1}{r_1}, \qquad \cos\beta_1 = \frac{y_1}{r_1}, \qquad \cos\gamma_1 = \frac{z_1}{r_1}$$

$$\cos\alpha_2 = \frac{x_2}{r_2}, \qquad \cos\beta_2 = \frac{y_2}{r_2}, \qquad \cos\gamma_2 = \frac{z_2}{r_2}$$

So by substituting the values of x_1/r_1, etc., into eq. (13-7), we get a general expression for θ in terms of the direction cosines of the lines:

ANGLE BETWEEN TWO LINES

$$\cos\theta = \cos\alpha_1\cos\alpha_2 + \cos\beta_1\cos\beta_2 + \cos\gamma_1\cos\gamma_2 \qquad \textbf{(13-8)}$$

If the lines are perpendicular, $\cos\theta = 0$, and we have

angle between perpendicular lines

$$\cos\alpha_1\cos\alpha_2 + \cos\beta_1\cos\beta_2 + \cos\gamma_1\cos\gamma_2 = 0 \qquad \textbf{(13-8a)}$$

If the lines are parallel, $\cos\theta = 1$ or -1 (depending on the direction of the lines), and we have

angle between parallel lines

$$\cos\alpha_1\cos\alpha_2 + \cos\beta_1\cos\beta_2 + \cos\gamma_1\cos\gamma_2 = \pm 1 \qquad \textbf{(13-8b)}$$

EXAMPLE 13-4: Find the angle that the line through $(-2, 5, -2)$ and $(0, 1, 3)$ makes with the line joining $(1, -1, -3)$ to $(1, -2, -1)$.

Solution: To solve this problem you'll need to use the direction cosine formula (eqs. 13-5) to find the directions of the two lines, then eq. (13-8) to determine the angle (θ) between them.

Working with the set of coordinate points for the first line, $(-2, 5, -2)$ and $(0, 1, 3)$, use the distance formula (eq. 13-1) to find d_1:

$$d_1 = \sqrt{(0 + 2)^2 + (1 - 5)^2 + (3 + 2)^2} = \sqrt{4 + 16 + 25} = 3\sqrt{5}$$

And the direction numbers are

$$a_1 = x_2 - x_1 = (0 + 2) = 2 \qquad b_1 = y_2 - y_1 = (1 - 5) = -4$$

$$c_1 = z_2 - z_1 = (3 + 2) = 5$$

Therefore, from eqs. (13-5)

$$\cos\alpha_1 = \frac{a_1}{r_1} = \frac{2}{3\sqrt{5}}, \qquad \cos\beta_1 = \frac{b_1}{r_1} = \frac{-4}{3\sqrt{5}}, \qquad \cos\gamma_1 = \frac{c_1}{r_1} = \frac{5}{3\sqrt{5}}$$

Similarly, for the points on the second line, $(1, -1, -3)$ and $(1, -2, -1)$, you get

$$d_2 = \sqrt{(1 - 1)^2 + (-2 + 1)^2 + (-1 + 3)^2} = \sqrt{0 + 1 + 4} = \sqrt{5}$$

and

$$a_2 = 1 - 1 = 0, \qquad b_2 = -2 + 1 = -1, \qquad c_2 = -1 + 3 = 2$$

Therefore

$$\cos\alpha_2 = \frac{a_2}{r_2} = \frac{0}{\sqrt{5}} = 0, \qquad \cos\beta_2 = \frac{-1}{\sqrt{5}}, \qquad \cos\gamma_2 = \frac{2}{\sqrt{5}}$$

Accordingly, from eq. (13-8)

$$\cos\theta = \cos\alpha_1\cos\alpha_2 + \cos\beta_1\cos\beta_2 + \cos\gamma_1\cos\gamma_2$$
$$= \frac{2}{3\sqrt{5}}(0) + \frac{-4}{3\sqrt{5}}\left(\frac{-1}{\sqrt{5}}\right) + \frac{5}{3\sqrt{5}}\left(\frac{2}{\sqrt{5}}\right) = \frac{14}{15}$$

so that

$$\theta = \arccos\left(\frac{14}{15}\right) \cong 21^\circ$$

SUMMARY

1. In solid analytic geometry a point in space is located by describing its perpendicular distance from three mutually perpendicular coordinate planes that divide the space into octants.
2. To every point P in three-dimensional space there correspond three directed distances x, y, and z, measured along lines perpendicular to the YZ-, ZX-, and XY-planes, respectively; these distances are the coordinates (x, y, z) of the point P.
3. The equation for the distance between two points in space is
$$d = \sqrt{(x_2 - x_1)^2 + (y_2 - y_1)^2 + (z_2 - z_1)^2}$$
4. The angles that a directed line makes with the positive directions of the coordinate axes are called the direction angles of the line, and the cosines of these angles are known as the direction cosines of the line.
5. The direction cosines of a point $P(a, b, c)$ are
$$\cos\alpha = \frac{a}{r}, \qquad \cos\beta = \frac{b}{r}, \qquad \cos\gamma = \frac{c}{r} \qquad \text{(where } r = \pm\sqrt{a^2 + b^2 + c^2}\text{)}$$
The sum of the squares of the direction cosines of a line is unity.
6. The direction cosines of a line are proportional to the three direction numbers a, b, and c, such that
$$\frac{\cos\alpha}{a} = \frac{\cos\beta}{b} = \frac{\cos\gamma}{c}$$
7. The angle θ between two given directed lines in space may be defined as the angle between the two lines that pass through the origin with the same direction as the given lines, such that
$$\cos\theta = \cos\alpha_1\cos\alpha_2 + \cos\beta_1\cos\beta_2 + \cos\gamma_1\cos\gamma_2$$
If the two lines are perpendicular, $\cos\theta = 0$; if the two lines are parallel, $\cos\theta = \pm 1$.

RAISE YOUR GRADES

Can you . . . ?

☑ find the distance between two points in space, given their coordinates
☑ find the direction cosines of a line that extends between two given points
☑ determine the direction cosines of a line, given the direction and the direction numbers of the line
☑ find the angle between two lines, given the coordinates of the terminal points

SOLVED PROBLEMS

Distance between Two Points

PROBLEM 13-1 Find the distance between points $(5, -4, -2)$ and $(2, 0, -3)$.

Solution: Using the distance formula (13-1), you get

$$\begin{aligned} d &= \sqrt{(x_2 - x_1)^2 + (y_2 - y_1)^2 + (z_2 - z_1)^2} \\ &= \sqrt{(2 - 5)^2 + [0 - (-4)]^2 + [(-3) - (-2)]^2} \\ &= \sqrt{(-3)^2 + 4^2 + (-1)^2} = \sqrt{26} \end{aligned}$$

PROBLEM 13-2 Find the distance between $P_1(5, 4, -1)$ and $P_2(8, -2, 1)$.

Solution: Substituting the given values in the distance formula yields

$$\begin{aligned} P_1P_2 &= \sqrt{(8 - 5)^2 + (-2 - 4)^2 + [1 - (-1)]^2} \\ &= \sqrt{3^2 + (-6)^2 + 2^2} = 7 \end{aligned}$$

PROBLEM 13-3 Find the distance between $P_1(-4, 4, 1)$ and $P_2(-3, 5, -4)$.

Solution:

$$\begin{aligned} P_1P_2 &= \sqrt{(-3 + 4)^2 + (5 - 4)^2 + (-4 - 1)^2} \\ &= \sqrt{1 + 1 + 25} = 3\sqrt{3} \end{aligned}$$

Direction Cosines of a Line

PROBLEM 13-4 Find the direction cosines of the line segment directed from $P(2, 3, -4)$ to $Q(0, -2, 3)$.

Solution: From the distance formula (13-1)

$$d = \sqrt{(0 - 2)^2 + (-2 - 3)^2 + (3 + 4)^2} = \sqrt{78}$$

And from eqs. (13-2)

$$\cos\alpha = \frac{x_2 - x_1}{d} = \frac{(0 - 2)}{\sqrt{78}} = -\frac{2}{\sqrt{78}}$$

$$\cos\beta = \frac{y_2 - y_1}{d} = \frac{(-2 - 3)}{\sqrt{78}} = -\frac{5}{\sqrt{78}}$$

$$\cos\gamma = \frac{z_2 - z_1}{d} = \frac{(3 + 4)}{\sqrt{78}} = \frac{7}{\sqrt{78}}$$

note: The signs would be reversed for the directed line segment QP.

PROBLEM 13-5 Find the direction numbers for the segment PQ in Problem 13-4.

Solution: The direction numbers are simply proportionality constants, one set of which has the values of the numerators (a, b, and c) of the direction cosines found from eqs. (13-2). So from the above problem, one set of direction numbers consists of the proportionality constants -2, -5, and 7; another set would be -4, -10, and 14; and so on. In other words, *a directed line has an infinite array of direction numbers, but only one set of direction cosines.*

PROBLEM 13-6 Two of the direction angles of a line are $\alpha = 120°$ and $\gamma = 45°$: Find all possible values of $\cos\beta$ and each corresponding direction angle.

Solution: Making use of the fact that the sum of the squares of the direction cosines is unity (from eq. 13-3), you can write

$$\cos^2\alpha + \cos^2\beta + \cos^2\gamma = 1$$

$$\cos^2 120^\circ + \cos^2\beta + \cos^2 45^\circ = 1$$

$$1/4 + \cos^2\beta + 1/2 = 1$$

$$\cos^2\beta = 1/4$$

$$\cos\beta = \pm 1/2$$

$$\beta = \arccos(\pm 1/2) = 60^\circ, 120^\circ$$

PROBLEM 13-7 What are the two possible values of the third direction cosine if $\cos\alpha = \cos\beta = 1/2$?

Solution: From eq. (13-3)

$$(1/2)^2 + (1/2)^2 + \cos^2\gamma = 1$$

$$1/4 + 1/4 + \cos^2\gamma = 1$$

$$\cos^2\gamma = 1 - 1/2 = 1/2$$

$$\cos\gamma = \pm 1/\sqrt{2} = \pm\sqrt{2}/2$$

PROBLEM 13-8 Find the value of the third direction cosine if $\cos\alpha = -2/3$ and $\cos\gamma = 1/3$.

Solution: Using eq. (13-3) and substituting the given values, you get

$$(-2/3)^2 + \cos^2\beta + (1/3)^2 = 1$$

$$\cos^2\beta = 1 - 5/9 = 4/9$$

$$\cos\beta = \pm 2/3$$

PROBLEM 13-9 Find the third direction cosine if $\cos\alpha = 1$ and $\cos\beta = 0$.

Solution: You know from eq. (13-3) that

$$\cos^2\alpha + \cos^2\beta + \cos^2\gamma = 1$$

and since $\cos\alpha = 1$, the value of $\cos\gamma$ must be 0—or the sum of the three values would be greater than 1.

PROBLEM 13-10 Prove that it is impossible for $1/3, 2/5$ and $-1/2$ to be the direction cosines of a line.

Solution: From eq. (13-3) you know that the sum of the squares of the direction cosines is $\cos^2\alpha + \cos^2\beta + \cos^2\gamma = 1$. Substituting the given values of the direction cosines, you get

$$(1/3)^2 + (2/5)^2 + (-1/2)^2 \stackrel{?}{=} 1$$

$$1/9 + 4/25 + 1/4 \neq 1$$

Since the given values do not satisfy eq. (13-3), they cannot be the direction cosines of a line.

PROBLEM 13-11 Find the direction cosines of each of the coordinate axes.

Solution: Equation (13-4) tells you that the direction cosines are given by the relationships

$$x = d\cos\alpha, \qquad y = d\cos\beta, \qquad z = d\cos\gamma$$

For the sake of simplicity, choose $d = 1$. Then for the X-axis, α is 0°; and since the cosine of 0° is 1, you have $x = 1(1) = 1$. And because there are no β or γ angles, the direction cosines for the X-axis are $1, 0, 0$. Similarly, for the Y-axis the direction cosines are $0, 1, 0$; and for the Z-axis they are $0, 0, 1$.

Angle between Two Lines

PROBLEM 13-12 Find the direction cosine of the angle θ between the pair of directed lines having the direction numbers $2, 3, 4$ and $-1, 5, -2$.

Solution: You can derive the direction cosine of this angle directly from eq. (13-7), where $x_1 = 2$, $x_2 = -1$, and so on:

$$\cos\theta = \frac{x_1x_2 + y_1y_2 + z_1z_2}{\sqrt{x_1^2 + y_1^2 + z_1^2}\sqrt{x_2^2 + y_2^2 + z_2^2}}$$

$$= \frac{2(-1) + 3(5) + 4(-2)}{\sqrt{(4 + 9 + 16)}\sqrt{(1 + 25 + 4)}}$$

$$= \frac{5}{\sqrt{29}\sqrt{30}}$$

PROBLEM 13-13 If the direction numbers of two lines are $3, -1, -2$ and $2, 4, 5$, what is the direction cosine of the angle between them?

Solution: Here, $x_1 = 3$, $x_2 = 2$, and so on; therefore, from eq. (13-7)

$$\cos\theta = \frac{6 - 4 - 10}{\sqrt{9 + 1 + 4}\sqrt{4 + 16 + 25}}$$

$$= \frac{-8}{\sqrt{14}\sqrt{45}}$$

PROBLEM 13-14 Find the cosine of the angle between the lines through the pairs of points $(3, 4, 5)$, $(2, -1, 4)$ and $(1, 2, 3)$, $(-3, 2, 1)$. Use the direction from the first to the second point as the positive direction for each line.

Solution: Since the coordinates of the points through which the lines pass are given, you can use the distance formula (13-1) to find r_1 and r_2, the distances between the points for each line. Then use eqs. (13-5) to find the direction cosines of each line, and finally use eq. (13-8) to determine the angle θ between the lines. Then, from eq. (13-1), $d = \sqrt{(x_2 - x_1)^2 + (y_2 - y_1)^2 + (z_2 - z_1)^2}$, so for the first set of points

$$r_1 = \sqrt{(2 - 3)^2 + (-1 - 4)^2 + (4 - 5)^2} = \sqrt{1 + 25 + 1} = \sqrt{27}$$

and for the second set

$$r_2 = \sqrt{(-3 - 1)^2 + (2 - 2)^2 + (1 - 3)^2} = \sqrt{16 + 4} = \sqrt{20}$$

Taking the algebraic sum of each of the coordinate pairs for each line, so that $a_1 = 2 - 3 = -1$, $b_1 = -5$, $c_1 = -1$ and $a_2 = -3 - 1 = -4$, $b_2 = 0$, $c_2 = -2$, substitute these and the r_1 and r_2 values into eq. (13-5):

$$\cos\alpha_1 = \frac{-1}{\sqrt{27}}, \qquad \cos\beta_1 = \frac{-5}{\sqrt{27}}, \qquad \cos\gamma_1 = \frac{-1}{\sqrt{27}}$$

$$\cos\alpha_2 = \frac{-4}{\sqrt{20}}, \qquad \cos\beta_2 = 0, \qquad \cos\gamma_2 = \frac{-2}{\sqrt{20}}$$

Now use eq. (13-8) to find the angle between the lines:

$$\cos\theta = \cos\alpha_1\cos\alpha_2 + \cos\beta_1\cos\beta_2 + \cos\gamma_1\cos\gamma_2$$

$$= \frac{-1}{\sqrt{27}}\left(\frac{-4}{\sqrt{20}}\right) + \frac{-5}{\sqrt{27}}(0) + \frac{-1}{\sqrt{27}}\left(\frac{-2}{\sqrt{20}}\right)$$

$$= \frac{4}{\sqrt{27}\sqrt{20}} + \frac{2}{\sqrt{27}\sqrt{20}} = \frac{6}{\sqrt{27}\sqrt{20}} = \frac{6}{6\sqrt{15}} = \frac{1}{\sqrt{15}}$$

PROBLEM 13-15 Given two directed lines defined by the coordinate pairs (0, 1, 0), (3, −2, −1) and (5, 3, 1), (−2, −3, 0), find the cosine of the angle between them.

Solution: From eq. (13-1)

$$r_1 = \sqrt{(3-0)^2 + (-2-1)^2 + (-1-0)^2} = \sqrt{19}$$
$$r_2 = \sqrt{(-2-5)^2 + (-3-3)^2 + (0-1)^2} = \sqrt{86}$$

so the direction numbers are

$$a_1 = 3, \quad b_1 = -3, \quad c_1 = -1; \qquad a_2 = -7, \quad b_2 = -6, \quad c_2 = -1$$

Substituting these values in eq. (13-5) gives

$$\cos\alpha_1 = \frac{3}{\sqrt{19}}, \qquad \cos\beta_1 = \frac{-3}{\sqrt{19}}, \qquad \cos\gamma_1 = \frac{-1}{\sqrt{19}}$$
$$\cos\alpha_2 = \frac{-7}{\sqrt{86}}, \qquad \cos\beta_2 = \frac{-6}{\sqrt{86}}, \qquad \cos\gamma_2 = \frac{-1}{\sqrt{86}}$$

and substituting these direction cosines into eq. (13-8) gives

$$\cos\theta = \frac{3}{\sqrt{19}}\left(\frac{-7}{\sqrt{86}}\right) + \frac{-3}{\sqrt{19}}\left(\frac{-6}{\sqrt{86}}\right) + \frac{-1}{\sqrt{19}}\left(\frac{-1}{\sqrt{86}}\right) = \frac{-21+18+1}{\sqrt{19}\sqrt{86}}$$
$$= \frac{-2}{\sqrt{19}\sqrt{86}}$$

Supplementary Exercises

PROBLEM 13-16 In which octant are *all* values of x, y, z negative?

PROBLEM 13-17 What coordinate is zero for any point in **(a)** the XY-plane? **(b)** the ZX-plane? **(c)** the YZ-plane?

PROBLEM 13-18 Find the distance from the origin to the point (2, 3, −4).

PROBLEM 13-19 What line is determined by **(a)** $x = 0, y = 0$? **(b)** $x = 0, z = 0$? **(c)** $y = 0, z = 0$?

PROBLEM 13-20 Find the distance between the points (−2, −3, 4) and (5, −1, 2).

PROBLEM 13-21 Find the lengths of the sides of the triangles whose vertices are given below, and state in each case whether the triangle is scalene, isosceles, or equilateral.

(a) (0, 0, 0), (3, 4, 5), (2, 1, −2)
(b) (1, 2, 3), (6, 6, 6), (3, 4, 5)

PROBLEM 13-22 Do the lines joining the points (1, 5, 0), (8, 5, 0), and (8, −2, 0) form an isosceles right triangle?

PROBLEM 13-23 Find the direction cosines of the lines joining the following pairs of points:

(a) (0, 0, 0) to (1, 5, 3)
(b) (−1, 2, −3) to (3, −4, 2)
(c) (−1, 2, −5) to (−4, −3, 6)

PROBLEM 13-24 Find the cosine of the angle θ between the pairs of directed lines having the direction numbers 6, −3, 1 and −2, 4, 3.

PROBLEM 13-25 Find the cosine of the angle between the lines through the pairs of points (2, 1, −1), (5, 3, 2) and (3, 0, 2), (−1, 3, 4).

PROBLEM 13-26 What are the two possible values of the third direction cosine if $\cos\alpha = 0$ and $\cos\gamma = 2/3$?

PROBLEM 13-27 Find the third direction cosine if $\cos\alpha = \cos\gamma = 3/4$.

PROBLEM 13-28 Find (to the nearest degree) the angle between each axis and the line from the origin to the point (3, 3, 1).

PROBLEM 13-29 Given a line extending from the origin to the point (3, −2, −1), find (to the nearest degree) the angle between it and each axis.

PROBLEM 13-30 A line makes equal angles with the coordinate axes; find its direction cosines.

Answers to Supplementary Exercises

13-16: VII (by the system of numbering used in this book)

13-17: (**a**) z; (**b**) y; (**c**) x

13-18: $\sqrt{29}$

13-19: (**a**) Z-axis; (**b**) Y-axis; (**c**) X-axis

13-20: $\sqrt{57}$

13-21: (**a**) $\sqrt{50}$, 3, $\sqrt{59}$; scalene and right
(**b**) $\sqrt{50}$, $\sqrt{12}$, $\sqrt{14}$; scalene

13-22: Yes

13-23: (**a**) $\dfrac{1}{\sqrt{35}}$; $\dfrac{5}{\sqrt{35}}$; $\dfrac{3}{\sqrt{35}}$

(**b**) $\dfrac{4}{\sqrt{77}}$; $\dfrac{-6}{\sqrt{77}}$; $\dfrac{5}{\sqrt{77}}$

(**c**) $\dfrac{-3}{\sqrt{155}}$; $\dfrac{-5}{\sqrt{155}}$; $\dfrac{11}{\sqrt{155}}$

13-24: $\dfrac{-21}{\sqrt{46}\sqrt{29}}$

13-25: 0

13-26: $\dfrac{\pm\sqrt{5}}{3}$

13-27: impossible

13-28: 46°, 46°, 77°

13-29: 37°, 122°, 106°

13-30: $\dfrac{1}{\sqrt{3}}$; $\dfrac{1}{\sqrt{3}}$; $\dfrac{1}{\sqrt{3}}$

14 THE PLANE IN THREE-DIMENSIONAL SPACE

THIS CHAPTER IS ABOUT

- ☑ Equation of a Plane
- ☑ Parallel and Perpendicular Planes
- ☑ Angle between Two Planes
- ☑ Perpendicular Distance from a Plane to a Point

14-1. Equation of a Plane

While an equation in two variables plots a curve in two dimensions, an equation in three variables plots a surface in three-dimensional space. The simplest equation in three variables is the linear equation $Ax + By + Cz + D = 0$, where the left-hand side is a first-degree polynomial in the three variables x, y, and z. This equation can take several forms, depending upon the information given and the information sought.

A. Normal form

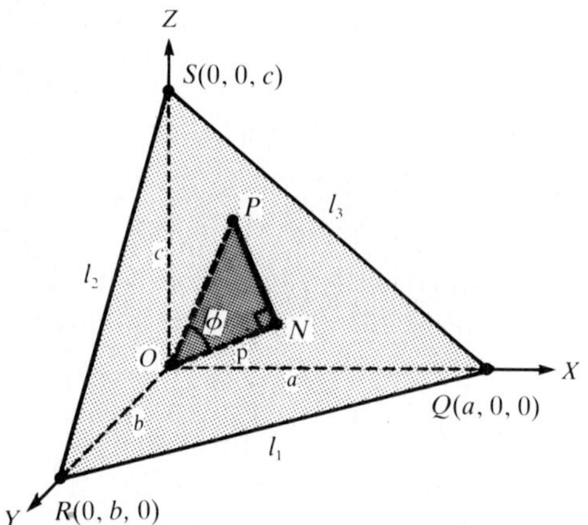

Figure 14-1. Normal form of the equation of a plane.

Let a plane intersect the coordinate axes at the points $Q(a, 0, 0)$, $R(0, b, 0)$, and $S(0, 0, c)$, as shown in Figure 14-1. Then the directed lengths a, b, and c are called the X-, Y-, and Z-**intercepts**, respectively; and the lines l_1, l_2, and l_3 where the plane intersects the coordinate planes are called the **traces** of the cutting plane.

Draw a line (with direction angles α, β, and γ) through O perpendicular to the plane and intersecting the plane at N: This line is called the **normal** to the plane, and its length ON—usually represented by p—is a positive number when measured from the origin to the plane.

Now let $P(x, y, z)$ be any point on the plane. Draw the lines OP and NP, and let the direction angles of OP be represented by α_1, β_1, and γ_1. Then, if we let ϕ be the angle between ON and OP, we can use eq. (13-8) to write

$$\cos\phi = \cos\alpha\cos\alpha_1 + \cos\beta\cos\beta_1 + \cos\gamma\cos\gamma_1$$

But $\cos\phi = p/OP$; therefore, triangle ONP is a right triangle. Moreover, $\cos\alpha_1 = x/OP$, $\cos\beta_1 = y/OP$, and $\cos\gamma_1 = z/OP$. Substituting these values, we have

$$\frac{p}{OP} = \frac{x}{OP}\cos\alpha + \frac{y}{OP}\cos\beta + \frac{z}{OP}\cos\gamma$$

or, dividing by OP,

EQUATION OF A PLANE: NORMAL FORM

$$x\cos\alpha + y\cos\beta + z\cos\gamma - p = 0 \qquad \textbf{(14-1)}$$

EXAMPLE 14-1: If the perpendicular distance of a plane from the origin is 3 units, and if the direction cosines of a line along this perpendicular are $\frac{1}{3}, \frac{2}{3}$, and $\frac{2}{3}$, what is the equation of the plane?

Solution: Here, $p = 3$ and $\cos\alpha = \frac{1}{3}$, $\cos\beta = \frac{2}{3}$, $\cos\gamma = \frac{2}{3}$, so that by eq. (14-1)

$$\tfrac{1}{3}x + \tfrac{2}{3}y + \tfrac{2}{3}z - 3 = 0$$

$$x + 2y + 2z - 9 = 0$$

is the required equation in normal form.

EXAMPLE 14-2: Find the direction cosines of the normal to the plane $3x - 4y + z = 5$.

Solution: From eq. (13-5)

$$\cos\alpha = \frac{a}{r} = \frac{3}{\sqrt{3^2 + (-4)^2 + 1^2}} = \frac{3}{\sqrt{26}}$$

Similarly, $$\cos\beta = -\frac{4}{\sqrt{26}} \quad \text{and} \quad \cos\gamma = \frac{1}{\sqrt{26}}$$

B. General form

- *A plane may be represented by the general equation*

EQUATION OF A PLANE: GENERAL FORM $$Ax + By + Cz + D = 0 \qquad \textbf{(14-2)}$$

where the coefficients A, B, and C are real and at least one of them is not zero. Conversely, the equation of every plane can be written in this general form.

Since the coefficients A, B, and C are *direction numbers* of lines perpendicular to the plane, it is easy to convert them to direction cosines by dividing the equation by $\sqrt{A^2 + B^2 + C^2}$, so that

$$\frac{Ax + By + Cz + D}{\sqrt{A^2 + B^2 + C^2}} = 0 \qquad \textbf{(14-2a)}$$

The coefficients of x, y, and z are now the *direction cosines* of lines perpendicular to the plane. The equation can therefore be written in the form $(\cos\alpha)x + (\cos\beta)y + (\cos\gamma)z - p = 0$, where p is the perpendicular distance from the origin to the plane. Comparing this with eq. (14-1), we see that it is identical. This gives us the method of reducing the general equation of the plane to normal form: We choose the sign before the radical so that p is positive (i.e., the sign of p is opposite to that of D) and use the conversion formula

THE PLANE: GENERAL TO NORMAL FORM

$$\frac{Ax}{\pm\sqrt{A^2 + B^2 + C^2}} + \frac{By}{\pm\sqrt{A^2 + B^2 + C^2}} + \frac{Cz}{\pm\sqrt{A^2 + B^2 + C^2}} + \frac{D}{\pm\sqrt{A^2 + B^2 + C^2}} = 0 \qquad \textbf{(14-2b)}$$

EXAMPLE 14-3: Reduce the equation $2x - 5y + 4z - 12 = 0$ to the normal form.

Solution: Since D is negative, divide each term by the positive radical, $\sqrt{A^2 + B^2 + C^2} = \sqrt{4 + 25 + 16} = 3\sqrt{5}$:

$$\frac{2x}{3\sqrt{5}} - \frac{5y}{3\sqrt{5}} + \frac{4z}{3\sqrt{5}} - \frac{12}{3\sqrt{5}} = 0$$

EXAMPLE 14-4: Reduce $x + 3y - 2z + 5 = 0$ to normal form.

Solution: The direction numbers of the normal are, from the given equation, 1, 3, and -2. And since the square root of the sum of the squares of the coefficients of the x, y, and z terms is $-\sqrt{14}$ (minus, because it must be opposite to the sign of D), the direction cosines are $1/\sqrt{14}$, $3/\sqrt{14}$, and $-2/\sqrt{14}$. Therefore the normal form of the equation is

$$\frac{x + 3y - 2z + 5}{-\sqrt{14}} = 0$$

C. Intercept form

We can determine the equation of a particular plane if the conditions of the plane are such that three of the coefficients A, B, C, and D can be found in terms of the fourth.

EXAMPLE 14-5: Find the equation of the plane passing through the points $(a, 0, 0)$, $(0, b, 0)$, and $(0, 0, c)$.

Solution: Substituting the coordinates into the general equation

$$Ax + By + Cz + D = 0$$

we have

$$aA + D = 0, \qquad bB + D = 0, \qquad cC + D = 0$$

from which

$$A = -\frac{D}{a}, \qquad B = -\frac{D}{b}, \qquad C = -\frac{D}{c}$$

and our equation becomes

$$-\frac{Dx}{a} - \frac{Dy}{b} - \frac{Dz}{c} + D = 0$$

or, dividing by $-D$,

EQUATION OF A PLANE: INTERCEPT FORM

$$\frac{x}{a} + \frac{y}{b} + \frac{z}{c} = 1 \qquad \textbf{(14-3)}$$

This form is called the **intercept form** of the equation of the plane since it has intercepts a, b, and c on the X-, Y-, and Z-axes, respectively.

EXAMPLE 14-6: Reduce $x - 5y + 2z - 3 = 0$ to intercept form and write the coordinates of the intercepts.

Solution: Writing the given equation in the form $x - 5y + 2z = 3$ and then dividing through by 3 to make the right member equal to 1, we get the intercept form (eq. 14-3):

$$\frac{x}{a} + \frac{y}{b} + \frac{z}{c} = 1$$

$$\frac{x}{3} - \frac{5y}{3} + \frac{2z}{3} = 1$$

$$\frac{x}{3} + \frac{y}{-3/5} + \frac{z}{3/2} = 1$$

So the intercepts are $(3, 0, 0)$, $(0, -\frac{3}{5}, 0)$, and $(0, 0, \frac{3}{2})$.

14-2. Parallel and Perpendicular Planes

Consider two planes:

$$A_1x + B_1y + C_1z = D_1 \qquad (D_1 \neq 0) \qquad \textbf{(1)}$$

$$A_2x + B_2y + C_2z = D_2 \qquad (D_2 \neq 0) \qquad \textbf{(2)}$$

Let $K = \pm\sqrt{A_1^2 + B_1^2 + C_1^2}$ and $K_2 = \pm\sqrt{A_2^2 + B_2^2 + C_2^2}$, where K_1 is given the sign of D_1 and K_2 that of D_2. The direction cosines of the normals to planes (1) and (2) are then A_1/K_1, B_1/K_1, C_1/K_1 and A_2/K_2, B_2/K_2, C_2/K_2, respectively.

If the planes are parallel, so are their normals; therefore $A_1/K_1 = A_2/K_2$ or $A_1/A_2 = K_1/K_2$. Similarly, $B_1/B_2 = C_1/C_2 = K_1/K_2$. Conversely, if $A_1/A_2 = B_1/B_2 = C_1/C_2 = k$, then

$$A_1 = kA_2, \qquad B_1 = kB_2, \qquad C_1 = kC_2 \qquad \textbf{(3)}$$

Substituting the values in eq. (3) into eq. (1) and dividing by k, we get

$$A_2x + B_2y + C_2z = \frac{D_1}{k} \qquad \textbf{(4)}$$

Therefore the normals of plane (1) are parallel to the normals of plane (2) and so planes (1) and (2) are parallel. This gives us a test for parallel planes:

- If the planes $A_1x + B_1y + C_1z = D_1$ and $A_2x + B_2y + C_2z = D_2$ are parallel, then

TEST FOR PARALLEL PLANES

$$\frac{A_1}{A_2} = \frac{B_1}{B_2} = \frac{C_1}{C_2} \qquad \textbf{(14-4)}$$

and conversely.

This test holds for any values of D_1 and D_2, including $D_1 = D_2 = 0$.

If the planes are perpendicular, so are their normals. Therefore, using eq. (14-4) and the fact that the direction cosines of the normals to the two planes are proportional to A_1, B_1, C_1, A_2, B_2, and C_2, respectively, we have the result that $A_1A_2 + B_1B_2 + C_1C_2 = 0$.

- The planes $A_1x + B_1y + C_1z = D_1$ and $A_2x + B_2y + C_2z = D_2$ will be mutually perpendicular if and only if

TEST FOR PERPENDICULARITY

$$A_1A_2 + B_1B_2 + C_1C_2 = 0 \qquad \textbf{(14-5)}$$

EXAMPLE 14-7: A plane contains the Z-axis and the point $(4, 2, 0)$, as shown in Figure 14-2. Find the equation of the plane.

Solution: Since this plane contains the Z-axis, it is perpendicular to the XY-plane and its equation is therefore of the form $Ax + By + D = 0$. It passes through the origin, and therefore $D = 0$. Finally, $4A + 2B = 0$. To make this equality true, A must be proportional to 1 and B must be proportional to -2, so that $4(1) + 2(-2) = 0$. Using these values for A and B, we get $x - 2y = 0$ for the equation of the plane.

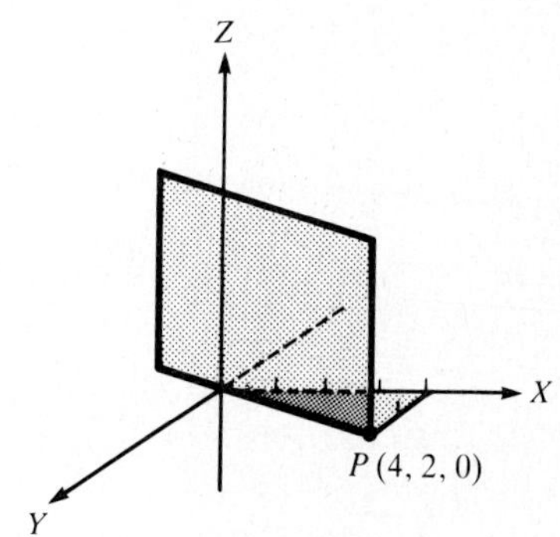

Figure 14-2

EXAMPLE 14-8: Write the equation of the plane that passes through $(1, 1, 2)$ and $(3, 5, 4)$ and is perpendicular to the XY-plane.

Solution: The plane is perpendicular to the XY-plane, so its equation is of the form $Ax + By + D = 0$. And the plane passes through the given points, so

$$A + B + D = 0 \qquad \text{and} \qquad 3A + 5B + D = 0$$

Solving these two equations simultaneously, we get $A = -2D$ and $B = D$. Substituting these values into $Ax + By + D = 0$ and dividing by $-D$, we have

$$Ax + By + D = 0$$
$$-2Dx + Dy + D = 0$$
$$2x - y - 1 = 0$$

14-3. Angle between Two Planes

• *The angle between two parallel lines is zero. The angle between two intersecting planes is the acute angle or right angle between their normals.*

Consider two planes (1) and (2) whose equations are

$$A_1x + B_1y + C_1z = D_1 \qquad \textbf{(1)}$$
$$A_2x + B_2y + C_2z = D_2 \qquad \textbf{(2)}$$

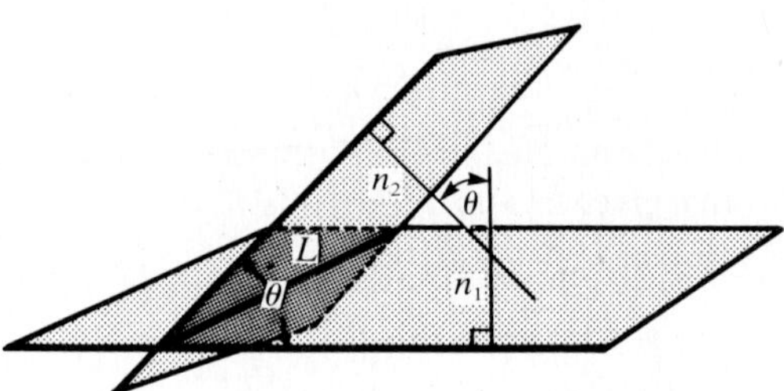

Figure 14-3. Angle between two planes.

Let these planes intersect at a line L, as in Figure 14-3. Let lines n_1 and n_2 be normals to plane (1) and plane (2), respectively. Then, the acute angle θ between n_1 and n_2 is, by definition, equal to the angle between the planes. And since the direction cosines of n_1 and n_2 are proportional to the respective coefficients in equations (1) and (2), we can write by eq. (13-7)

ANGLE BETWEEN TWO PLANES

$$\cos\theta = \pm\frac{A_1A_2 + B_1B_2 + C_1C_2}{\sqrt{(A_1{}^2 + B_1{}^2 + C_1{}^2)(A_2{}^2 + B_2{}^2 + C_2{}^2)}} \qquad \textbf{(14-6)}$$

where the sign is chosen to make $\cos\theta$ positive. Of course, if the planes are mutually perpendicular, then $\cos\theta = 0$ and so

$$A_1A_2 + B_1B_2 + C_1C_2 = 0$$

Conversely, if $A_1A_2 + B_1B_2 + C_1C_2 = 0$ is true, then $\cos\theta = 0$, $\theta = 90°$, and the planes are perpendicular.

EXAMPLE 14-9: Find the angle between the planes $2x + y - z = 4$ and $3x - 2y + 5z = 0$.

Solution: From eq. (14-6)

$$\cos\theta = \pm\frac{2(3) + 1(-2) + (-1)5}{\sqrt{[2^2 + 1^2 + (-1)^2][3^2 + (-2)^2 + 5^2]}} = -\left(\frac{-1}{\sqrt{228}}\right)$$

Therefore, the acute angle between the planes is

$$\theta = \arccos\left(\frac{1}{\sqrt{228}}\right) \cong \arccos(0.066) \cong 86.2°$$

14-4. Perpendicular Distance from a Plane to a Point

To find the shortest distance from the given plane

$$Ax + By + Cz + D = 0 \quad \textbf{(1)}$$

to the point $P_1(x_1, y_1, z_1)$, consider the equation

$$Ax + By + Cz - (Ax_1 + By_1 + Cz_1) = 0 \quad \textbf{(2)}$$

This equation is that of a plane parallel to the given plane (1) and passing through P_1, whose coordinates satisfy eq. (2). The distances p_1 and p_2 from the planes (1) and (2) to the origin are given by the respective formulas

$$p_1 = \frac{D}{\pm\sqrt{A^2 + B^2 + C^2}} \qquad \text{and} \qquad p_2 = \frac{-(Ax_1 + By_1 + Cz_1)}{\pm\sqrt{A^2 + B^2 + C^2}}$$

If the radical is given the same sign in both of these expressions, the distance d between the planes, or the perpendicular distance from the plane (1) to P_1, is

$$\pm(p_1 - p_2) = \pm\frac{Ax_1 + By_1 + Cz_1 + D}{\sqrt{A^2 + B^2 + C^2}}$$

Thus, we can write the distance as

DISTANCE FROM A PLANE TO A POINT

$$d = \left|\frac{Ax_1 + By_1 + Cz_1 + D}{\sqrt{A^2 + B^2 + C^2}}\right| \quad \textbf{(14-7)}$$

EXAMPLE 14-10: Find the shortest distance from the plane $2x + 3y - 5z - 6 = 0$ to the point $(3, -2, 4)$.

Solution: By eq. (14-7)

$$d = \left|\frac{2(3) + 3(-2) - 5(4) - 6}{\sqrt{2^2 + 3^2 + (-5)^2}}\right| = \left|\frac{-26}{\sqrt{38}}\right| = \frac{13\sqrt{38}}{19}$$

SUMMARY

1. An equation in three variables represents a surface in three-dimensional space.
2. The simplest equation in three variables is the linear equation $Ax + By + Cz + D = 0$.
3. The normal form of the equation of a plane is

$$x\cos\alpha + y\cos\beta + z\cos\gamma - p = 0$$

   where p represents the length of the normal, measured from the origin to the plane.
4. The general form of the equation of a plane is

$$Ax + By + Cz + D = 0$$

   where the coefficients A, B, and C are real and at least one of them is not zero.
5. Since the coefficients A, B, and C (in the general equation) are direction numbers of lines perpendicular to the plane, they can be converted into direction cosines by dividing the equation by $\sqrt{A^2 + B^2 + C^2}$.
6. The intercept form of the equation of a plane is

$$\frac{x}{a} + \frac{y}{b} + \frac{z}{c} = 1$$

   where a, b, and c are intercepts on the X-, Y-, and Z-axes, respectively.

7. If the planes $A_1x + B_1y + C_1z = D_1$ and $A_2x + B_2y + C_2z = D_2$ are parallel, then $A_1/A_2 = B_1/B_2 = C_1/C_2$, and conversely.
8. Two planes will be perpendicular to each other if and only if $A_1A_2 + B_1B_2 + C_1C_2 = 0$.
9. The angle between two planes is given by the equation

$$\cos\theta = \pm\frac{A_1A_2 + B_1B_2 + C_1C_2}{\sqrt{(A_1{}^2 + B_1{}^2 + C_1{}^2)(A_2{}^2 + B_2{}^2 + C_2{}^2)}}$$

10. The distance from a plane to a point is given by the formula

$$d = \left|\frac{Ax_1 + By_1 + Cz_1 + D}{\sqrt{A^2 + B^2 + C^2}}\right|$$

RAISE YOUR GRADES

Can you . . .?

- ☑ find the direction cosines of the normals to a plane whose equation is given
- ☑ find the equation of a plane, given the perpendicular distance of the plane from the origin and the direction cosines of a line along this perpendicular
- ☑ reduce the equation of a plane in general form to the normal form
- ☑ reduce the equation of a plane in the general form to the intercept form
- ☑ write the equation of a plane that passes through two given points and is perpendicular to a given plane
- ☑ find the angle between two planes whose equations are given
- ☑ find the distance from a plane to a point, given the equation of the plane and the coordinates of the point in space

SOLVED PROBLEMS

Equation of a Plane

PROBLEM 14-1 Change the equation $3x - 4y = 6$ to normal form.

Solution: Using eq. (13-5), you get the direction cosines of the normals to the plane:

$$\cos\alpha = \frac{a}{r} = \frac{3}{\sqrt{3^2 + (-4)^2 + 0^2}} = \frac{3}{\sqrt{25}} = \frac{3}{5}$$

Similarly,

$$\cos\beta = -\frac{4}{5} \quad \text{and} \quad \cos\gamma = \frac{0}{5} = 0$$

Thus, from eq. (14-1), you have

$$x\cos\alpha + y\cos\beta + z\cos\gamma - p = \frac{3x - 4y - 6}{5} = 0$$

PROBLEM 14-2 The line joining $P_1(3, 2, 1)$ and $P_2(-1, 2, 4)$ lies in a plane that passes through the origin. Find the equation of the plane.

Solution: Since the plane passes through the origin, its equation will be of the form $Ax + By + Cx = 0$. Also, since you're given the coordinates of the end points of the line through which the plane passes, you can write

$$3A + 2B + C = 0 \qquad \text{and} \qquad -A + 2B + 4C = 0$$

Let $C = 1$ and solve simultaneously:

$$3A + 2B = -1$$

$$-A + 2B = -4$$

from which $A = \frac{3}{4}$ and $B = -\frac{13}{8}$. The equation of the plane is therefore

$$\frac{3x}{4} - \frac{13y}{8} + z = 0 \qquad \text{or} \qquad 6x - 13y + 8z = 0$$

PROBLEM 14-3 Show that the three points $P_1(1, 1, 5)$, $P_2(-2, -1, -5)$, and $P_3(4, 2, 2)$ are noncollinear.

Solution: The direction numbers are

for P_1P_2: $a = (x_2 - x_1) = (-2 - 1) = -3$ $\qquad$ for P_3P_1: $a = (x_3 - x_1) = (4 - 1) = 3$

$b = (y_2 - y_1) = (-1 - 1) = -2$ $\qquad$ $b = (y_3 - y_1) = (2 - 1) = 1$

$c = (z_2 - z_1) = (-5 - 5) = -10$ $\qquad$ $c = (z_3 - z_1) = (2 - 5) = -3$

Since these sets of direction numbers are not proportional, the three points cannot lie on the same line; i.e., they are *noncollinear.*

PROBLEM 14-4 Find the equation of the plane that is perpendicular to the line joining $P_1(2, 5, -3)$, $P_2(4, -1, 0)$ and passes through $Q(1, 4, -7)$.

Solution: The direction numbers of P_1P_2 are

$$a = (x_2 - x_1) = (4 - 2) = 2$$

$$b = (y_2 - y_1) = (-1 - 5) = -6$$

$$c = (z_2 - z_1) = (0 + 3) = 3$$

Using these direction numbers and the coordinates of the point through which the plane passes, you get

$$2(x - 1) - 6(y - 4) + 3(z + 7) = 0$$

$$2x - 6y + 3z + 43 = 0$$

PROBLEM 14-5 The directed normal from the origin to a plane has direction cosines $\cos\alpha = \frac{1}{\sqrt{5}}$, $\cos\beta = \frac{-1}{\sqrt{5}}$, and $\cos\gamma = \frac{\sqrt{3}}{\sqrt{5}}$; and the distance from the origin to the plane (along this normal) is 7 units, as shown in Figure 14-4. Find the equation of the plane.

Solution: From eq. (14-1), the equation in normal form is

$$\frac{x}{\sqrt{5}} - \frac{y}{\sqrt{5}} + \frac{z\sqrt{3}}{\sqrt{5}} - 7 = 0$$

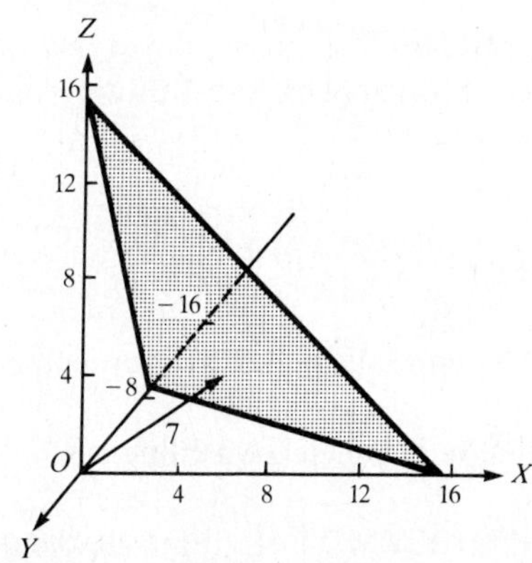

Figure 14-4

PROBLEM 14-6 A plane passes through $P(4,0,0)$, $Q(0,-2,0)$, and $R(0,0,5)$. Find its equation.

Solution: Since the X-, Y-, and Z-intercepts are 4, -2, and 5, respectively, you can write the equation in intercept form, by eq. (14-3):

$$\frac{x}{a}+\frac{y}{b}+\frac{z}{c}=1$$

$$\frac{x}{4}+\frac{y}{-2}+\frac{z}{5}=1$$

PROBLEM 14-7 Reduce $5x+2y-4z+3=0$ to intercept form.

Solution: Rewrite the given equation and divide by -3:

$$5x+2y-4z=-3$$

$$\frac{x}{-3/5}+\frac{y}{-3/2}+\frac{z}{3/4}=1$$

PROBLEM 14-8 Reduce $3x+2y-z+5=0$ to normal form.

Solution: Since the coefficients 3, 2, and -1 are direction numbers of lines perpendicular to the plane, you simply convert them into direction cosines (in accordance with eq. 14-1) by dividing the equation by $\sqrt{A^2+B^2+C^2}=\sqrt{3^2+2^2+(-1)^2}=\sqrt{14}$, and choose the sign of the radical so it is the opposite of $+5$: Thus

$$\frac{3x+2y-z+5}{-\sqrt{14}}=0$$

is the normal form of the equation.

Parallel and Perpendicular Planes

PROBLEM 14-9 Show that the two planes $4x-y+6z=0$ and $8x-2y+12z-18=0$ are parallel.

Solution: In order to show that the planes are parallel, you have to show that the proportionality condition (eq. 14-4) $A_1/A_2=B_1/B_2=C_1/C_2$ exists; that is, the coefficients of x, y, and z must have a constant of proportionality, which is usually designated as k. Thus from the equations of the given planes, you can write

$$\frac{4}{8}=\frac{-1}{-2}=\frac{6}{12}\qquad\text{and}\qquad k=\frac{1}{2}$$

Therefore the planes are parallel.

PROBLEM 14-10 Show that the two planes $3x-6y+6z-1=0$ and $2x+2y+z=0$ are perpendicular.

Solution: The given planes will be perpendicular if and only if $A_1A_2+B_1B_2+C_1C_2=0$ (eq. 14-5) applies. Substituting from the given equations, you get

$$(3)(2)+(-6)(2)+(6)(1)=0$$

$$6-12+6=0$$

$$0=0$$

Therefore the planes are perpendicular to each other.

Angle between Two Planes

PROBLEM 14-11 Find the acute angle between the two planes $x+y+z-4=0$ and $x-y-z+7=0$.

Solution: From eq. (14-6), the angle is given by

$$\cos\theta = \pm\frac{A_1A_2 + B_1B_2 + C_1C_2}{\sqrt{(A_1{}^2 + B_1{}^2 + C_1{}^2)(A_2{}^2 + B_2{}^2 + C_2{}^2)}}$$

$$= \frac{|1(1) + 1(-1) + 1(-1)|}{\sqrt{(1+1+1)(1+1+1)}} = \frac{|1-1-1|}{\sqrt{3}\sqrt{3}} = \frac{1}{3}$$

Therefore the angle $\theta = \arccos(\frac{1}{3})$, or approximately 70°.

PROBLEM 14-12 Determine the angle between $x + y - z + 7 = 0$ and $3x - y - 6 = 0$.

Solution: From eq. (14-6)

$$\cos\theta = \frac{|1(3) - 1(1) - 0|}{\sqrt{3}\sqrt{10}} = \frac{|3-1|}{\sqrt{3}\sqrt{10}} = \frac{2}{\sqrt{30}}$$

$$\theta = \arccos\left(\frac{2}{\sqrt{30}}\right) \cong \arccos(0.37) \cong 1.2 \text{ radians}$$

Perpendicular Distance from a Plane to a Point

PROBLEM 14-13 Find the distance from the plane $2x + 3y - 5z - 6 = 0$ to the point $(3, -2, 1)$.

Solution: From eq. (14-7)

$$d = \left|\frac{Ax_1 + By_1 + Cz_1 + D}{\sqrt{A^2 + B^2 + C^2}}\right|$$

$$= \left|\frac{2(3) + 3(-2) - 5(1) - 6}{\sqrt{2^2 + 3^2 + (-5)^2}}\right| = \frac{11}{\sqrt{38}} = \frac{11\sqrt{38}}{38}$$

PROBLEM 14-14 Find the distance from the plane $x + y - z + 2 = 0$ to the point $(0, -2, 3)$.

Solution: From eq. (14-7)

$$d = \left|\frac{1(0) + 1(-2) - 1(3) + 2}{\sqrt{1^2 + 1^2 + (-1)^2}}\right| = \frac{3}{\sqrt{3}} = \sqrt{3}$$

Supplementary Exercises

PROBLEM 14-15 Find the equation of the plane determined by the three given points:

(a) $(2, -1, -1), (5, 0, 0), (-4, -1, -4)$
(b) $(6, -4, 1), (0, 1, -3), (2, 2, -7)$

PROBLEM 14-16 Find the equation of the plane that is perpendicular to the line joining P_1 and P_2 and passes through Q:

(a) $P_1(4, 7, -2)$, $P_2(1, 3, 2)$, $Q(2, 5, 7)$
(b) $P_1(3, 1, 1)$, $P_2(-1, 2, 4)$, $Q(1, -1, -1)$

PROBLEM 14-17 A directed line segment extends from the origin O to P. Find the equation of the plane perpendicular to OP at P if OP has the following properties:

(a) The direction cosines of OP are $1/\sqrt{3}, 1/\sqrt{3}, 1/\sqrt{3}$; OP is 4 units long.
(b) The direction numbers of OP are $2, 5, -3$; the coordinates of P are $(-5, 2, -3)$.

PROBLEM 14-18 Find the locus of points whose numerical distance from the plane $x + 2y - 3z + 4 = 0$ is 5 units.

PROBLEM 14-19 Write the equation of the plane whose X-, Y-, and Z-intercepts are 4, 5, and 7, respectively.

PROBLEM 14-20 Find the equation of the plane that passes through $(1, 4, 3)$, $(-2, 1, 0)$ and is perpendicular to the XY-plane.

PROBLEM 14-21 Find the equation of the plane that passes through $(2, 4, -1)$ and is perpendicular to the line joining $P(1, 2, 7)$ and $Q(-5, 3, 1)$.

PROBLEM 14-22 Find the equation of the plane that passes through $(-1, -3, 6)$ and is parallel to the plane $4x - 9y + 7z + 2 = 0$.

PROBLEM 14-23 Find the cosine of the acute angle between the planes $3x - y + z - 5 = 0$ and $x + 2y + 2z + 2 = 0$.

PROBLEM 14-24 Find the distance from $2x + 7y + 4z - 3 = 0$ to $P(2, 3, 3)$.

Answers to Supplementary Exercises

14-15: (**a**) $x - y - 2z - 5 = 0$
(**b**) $x + 2y + z + 1 = 0$

14-16: (**a**) $3x + 4y - 4z + 2 = 0$
(**b**) $4x - y - 3z - 8 = 0$

14-17: (**a**) $x + y + z - 4\sqrt{3} = 0$
(**b**) $2x + 5y - 3z - 9 = 0$

14-18: $x + 2y - 3z + 4 \pm 5\sqrt{14} = 0$

14-19: $x/4 + y/5 + z/7 = 1$

14-20: $x - y + 3 = 0$

14-21: $6x - y + 6z - 2 = 0$

14-22: $4x - 9y + 7z - 65 = 0$

14-23: $\cos\theta = 1/\sqrt{11}$

14-24: $34/\sqrt{69}$

EXAM 5 (chapters 13 and 14)

1. Find the distance between points $P_1(2, 5, 8)$ and $P_2(1, -3, 6)$.

2. Find the direction cosines of the line that extends from $P_1(1, 2, 3)$ to $P_2(1, -1, 1)$.

3. Find the direction numbers for the line that extends from $P_1(4, 2, -1)$ to $P_2(3, -6, 9)$.

4. If the direction numbers for a certain line are 3, -4, and 7, what are the direction cosines?

5. Find the angle between the line $P_1(0, 1, 0)$, $P_2(1, 0, 1)$ and the line $P_3(4, 2, 3)$, $P_4(-1, -1, -1)$.

6. Are the lines $P_1(-1, 0, 2)$, $P_2(4, 3, 1)$ and $P_3(0, 1, 8)$, $P_4(10, 7, 6)$ parallel?

7. Show that line $P_1(4, 8, -13)$, $P_2(6, -5, -2)$ and line $P_3(1, 2, -3)$, $P_4(2, 3, -2)$ are perpendicular.

8. Find the equation of the plane determined by the three points $(1, 1, 0)$, $(0, 1, 3)$, and $(2, 0, -4)$.

9. Find the equation of the plane that is perpendicular to the line joining $P_1(6, 3, 5)$, $P_2(4, 1, 4)$ and passes through $Q(2, -3, -1)$.

10. A directed line segment extends from the origin O to point P. Find the equation of the plane perpendicular to OP at P if OP is parallel to RS, given that the end points of RS are $R(1, -1, 2)$, $S(3, 1, 1)$ and that OP is 7 units long.

11. Write the equation of the plane whose X-, Y-, Z-intercepts are 1, -4, -2, respectively.

12. Find the equation of the plane that contains $(1, 4, 3)$, $(-2, 1, 0)$ and is perpendicular to the plane $x + y - z - 1 = 0$.

13. Find the equation of the plane that contains $(2, 4, -1)$ and is perpendicular to the YZ-plane.

14. Find the equation of the plane that passes through $(-1, -3, 6)$ and is parallel to the line joining $(2, 1, -3)$ and $(0, 5, 5)$.

15. Find $\cos\theta$ where θ is the acute angle between the lines joining $(1, 4, 8)$, $(2, 0, 3)$ and $(0, 1, 4)$, $(1, 0, 1)$.

Answers to Exam 5

1. $\sqrt{69}$
2. $0, -3/\sqrt{13}, -2/\sqrt{13}$
3. $-1, -8, 10$
4. $\pm 3/\sqrt{74}, \pm 4/\sqrt{74}, \pm 7/\sqrt{74}$
5. $\cos\theta = 6/5\sqrt{6}$; $\theta \cong 60.67°$
6. Yes—The direction numbers are proportional, $k = 2$; $5{:}3{:}-1 = 10{:}6{:}-2$
7. $A_1A_2 + B_1B_2 + C_1C_2 = (2)(1) + (-13)(1) + (11)(1) = 0$
8. $3x - y + z - 2 = 0$
9. $2x + 2y + z + 3 = 0$
10. $2x + 2y - z - 21 = 0$
11. $\frac{x}{1} - \frac{y}{4} - \frac{z}{2} = 1$
12. $x - y + 3 = 0$
13. $By + Cz + D = 0$, where B, C, D are any numbers such that $4B - C + D = 0$
14. $A(x + 1) + B(y + 3) + C(z - 6) = 0$, where A, B, C are any numbers such that $A - 2B - 4C = 0$
15. $\cos\theta = \dfrac{20}{\sqrt{11}\sqrt{42}}$

15 THE LINE IN THREE-DIMENSIONAL SPACE

THIS CHAPTER IS ABOUT

☑ Symmetric Equations of a Line
☑ Two-Point Form of a Line
☑ General Equations of a Line

15-1. Symmetric Equations of a Line

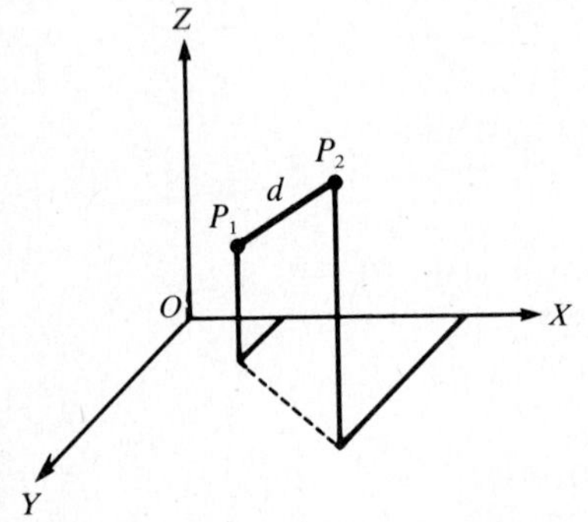

Figure 15-1. Symmetric equation of a line.

Consider a line segment through the points $P_1(x_1, y_1, z_1)$ and $P_2(x_2, y_2, z_2)$, as shown in Figure 15-1. From eq. (13-2) we know that

$$x_2 - x_1 = d\cos\alpha$$

$$y_2 - y_1 = d\cos\beta$$

$$z_2 - z_1 = d\cos\gamma$$

where $d = P_1P_2$ and α, β, γ are the direction angles of the line through P_1 and P_2. If we solve each of these equations for d and equate values, we get

$$\frac{x_2 - x_1}{\cos\alpha} = \frac{y_2 - y_1}{\cos\beta} = \frac{z_2 - z_1}{\cos\gamma}$$

which tells us that the projections of a line segment on the coordinate axes are proportional to the direction cosines of the line. When the points P_1 and P_2 are given, the direction cosines of the line joining them can be obtained. Likewise, if only one point (x_1, y_1, z_1) and the direction cosines are given, a line is determined. Therefore, if $P_2(x_2, y_2, z_2)$ is taken as the arbitrary point and written $P(x, y, z)$, we may write the equations of a straight line through the point (x_1, y_1, z_1)

LINE THROUGH A POINT

$$\frac{x - x_1}{\cos\alpha} = \frac{y - y_1}{\cos\beta} = \frac{z - z_1}{\cos\gamma} \qquad \textbf{(15-1)}$$

where the direction cosines of the line are known.

By replacing the direction cosines with direction numbers, we have

SYMMETRIC FORM OF A LINE

$$\frac{x - x_1}{a} = \frac{y - y_1}{b} = \frac{z - z_1}{c} \qquad \textbf{(15-2)}$$

which is the **symmetric form** of the equations of a straight line.

These equations may be written as the equations of three planes—but they are not independent, since any two may be combined to give the equation of the third plane. Because the coordinates of every point on the line must satisfy each of these three equations, each plane contains the line and is perpendicular to one of the coordinate axes. These planes are called the **projecting planes** of the line.

EXAMPLE 15-1: Find the equations of the line that passes through the point $(1, 3, 5)$ with $\alpha = 30°$, $\beta = 45°$, and $\gamma = 60°$.

Solution: Recalling from trigonometry that $\cos 30° = \sqrt{3}/2$, $\cos 45° = \sqrt{2}/2$, and $\cos 60° = 1/2$, we can write the equations of the line by eq. (15-1):

$$\frac{x - x_1}{\cos\alpha} = \frac{y - y_1}{\cos\beta} = \frac{z - z_1}{\cos\gamma}$$

$$\frac{x - 1}{\sqrt{3}/2} = \frac{y - 3}{\sqrt{2}/2} = \frac{z - 5}{1/2}$$

$$\frac{x - 1}{\sqrt{3}} = \frac{y - 3}{\sqrt{2}} = \frac{z - 5}{1}$$

EXAMPLE 15-2: A line with direction numbers 2, -3, and 4 passes through the point $(-1, 4, 3)$. Write its equations and find its direction angles.

Solution: Since we know the direction numbers, we can write the equations of the line in symmetric form by eq. (15-2):

$$\frac{x - x_1}{a} = \frac{y - y_1}{b} = \frac{z - z_1}{c}$$

$$\frac{x + 1}{2} = \frac{y - 4}{-3} = \frac{z - 3}{4}$$

Then we can find the direction angles from eq. (13-5):

$\cos\alpha = \frac{a}{d} = \frac{2}{\sqrt{2^2 + (-3)^2 + 4^2}}$	$\cos\beta = \frac{b}{d}$	$\cos\gamma = \frac{c}{d}$
$= \frac{2}{\sqrt{29}}$ or $\frac{-2}{\sqrt{29}}$	$= \frac{-3}{\sqrt{29}}$ or $\frac{3}{\sqrt{29}}$	$= \frac{4}{\sqrt{29}}$ or $\frac{-4}{\sqrt{29}}$
so $\alpha = \arccos\left(\frac{2}{\sqrt{29}}\right) \cong 68.2°$	so $\beta = \arccos\left(\frac{-3}{\sqrt{29}}\right) \cong 123.9°$	so $\gamma = \arccos\left(\frac{4}{\sqrt{29}}\right) \cong 42.0°$
or $\alpha = \arccos\left(\frac{-2}{\sqrt{29}}\right) \cong 111.8°$	or $\beta = \arccos\left(\frac{3}{\sqrt{29}}\right) \cong 56.1°$	or $\gamma = \arccos\left(\frac{-4}{\sqrt{29}}\right) \cong 138.0°$

15-2. Two-Point Form of a Line

If a straight line is determined by two points $P_1(x_1, y_1, z_1)$ and $P_2(x_2, y_2, z_2)$, we can write the equations of the line through these two points by using eq. (15-2):

TWO-POINT FORM OF A LINE

$$\frac{x - x_1}{x_2 - x_1} = \frac{y - y_1}{y_2 - y_1} = \frac{z - z_1}{z_2 - z_1} \qquad \textbf{(15-3)}$$

EXAMPLE 15-3: Find the equations of the line through the points $(3, 4, 5)$ and $(5, -2, 3)$.

Solution: Substituting these coordinates into the two-point form (eq. 15-3), we have

$$\frac{x - 3}{2} = \frac{y - 4}{-6} = \frac{z - 5}{-2} \quad \text{or} \quad \frac{x - 5}{-2} = \frac{y + 2}{6} = \frac{z - 3}{2}$$

depending upon which point we select as P_1.

EXAMPLE 15-4: Find the equations of the line through the points $(-5, 3, 0)$ and $(2, -4, 2)$.

Solution: Using first $(-5, 3, 0)$ and then $(2, -4, 2)$ as the point (x_1, y_1, z_1) in eq. (15-3), we have either

$$\frac{x+5}{7} = \frac{y-3}{-7} = \frac{z}{2} \qquad \text{or} \qquad \frac{x-2}{-7} = \frac{y+4}{7} = \frac{z-2}{-2}$$

The alternate answers give the same projecting planes.

15-3. General Equations of a Line

A straight line is determined when two planes intersect in space. If

$$A_1x + B_1y + C_1z + D_1 = 0 \qquad \text{and} \qquad A_2x + B_2y + C_2z + D_2 = 0$$

are the equations of two intersecting planes, any point whose coordinates satisfy both equations is a point on the line determined by the two planes. Conversely, the coordinates of any point on the line will satisfy both equations.

- The equations of two intersecting planes may be considered as the equations of a line.

The general equation of a line may be reduced to the symmetric form by eliminating first one variable, say x, and so obtaining a projecting plane in the other two variables; and then by eliminating a second variable, say y, and so obtaining another projecting plane in x and z. If the two resulting equations are solved for z, the symmetric form may be obtained by equating these values of z.

EXAMPLE 15-5: Reduce the equations of the line $3x + 2y + 4z = -5$ and $x - y + 2z = 4$ to the symmetric form.

Solution: Solve the pair of equations simultaneously— first to eliminate y, then to eliminate x:

$$z = \frac{3-5x}{8} \qquad \text{and} \qquad z = \frac{5y+17}{2}$$

Equating these values of z, rearranging terms, and reducing, you get

$$\frac{-5x+3}{8} = \frac{5y+17}{2} = z$$

$$\frac{x-3/5}{-8/5} = \frac{y+17/5}{2/5} = \frac{z-0}{1}$$

$$\frac{x-3/5}{-8} = \frac{y+17/5}{2} = \frac{z-0}{5}$$

If you compare this relation with eq. (15-1), you'll see that the direction cosines of the line are proportional to the denominators; i.e., the denominators are direction numbers.

EXAMPLE 15-6: Reduce the equations of the line $x - y - z + 3 = 0$ and $2x + y + 2z - 1 = 0$ to symmetric form. Sketch the line.

Solution: Eliminate x, then y:

$$z = \frac{y-7/3}{-4/3} \qquad \text{and} \qquad z = \frac{x+2/3}{-1/3}$$

These two equations for z in terms of y and x are the projecting planes on the

YZ- and *XZ*-planes, respectively. Therefore the symmetric equations of the line are

$$\frac{x + 2/3}{-1/3} = \frac{y - 7/3}{-4/3} = \frac{z}{1}$$

In Figure 15-2, *AB* is the line, *ABFE* is the *YZ* projecting plane, *ABC* is the *XY* projecting plane, and *ABD* is the *XZ* projecting plane. (A projecting plane is simply one that contains the line and is perpendicular to one of the coordinate axes.)

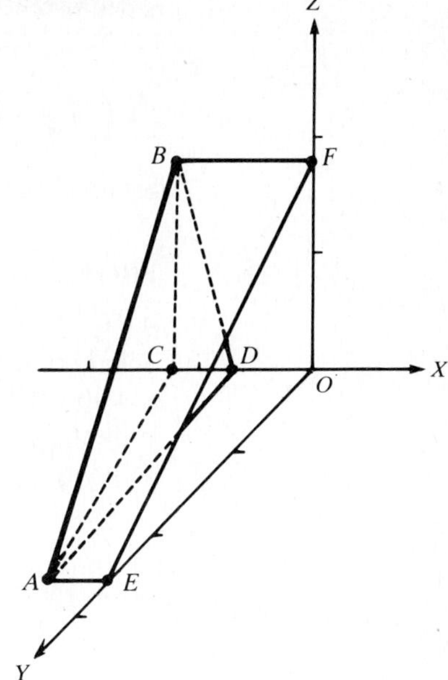

Figure 15-2

SUMMARY

1. A straight line is determined when two planes intersect in space.
2. The equations of a straight line determined by a given point and given direction cosines may be written as

$$\frac{x - x_1}{\cos\alpha} = \frac{y - y_1}{\cos\beta} = \frac{z - z_1}{\cos\gamma}$$

3. The symmetric form of the equations of a straight line (in which the direction cosines are replaced by the direction numbers) is

$$\frac{x - x_1}{a} = \frac{y - y_1}{b} = \frac{z - z_1}{c}$$

4. If a straight line is determined by two known points, its equations may be written in two-point form:

$$\frac{x - x_1}{x_2 - x_1} = \frac{y - y_1}{y_2 - y_1} = \frac{z - z_1}{z_2 - z_1}$$

5. The equations of the two planes that intersect to form a line may be considered as the equations of the line.
6. The general equations of a line (consisting of the equations of the two intersecting planes that form the line) may be reduced to the symmetric form by the following steps:
   - eliminating first one variable, say x, to obtain a projecting plane in the other two variables, y and z
   - eliminating a second variable, say y, to obtain another projecting plane in x and z
   - equating the resulting values, solved for the third variable, z

RAISE YOUR GRADES

Can you . . . ?

☑ find the equations of a line, given its direction cosines and the coordinates of a point in space through which it passes

☑ find the equations of a line, given its direction angles (α, β, γ) and the coordinates of a point in space through which it passes

☑ find the equations of a straight line, given the direction numbers of the line and a point through which it passes

☑ write the equations of a line that passes through two given points

☑ find the equations of the line of intersection of two intersecting planes; i.e., reduce the general equations of a line to symmetric form

SOLVED PROBLEMS

Symmetric Equations of a Line

PROBLEM 15-1 Find the equations of the line through $(2, 1, -3)$ whose direction angles are $\alpha = 90°$, $\beta = 30°$, and $\gamma = 60°$.

Solution: If $\alpha = 90°$, then $\cos\alpha = 0$, so the first member of eq. (15-1) can't be used. But since $\alpha = 90°$, the line is parallel to the YZ-plane. And since it passes through $(2, 1, -3)$, one of its projecting planes is $x = 2$. The second and third members of eq. (15-1) yield the equation of the second projecting plane:

$$\frac{y-1}{\cos 30°} = \frac{z+3}{\cos 60°}$$

$$\frac{y-1}{\sqrt{3}/2} = \frac{z+3}{1/2}$$

$$y - 1 = \sqrt{3}(z+3)$$

Therefore the desired equations are

$$x = 2 \qquad \text{and} \qquad y - 1 = \sqrt{3}(z+3)$$

PROBLEM 15-2 Find the equations of the line through $(1, 2, 3)$ that is parallel to the X-axis.

Solution: Here $\alpha = 0$ and $\beta = \gamma = 90°$. Accordingly, from eq. (15-1)

$$\frac{x-1}{1} = \frac{y-2}{0} = \frac{z-3}{0}$$

Of course, $(y-2)/0$ and $(z-3)/0$ are not defined, but you can interpret these expressions as indicating that one solution is $y = 2$, $z = 3$. Note that each of these planes contains the given point and that their intersection is parallel to the X-axis. Therefore any of the points $(a, 2, 3)$, where a is arbitrary, could have been used.

PROBLEM 15-3 A line has direction numbers $3, -5, 7$ and passes through $(4, -3, 6)$. Find its equations and the direction cosines of the line.

Solution: You can write the symmetric equations from eq. (15-2):

$$\frac{x-4}{3} = \frac{y+3}{-5} = \frac{z-6}{7}$$

and you can find the direction cosines from eq. (13-5):

$$\cos\alpha = \frac{a}{d} = \frac{3}{\sqrt{3^2 + (-5)^2 + 7^2}} = \frac{3}{\sqrt{83}}$$

$$\cos\beta = \frac{b}{d} = \frac{-5}{\sqrt{83}}$$

$$\cos\gamma = \frac{c}{d} = \frac{7}{\sqrt{83}}$$

PROBLEM 15-4 A line has direction numbers $1, -2, 6$ and passes through $(4, 5, -9)$. Find its equations and direction cosines.

Solution: From eq. (15-2) the equations of the line are

$$\frac{x-4}{1} = \frac{y-5}{-2} = \frac{z+9}{6}$$

and from eq. (13-5) the direction cosines are

$$\cos\alpha = \frac{1}{\sqrt{41}}, \qquad \cos\beta = \frac{-2}{\sqrt{41}}, \qquad \cos\gamma = \frac{6}{\sqrt{41}}$$

PROBLEM 15-5 Write the equations of the line through (1, 5, 5) and parallel to the line

$$\frac{x-3}{6} = \frac{y-1}{2} = \frac{z+7}{7}$$

Solution: From eq. (15-2), and using the coordinates of the given point, you have as numerators $x - 1$, $y - 5$, and $z - 5$. The denominators a, b, and c for the line you want will be the same as the direction numbers of the line it parallels—namely, 6, 2, and 7. Therefore the equations of the line are

$$\frac{x-1}{6} = \frac{y-5}{2} = \frac{z-5}{7}$$

Two-Point Form of a Line

PROBLEM 15-6 Write the equations of the line determined by $P_1(-2, 3, 1)$ and $P_2(4, 5, -9)$.

Solution: The two-point form (eq. 15-3) gives

$$\frac{x-x_1}{x_2-x_1} = \frac{y-y_1}{y_2-y_1} = \frac{z-z_1}{z_2-z_1}$$

$$\frac{x+2}{6} = \frac{y-3}{2} = \frac{z-1}{-10}$$

PROBLEM 15-7 Write the equations of the line determined by $P_1(1, 2, -3)$ and $P_2(6, -5, 1)$.

Solution: Substituting the coordinate values into eq. (15-3), you get

$$\frac{x-1}{5} = \frac{y-2}{-7} = \frac{z+3}{4}$$

General Equations of a Line

PROBLEM 15-8 Show that the lines

$$\frac{x-2}{1} = \frac{y-2}{-1} = \frac{z}{1} \quad \text{and} \quad \frac{x+6}{7} = \frac{y}{4} = \frac{z-1}{-3}$$

are perpendicular.

Solution: Two intersecting planes are perpendicular if

$$A_1A_2 + B_1B_2 + C_1C_2 = 0 \qquad \text{(eq. 14-5)}$$

And from the equations given for lines on the planes, the direction numbers are $A_1 = 1$, $B_1 = -1$, $C_1 = 1$, $A_2 = 7$, $B_2 = 4$, $C_2 = -3$. Substituting these values into eq. (14-5) shows that

$$(1)(7) + (-1)(4) + (1)(-3) = 0$$

$$7 - 4 - 3 = 0$$

$$0 = 0$$

and therefore the given lines, which are on perpendicular planes, must be perpendicular.

PROBLEM 15-9 Find the symmetric equations of the line formed by the intersection of the two planes $2x - 5y + z - 1 = 0$ and $x + y - 2z + 3 = 0$.

Solution: First eliminate y and z in turn:

$$\begin{array}{rl} 2x - 5y + z - 1 = 0 & 4x - 10y + 2z - 2 = 0 \\ 5x + 5y - 10z + 15 = 0 & x + y - 2z + 3 = 0 \\ \hline 7x - 9z + 14 = 0 & 5x - 9y + 1 = 0 \end{array}$$

Solving these for x, you find

$$7x = 9z - 14 = \frac{z - 14/9}{1/9} \qquad 5x = 9y - 1 = \frac{y - 1/9}{1/9}$$

$$x = \frac{z - 14/9}{7/9} \qquad x = \frac{y - 1/9}{5/9}$$

And the symmetric equations of the line are found by equating these results to x:

$$x = \frac{y - 1/9}{5/9} = \frac{z - 14/9}{7/9}$$

PROBLEM 15-10 Find the symmetric equations of the line of intersection of the planes $2x - 3y + 3z - 4 = 0$ and $x + 2y - z + 3 = 0$.

Solution: Eliminate z and y in turn, solve for x, and equate:

$$5x + 3y + 5 = 0 \qquad 7x + 3z + 1 = 0$$

$$x = \frac{3y + 5}{-5} = \frac{3z + 1}{-7}$$

$$\frac{x}{1} = \frac{y + 5/3}{-5/3} = \frac{z + 1/3}{-7/3}$$

$$\frac{x}{3} = \frac{y + 5/3}{-5} = \frac{z + 1/3}{-7}$$

Supplementary Exercises

PROBLEM 15-11 Find the equations of the line that **(a)** passes through $(2, -8, -6)$ and has direction numbers 3, 2, 4; **(b)** is perpendicular to the plane $7x + y - 6z + 1 = 0$ and passes through $(4, 2, -3)$.

PROBLEM 15-12 Write the equations of the line joining **(a)** $P_1(0, 0, 1)$ to $P_2(-1, 2, -2)$; **(b)** $P_1(4, 7, 3)$ to $P_2(2, 1, 6)$.

PROBLEM 15-13 Find the equations of the line that passes through the point $(3, 4, -5)$ and makes an angle of 120° with the X-axis and 60° with the Z-axis.

PROBLEM 15-14 Find the equations of the line that passes through the point $(1, -2, 3)$ and is perpendicular to the plane $6x + 7y - 5z = 10$.

PROBLEM 15-15 Reduce the equations of the line $x + 2y + 3z - 2 = 0$ and $3x + 2y - z - 4 = 0$ to the symmetric form and determine the direction cosines.

PROBLEM 15-16 Find the direction cosines for the line determined by $3x - 2y + z - 1 = 0$ and $x + y - 2z + 2 = 0$.

PROBLEM 15-17 Find the points at which the line determined by $x + 2y - 3z - 1 = 0$ and $3x - 2y + 5z - 3 = 0$ intersects the coordinate planes.

PROBLEM 15-18 Find the equations of the lines that pass through $(-3, 4, 1)$ with the direction numbers **(a)** 3, 1, 2; **(b)** -2, 3, 4.

PROBLEM 15-19 Find the equations of the line that passes through (4, 5, 6) and is parallel to the Z-axis.

PROBLEM 15-20 Reduce the equations of the line $3x + y - z = 7$ and $2x - y + 2z = 3$ to symmetric form.

Answers to Supplementary Exercises

15-11: **(a)** $\frac{x-2}{3} = \frac{y+8}{2} = \frac{z+6}{4}$

(b) $\frac{x-4}{7} = \frac{y-2}{1} = \frac{z+3}{-6}$

15-12: **(a)** $\frac{x}{-1} = \frac{y}{2} = \frac{z-1}{-3}$

(b) $\frac{x-4}{-2} = \frac{y-7}{-6} = \frac{z-3}{3}$

15-13: $\frac{x-3}{-1} = \frac{y-4}{2} = \frac{z+5}{1}$

15-14: $\frac{x-1}{6} = \frac{y+2}{7} = \frac{z-3}{-5}$

15-15: $\frac{x-1}{4} = \frac{y-1/2}{-5} = \frac{z-0}{2}$

$\frac{4}{3\sqrt{5}}, \frac{-5}{3\sqrt{5}}, \frac{2}{3\sqrt{5}}$

15-16: $\frac{3}{\sqrt{83}}, \frac{7}{\sqrt{83}}, \frac{5}{\sqrt{83}}$

15-17: XY: (1, 0, 0); YZ: $(0, -\frac{7}{2}, 2)$; XZ: (1, 0, 0)

15-18: **(a)** $\frac{x+3}{3} = \frac{y-4}{1} = \frac{z-1}{2}$

(b) $\frac{x+3}{-2} = \frac{y-4}{3} = \frac{z-1}{4}$

15-19: $x = 4$; $y = 5$

15-20: $\frac{x-2}{1} = \frac{y-1}{-8} = \frac{z}{-5}$

16 QUADRIC SURFACES

THIS CHAPTER IS ABOUT

- ☑ Traces
- ☑ The Cylinder
- ☑ The Cone
- ☑ The Sphere
- ☑ The Ellipsoid
- ☑ The Hyperboloid of One Sheet
- ☑ The Hyperboloid of Two Sheets
- ☑ The Elliptic Paraboloid
- ☑ The Hyperbolic Paraboloid

16-1. Traces

A **quadric surface** is defined by a second-degree equation. We already know that the general linear equation represents a plane and that two such equations determine a line. Now we can write a general equation of the second degree

$$Ax^2 + By^2 + Cz^2 + Dxy + Eyz + Fxz + Gx + Hy + Kz + L = 0$$

whose graph defines a quadric surface. Since any plane section of this surface is a *conic*, the quadric surface may also be called a **conicoid**.

In sketching a quadric surface, it is helpful to find the curves of its intersections with the coordinate planes and with planes parallel to the coordinate planes. Such curves are called **traces** of the surface: The *trace*, or *section*, made on a coordinate plane by a surface is obtained by setting the third coordinate in the given equation equal to zero. Thus, for example, the trace on the XZ-plane is found by setting $y = 0$. The following example illustrates the method of using traces.

EXAMPLE 16-1: The surface $4x^2 + y^2 = 8z$ is intersected by the planes **(a)** $y = 0$, **(b)** $x = 0$, and **(c)** $z = 2$. Find the trace of the surface on each plane.

Solution:

(a) Substituting $y = 0$ in the equation of the surface, we get the parabola $x^2 = 2z$, which is the curve, or the trace, of the surface in the XZ-plane. This parabola is shown in Figure 16-1a.

(b) If $x = 0$, we obtain the parabola $y^2 = 8z$, which is the curve of intersection, or trace, in the YZ-plane, as shown in Figure 16-1b.

(c) Letting $z = 2$, we have the ellipse $4x^2 + y^2 = 16$ as the curve of intersection of a plane parallel to the XY-plane and 2 units above it. This ellipse is shown in Figure 16-1c.

The complete surface is sketched by showing all these traces on the same reference frame, as in Figure 16-1c.

(a)

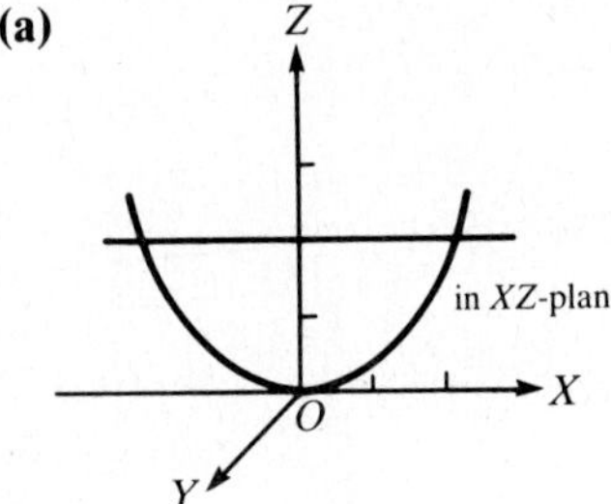

(b)

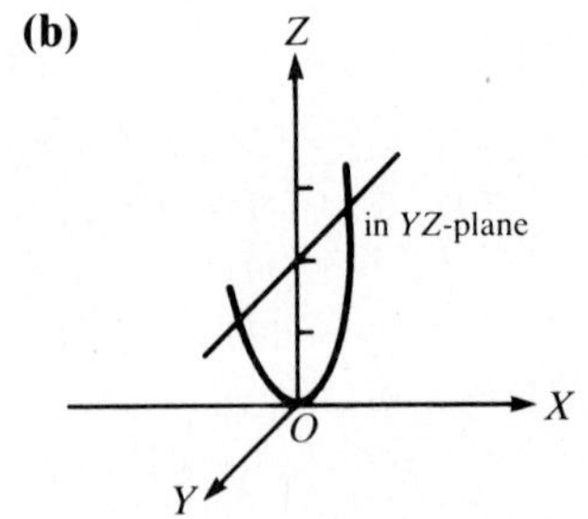

(c)

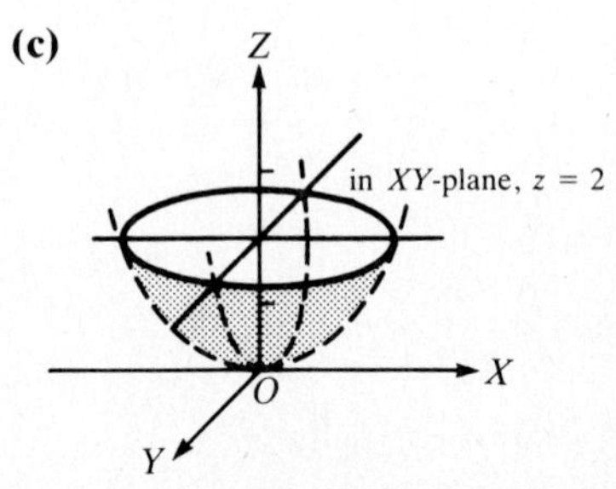

Figure 16-1

16-2. The Cylinder

- A **cylindrical surface** is generated by a straight line that moves so that it is always parallel to its original position and intersects a plane curve. The plane curve is called the *directrix*, and the moving line is called a *generator*, or *element*.

The solid bounded by the surface and any two parallel planes that cut all the elements is called a **cylinder**.

note: Now that we've made the distinction between a quadric surface and a solid, we're going to ignore it. Here—and throughout the chapter—we'll use the terms cylinder, cone, etc., to refer to the quadric surface only, not to the solid.

EXAMPLE 16-2: Find the equation of a right circular cylinder of radius a, such that the axis of the cylinder intersects the X-axis and is parallel to the Z-axis.

Solution: Consider a cylinder whose axis CD intersects the X-axis at the point C, as shown in Figure 16-2. Let $P(x, y, z)$ be any point on the cylindrical surface. Then, $ON = x$, $NM = y$, and $MP = z$. If DP is drawn perpendicular to CD, then $DP = CM = a$, which is the condition that the point P is on the cylinder. However, in the right triangle CNM,

$$(CM)^2 = (CN)^2 + (NM)^2$$

So, if we substitute $CM = a$, $CN = x - a$, and $NM = y$, we get the equation of the right circular cylinder:

$$a^2 = (x - a)^2 + y^2$$

CYLINDER or

$$x^2 + y^2 - 2ax = 0$$

The directrix of this cylinder is the circle $x^2 + y^2 - 2ax = 0$ in the XY-plane.

note: The equation of the cylinder contains only *two* variables: The third, "missing" variable has any and all values.

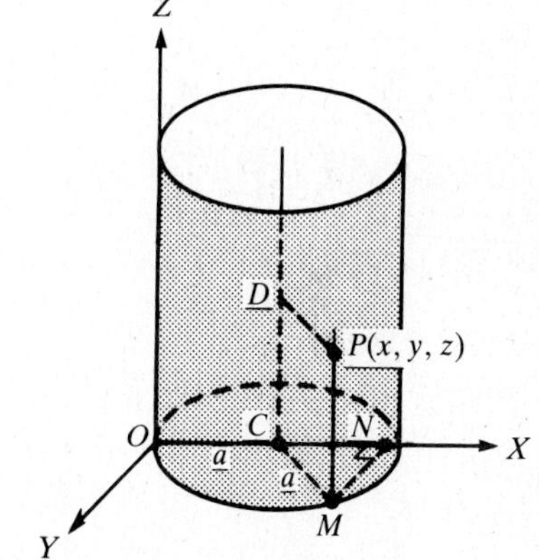

Figure 16-2. Cylinder: $x^2 + y^2 = 2ax$

16-3. The Cone

- A **conical surface** is generated by a line moving about a fixed point. The moving line is called the *generator* (or *generatrix*), and the fixed point is called the *vertex* of the conical surface.

The generator may be made to follow a directing curve (or directrix), a plane, or *skew* [a twisted curve, one that lies in more than one plane, as distinguished from a plane curve, which lies in only one plane].

A particular generator—or a position of the generator—is referred to as an *element* of the conical surface. The two similar portions of the cone separated by the vertex are called the *nappes* (see Figure 16-3). The solid bounded by one nappe and any plane that cuts all the elements is called a **cone** [see Chapter 8].

The equation of a cone has three variables, each of whose terms is of the second degree. The cone shown in Figure 16-3, for example, is represented by the standard equation

CONE

$$\frac{x^2}{a^2} + \frac{y^2}{b^2} - \frac{z^2}{c^2} = 0$$

where the vertex is at (0, 0, 0). Such a cone is called an **elliptic cone**, since every cross-section of the cone by a plane z = constant is an ellipse. The axis of this cone is the Z-axis.

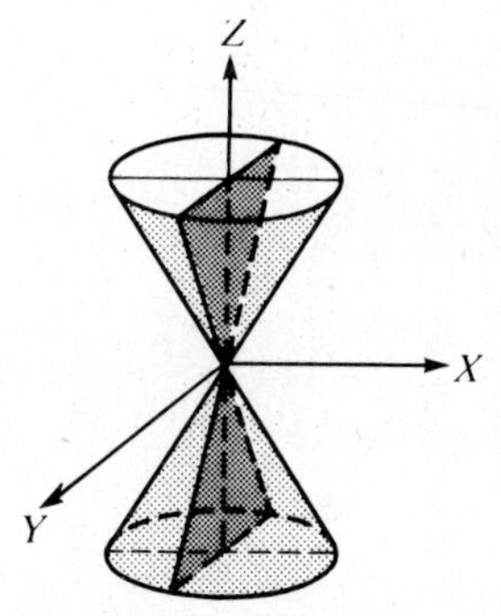

Figure 16-3. Cone: $\frac{x^2}{a^2} + \frac{y^2}{b^2} - \frac{z^2}{c^2} = 0$

EXAMPLE 16-3: Identify and describe the surface

$$4x^2 - 3y^2 + 12z^2 - 16x - 30y - 24z - 47 = 0$$

Solution: Completing the squares, we rewrite the equation in standard form:

$$4(x-2)^2 - 3(y+5)^2 + 12(z-1)^2 = 47 + 16 - 75 + 12$$

$$\frac{(x-2)^2}{3} - \frac{(y+5)^2}{4} + \frac{(z-1)^2}{1} = 0$$

This equation therefore represents a cone with vertex at $(2, -5, 1)$ and axis perpendicular to the XZ-plane.

16-4. The Sphere

- A **sphere** in the locus of a point that moves in such a way that it is always a constant distance from a fixed point. The fixed point is called the *center* of the sphere, and the fixed distance is called the *radius*.

To derive the equation of a sphere, let (h, k, l) denote the center and r the radius. Using the distance formula (from eq. 13-1), we have

SPHERE ($C = (h, k, l)$)

$$(x-h)^2 + (y-k)^2 + (z-l)^2 = r^2 \tag{16-1}$$

This equation is satisfied only by points on the sphere and is therefore the equation of the sphere with center (h, k, l). If the center is at the origin, then $h = k = l = 0$ and eq. (16-1) reduces to

SPHERE ($C = (0, 0, 0)$)

$$x^2 + y^2 + z^2 = r^2 \tag{16-2}$$

We obtain a general form of the equation of the sphere by expanding eq. (16-1) as follows:

SPHERE (general form)

$$x^2 + y^2 + z^2 + Ax + By + Cz + D = 0 \tag{16-3}$$

By completing the squares, we can transform this equation into

$$\left(x + \frac{A}{2}\right)^2 + \left(y + \frac{B}{2}\right)^2 + \left(z + \frac{C}{2}\right)^2 = \frac{A^2 + B^2 + C^2 - 4D}{4}$$

And by comparing this equation with eq. (16-1), we see that it represents a sphere with center $(-A/2, -B/2, -C/2)$ and radius $r = \frac{1}{2}\sqrt{A^2 + B^2 + C^2 - 4D}$. In order to have a *real sphere*, we must have $r > 0$, or $A^2 + B^2 + C^2 - 4D > 0$. If $r = 0$, the sphere is a *point sphere*. If $A^2 + B^2 + C^2 - 4D < 0$, there is *no locus*.

EXAMPLE 16-4: Find the equation of the sphere of radius 2/3 and center $(2, -3, 0)$.

Solution: In this case, $h = 2$, $k = -3$, $l = 0$, and $r = 2/3$. Substituting these values into eq. (16-1), we can write the equation of the sphere as

$$(x-2)^2 + (y+3)^2 + (z-0)^2 = \frac{4}{9}$$

Or, by simplifying, we can write the equation in the general form

$$9x^2 + 9y^2 + 9z^2 - 36x + 54y + 113 = 0$$

16-5. The Ellipsoid

The **ellipsoid** is a surface represented by an equation of the form

ELLIPSOID
$$\frac{x^2}{a^2} + \frac{y^2}{b^2} + \frac{z^2}{c^2} = 1 \qquad \textbf{(16-4)}$$

such that its traces are all ellipses. The ellipsoid is symmetric with respect to each coordinate plane. So, setting each of the variables equal to zero in turn, we find the trace equations of this ellipsoid to be

$$\frac{x^2}{a^2} + \frac{y^2}{b^2} = 1, \qquad \frac{x^2}{a^2} + \frac{z^2}{c^2} = 1, \qquad \frac{y^2}{b^2} + \frac{z^2}{c^2} = 1$$

XY-plane: $z = 0$ $\qquad$ XZ-plane: $y = 0$ $\qquad$ YZ-plane: $x = 0$

The traces are therefore all ellipses, as shown in Figure 16-4.

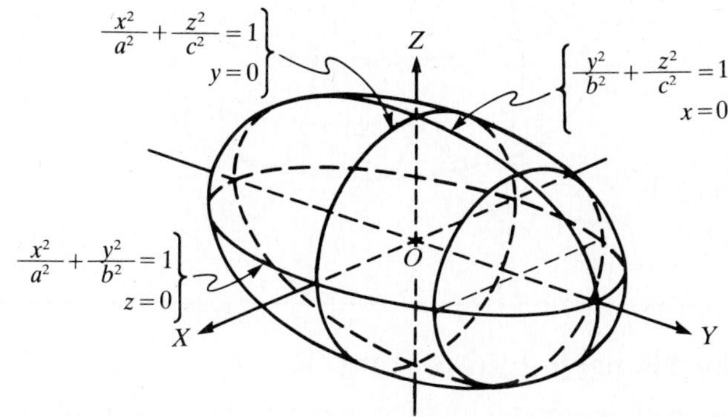

Figure 16-4. Ellipsoid: $\frac{x^2}{a^2} + \frac{y^2}{b^2} + \frac{z^2}{c^2} = 1$

Next we assign to y a definite value, $y = y_0$, such that $0 < y_0 < b$, and write the given equation in the form

$$\frac{x^2}{a^2} + \frac{z^2}{c^2} = 1 - \frac{{y_0}^2}{b^2}$$

This equation shows that sections made by planes parallel to the XZ-plane are also ellipses—and that the elliptic sections decrease in size as the intersecting plane moves farther from the XZ-plane, as Figure 16-4 illustrates. When the moving plane reaches a distance b from the XZ-plane, the equation of the section becomes simply

$$\frac{x^2}{a^2} + \frac{z^2}{c^2} = 0$$

and the section is therefore the point $(0, b, 0)$. We see then that each of the planes $y = b$ and $y = -b$ contains one point of the ellipsoid and that all other points of the surface lie between these planes. Elliptic sections can be found in a similar way for values of x between $-a$ and a, and for z between $-c$ and c.

note: When $a = b = c$ in the equation of the ellipsoid, the surface is a special case of the ellipsoid—a sphere.

EXAMPLE 16-5: Sketch the surface whose equation is $4x^2 + y^2 + 4z^2 = 16$.

Solution: Since replacing x by $-x$, y by $-y$, or z by $-z$ doesn't alter the equation, it is apparent that the surface is symmetric with respect to each of the coordinate planes. We next obtain and sketch the traces in each of the coordinate planes:

YZ-plane:	XZ-plane:	XY-plane:
$\dfrac{y^2}{16} + \dfrac{z^2}{4} = 1$	$x^2 + z^2 = 4$	$\dfrac{x^2}{4} + \dfrac{y^2}{16} = 1$
$x = 0$	$y = 0$	$z = 0$
Ellipse	Circle	Ellipse

Sketching these traces, we see that the whole surface is roughly that of a football, as shown in Figure 16-5.

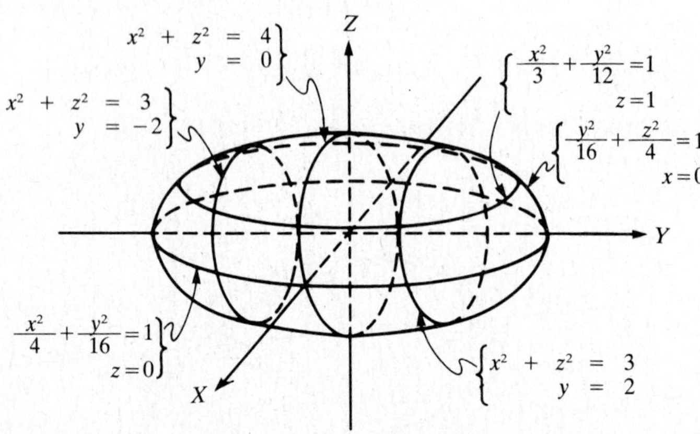

Figure 16-5. Ellipsoid: $4x^2 + y^2 + 4z^2 = 16$

16-6. The Hyperboloid of One Sheet

The **hyperboloid of one sheet** is a surface represented by an equation of the form

ONE-SHEET HYPERBOLOID

$$\frac{x^2}{a^2} + \frac{y^2}{b^2} - \frac{z^2}{c^2} = 1 \tag{16-5}$$

such that two of its sections are hyperbolas and one is an ellipse, as shown in Figure 16-6. Thus, in this hyperboloid, the sections parallel to the traces on the XZ- and YZ-planes are hyperbolas, and those parallel to and on the XY-plane are ellipses. The surface is symmetric with respect to each coordinate plane. The X- and Y-intercepts are $\pm a$ and $\pm b$, and there are no Z-intercepts. The surface is connected (one piece, or *sheet*), but unbounded.

The procedure for developing the locus of a hyperboloid of one sheet is illustrated in Example 16-6.

Figure 16-6. Hyperboloid of one sheet: $\dfrac{x^2}{a^2} + \dfrac{y^2}{b^2} - \dfrac{z^2}{c^2} = 1$

EXAMPLE 16-6: Draw the locus of the equation

$$\frac{x^2}{a^2} + \frac{y^2}{b^2} - \frac{z^2}{c^2} = 1$$

Solution: We know that the locus of this equation is a hyperboloid of one sheet (by eq. 16-5) and that the intercepts on the X-axis are $x = \pm a$, those on the Y-axis are $y = \pm b$, and those on the Z-axis are imaginary. Now we can use the method of traces.

(1) We find the traces on each of the coordinate planes by letting $x = 0$, $y = 0$, and $z = 0$, successively. Thus

for $x = 0$:	for $y = 0$:	for $z = 0$:
$\dfrac{y^2}{b^2} - \dfrac{z^2}{c^2} = 1$	$\dfrac{x^2}{a^2} - \dfrac{z^2}{c^2} = 1$	$\dfrac{x^2}{a^2} + \dfrac{y^2}{b^2} = 1$
Hyperbola	Hyperbola	Ellipse

so the hyperbola in the YZ-plane has transverse axis $2b$, the hyperbola in the XZ-plane has transverse axis $2a$, and the ellipse in the XY-plane has major axis $2a$ and minor axis $2b$.

(2) We pass a plane $z = k$ through the surface parallel to the XY-plane:

$$\frac{x^2}{a^2} + \frac{y^2}{b^2} = 1 + \frac{k^2}{c^2}$$

or

$$\frac{x^2}{(a^2/c^2)(c^2 + k^2)} + \frac{y^2}{(b^2/c^2)(c^2 + k^2)} = 1$$

which tells us that every section parallel to the XY-plane is an ellipse.

The surface shown in Figure 16-7 is the desired hyperboloid of one sheet.

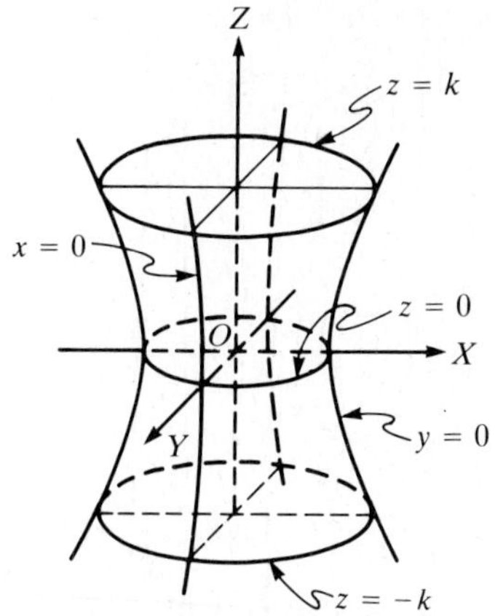

Figure 16-7

16-7. The Hyperboloid of Two Sheets

The **hyperboloid of two sheets** is a surface represented by an equation of the form

TWO-SHEET HYPERBOLOID

$$\frac{x^2}{a^2} - \frac{y^2}{b^2} - \frac{z^2}{c^2} = 1 \qquad \textbf{(16-6)}$$

This hyperboloid of two sheets (two, because the surface is made up of two pieces, or sheets) is shown in Figure 16-8, so we can see that one part is in the region $x \geq a$ and the other is in the region $x \leq -a$. The surface is symmetric with respect to each coordinate plane. The x-intercepts are $\pm a$, and there are no Y- or Z-intercepts. The real sections that are parallel to the YZ-plane are ellipses, and those parallel to or on the other coordinate planes are hyperbolas. The axis of this hyperboloid is the X-axis, its center is at the origin, and the points $(\pm a, 0, 0)$ are its vertices.

note: The positive term in the equation indicates which axis serves as the axis of the hyperboloid of two sheets.

The method of developing the locus of a hyperbola of two sheets is shown in Example 16-7.

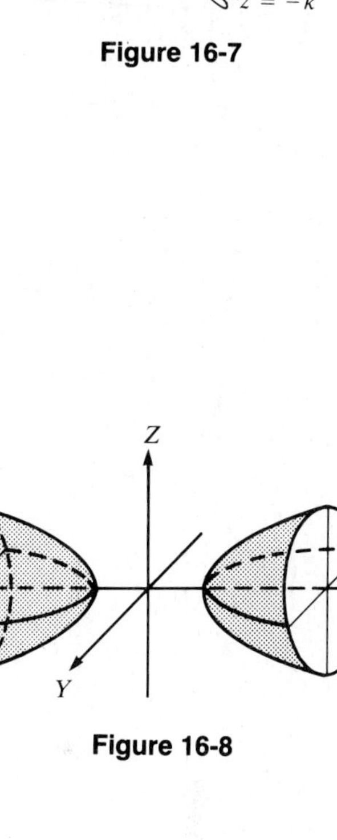

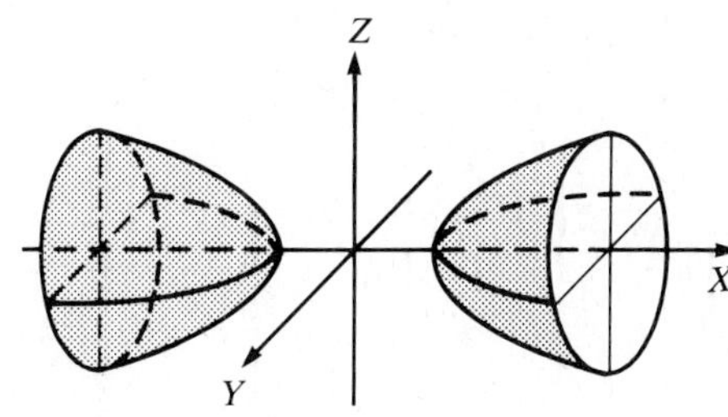

Figure 16-8

EXAMPLE 16-7: Draw the locus of the equation

$$\frac{z^2}{c^2} - \frac{x^2}{a^2} - \frac{y^2}{b^2} = 1$$

Solution: This equation represents a hyperboloid of two sheets that intersects the Z-axis at the points $z = \pm c$, while the X- and Y-intercepts are imaginary. Now we use the method of traces:

(1) The trace in the XZ-plane, found by letting $y = 0$, is the hyperbola whose equation is $z^2/c^2 - x^2/a^2 = 1$.

(2) The trace in the YZ-plane, where $x = 0$, is the hyperbola $z^2/c^2 - y^2/b^2 = 1$.

(3) Although there is no trace of this surface IN the XY-plane, we can find the trace in a plane PARALLEL TO the XY-plane if we let $z = k$. This gives us the equation of an ellipse:

$$\frac{x^2}{a^2(k^2/c^2 - 1)} + \frac{y^2}{b^2(k^2/c^2 - 1)} = 1$$

Notice that if $-c \leq k \leq c$, there is no real ellipse. If $k > c$ or $k < -c$, the traces are real ellipses that increase in size as the plane $z = k$ moves away from the XY-plane in either direction. Consequently, there is no part of the locus between the planes $z = c$ and $z = -c$; that is, the surface is divided into two parts, as shown in Figure 16-9.

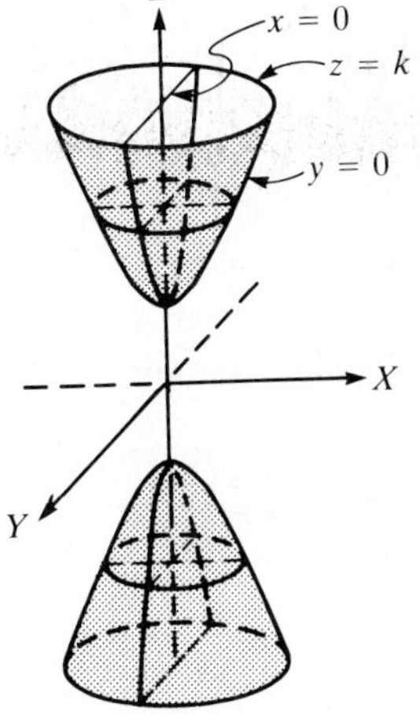

Figure 16-9. Hyperboloid of two sheets: $\frac{z^2}{c^2} - \frac{x^2}{a^2} - \frac{y^2}{c^2} = 1$

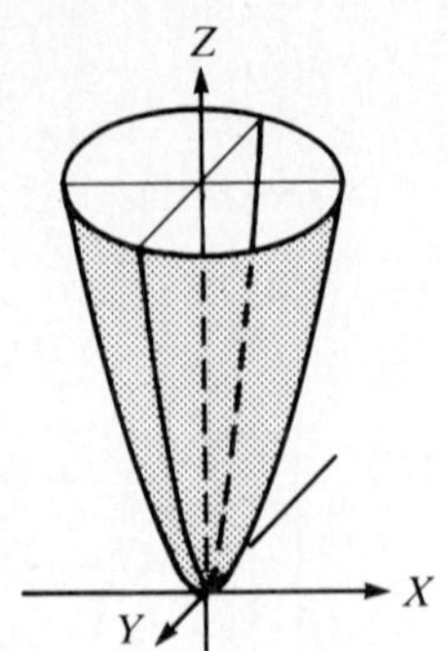

Figure 16-10. Elliptic paraboloid: $\frac{x^2}{a^2} + \frac{y^2}{b^2} = cz$

16-8. The Elliptic Paraboloid

The **elliptic paraboloid** is a surface represented by an equation of the form

ELLIPTIC PARABOLOID
$$\frac{x^2}{a^2} + \frac{y^2}{b^2} = cz \qquad \textbf{(16-7)}$$

In this paraboloid, the XY-trace, found by setting $z = 0$, is the origin. And if a, b, and c are positive constants, the surface (except for the origin) is above the XY-plane. A plane parallel to the XY-plane and cutting the surface makes an elliptic section that increases in size as the plane recedes from the origin. This surface can be represented as shown in Figure 16-10.

EXAMPLE 16-8: Identify the surface $5x^2 + 4z^2 - 10x - 140y - 32z + 69 = 0$.

Solution: Completing the squares, we get

$$5(x^2 - 2x + 1) + 4(z^2 - 8z + 16) = 5 + 64 - 69 + 140y$$
$$5(x - 1)^2 + 4(z - 4)^2 = 140y$$
$$\frac{(x - 1)^2}{4} + \frac{(z - 4)^2}{5} = 7y$$

This is the equation of an elliptic paraboloid with vertex at $(1, 0, 4)$ and axis parallel to the Y-axis.

16-9. The Hyperbolic Paraboloid

The **hyperbolic paraboloid** is a surface represented by an equation of the form

HYPERBOLIC PARABOLOID
$$\frac{x^2}{a^2} - \frac{y^2}{b^2} = cz \qquad \textbf{(16-8)}$$

In this hyperbolic paraboloid, the surface is symmetric with respect to the YZ- and XZ-planes. The XY-trace, where $z = 0$, is given by the pair of simultaneous equations

$$\frac{x^2}{a^2} - \frac{y^2}{b^2} = 0 \qquad \text{or} \qquad \left(\frac{x}{a} + \frac{y}{b}\right)\left(\frac{x}{a} - \frac{y}{b}\right) = 0$$

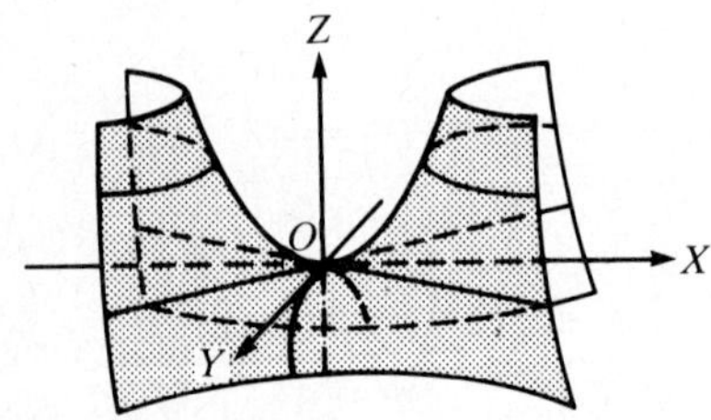

Figure 16-11. Hyperbolic paraboloid: $\frac{x^2}{a^2} - \frac{y^2}{b^2} = cz$

Therefore the XY-trace is a pair of lines intersecting at the origin. The section of a plane parallel to the XY-axis can be represented by the equation

$$\frac{x^2}{a^2} - \frac{y^2}{b^2} = cz_0$$

This is a hyperbola whose transverse axis is parallel to the Y-axis when z_0 is positive, and parallel to the X-axis when z_0 is negative. Sections parallel to the XZ- and the YZ-planes are parabolas. The whole surface of this hyperbolic paraboloid is saddle-shaped, as we see in Figure 16-11, where the *saddle point* is at the origin.

EXAMPLE 16-9: Describe the locus of $x^2/a^2 - y^2/b^2 = cz$, where $c > 0$.

Solution: This locus has zero intercepts on the X-, Y-, and Z-axes. The trace of the surface in the YZ-plane is the parabola $y^2 = -b^2cz$, with axis along the negative Z-axis. The trace in the XZ-plane is the parabola $x^2 = a^2cz$, whose axis is the positive Z-axis. In the XY-plane, the trace consists of two intersecting lines, $x/a + y/b = 0$ and $x/a - y/b = 0$.

The plane $z = k$ cuts the surface in the hyperbola $x^2/a^2 - y^2/b^2 = kc$. If $k < 0$, the transverse axis is parallel to the X-axis; and if $k > 0$, the transverse axis is parallel to the Y-axis. Also, the cross-section (saddle point) made by a plane parallel to the YZ-plane is a parabola that has a constant latus rectum and has its vertex on the boundary parabola in the XZ-plane. This surface is therefore a hyperbolic paraboloid, similar to that shown in Figure 16-11.

SUMMARY

1. A quadric surface is defined by a second-degree equation whose general form is $Ax^2 + By^2 + Cz^2 + Dxy + Eyz + Fxz + Gx + Hy + Kz + L = 0$.
2. The intersection of a surface with (or its projection upon) a coordinate plane is called a trace. Traces—which are found by setting the variables x, y, and z alternately equal to zero in the equation of the surface—are used in sketching the locus of a surface.
3. The standard equations for the quadric surfaces are as follows:

Cylinder: $x^2 + y^2 - 2ax = 0$

Cone: $\dfrac{x^2}{a^2} + \dfrac{y^2}{b^2} - \dfrac{z^2}{c^2} = 0$

Sphere: $x^2 + y^2 + z^2 = r^2$

Ellipsoid: $\dfrac{x^2}{a^2} + \dfrac{y^2}{b^2} + \dfrac{z^2}{c^2} = 1$

Hyperboloid of one sheet: $\dfrac{x^2}{a^2} + \dfrac{y^2}{b^2} - \dfrac{z^2}{c^2} = 1$

Hyperboloid of two sheets: $\dfrac{x^2}{a^2} - \dfrac{y^2}{b^2} - \dfrac{z^2}{c^2} = 1$

Elliptic paraboloid: $\dfrac{x^2}{a^2} + \dfrac{y^2}{b^2} = cz$

Hyperbolic paraboloid: $\dfrac{x^2}{a^2} - \dfrac{y^2}{b^2} = cz$

RAISE YOUR GRADES

Can you . . .?

☑ find the traces of a quadric surface and sketch its locus, given its equation

☑ identify and describe a quadric surface, given its equation in general form

☑ find the equation of a sphere, given its radius and the location of its center

☑ apply the tests for symmetry to quadric surface equations as an aid in sketching the locus

SOLVED PROBLEMS

Traces

PROBLEM 16-1 Given the equation of the surface $x^2 + 3y^2 + z^2 - 2x + 7y + 4z - 4 = 0$, find the equation of the trace on the XZ-plane and identify the trace on the plane $y = -1$.

Solution: Setting $y = 0$, you get

$$x^2 + z^2 - 2x + 4z - 4 = 0$$

as the equation of the trace on the XZ-plane. To find the trace on the $y = -1$ plane (the plane lying 1 unit behind the XZ-plane), first substitute $y = -1$ in the given equation:

$$x^2 + 3(-1)^2 + z^2 - 2x + 7(-1) + 4z - 4 = 0$$
$$x^2 + z^2 - 2x + 4z = 8$$

then complete the squares:

$$(x^2 - 2x + 1) + (z^2 + 4z + 4) = 8 + 1 + 4$$
$$(x - 1)^2 + (z + 2)^2 = 13$$

So the trace on the plane $y = -1$ is a circle.

PROBLEM 16-2 Determine the intercepts of the surface $x^2 + y^2 + x + 2z - 5 = 0$.

Solution: To obtain the intercepts on any one of the coordinate axes in a three-dimensional system, you set the other two coordinates equal to zero in the given equation and solve for the third variable. Thus

if $x = y = 0$:

$$2z - 5 = 0$$
$$z = \frac{5}{2}$$

if $x = z = 0$:

$$y^2 - 5 = 0$$
$$y = \pm\sqrt{5}$$

if $y = z = 0$:

$$x^2 + x - 5 = 0$$
$$x = \frac{-1 \pm \sqrt{21}}{2}$$

So the X-intercepts are $(-1 \pm \sqrt{21})/2$, the Y-intercepts are $\pm\sqrt{5}$, and the Z-intercept is $5/2$.

The Cylinder

PROBLEM 16-3 Identify and describe the surface whose equation is $y^2 = 4ax$.

Solution: In the XY-plane the equation $y^2 = 4ax$ represents a parabola whose vertex is at the origin (see Chapter 5). Thus if $Q(x, y, 0)$ represents any point of the parabola $y^2 = 4ax$, the coordinates (x, y, z) of the point P (in a plane parallel to the XY-plane) will also satisfy the equation and z may have any value, as shown in Figure 16-12. This means that any point on the line through Q parallel to the Z-axis will lie on the locus. Therefore all lines that pass through points on the parabola and are parallel to the Z-axis will lie on the surface represented by the equation $y^2 = 4ax$. And since this surface is generated by a line that moves so as to be parallel to its original position, the surface is called a **parabolic cylinder** and the given parabola is its directrix.

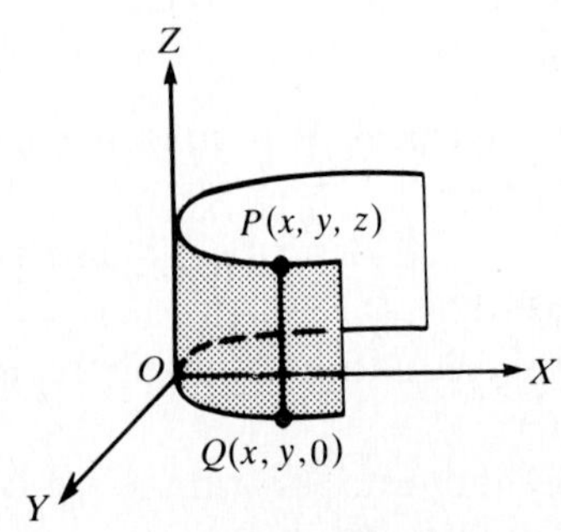

Figure 16-12

PROBLEM 16-4 Sketch the surface

$$\frac{x^2}{a^2} + \frac{y^2}{b^2} = 1$$

Solution: Since the third variable z is missing, this equation must represent a cylinder. And since the directrix of this cylinder is the ellipse $x^2/a^2 + y^2/b^2 = 1$ in the XY-plane, the cylinder must be an **elliptic cylinder** perpendicular to the XY-plane, as shown in Figure 16-13.

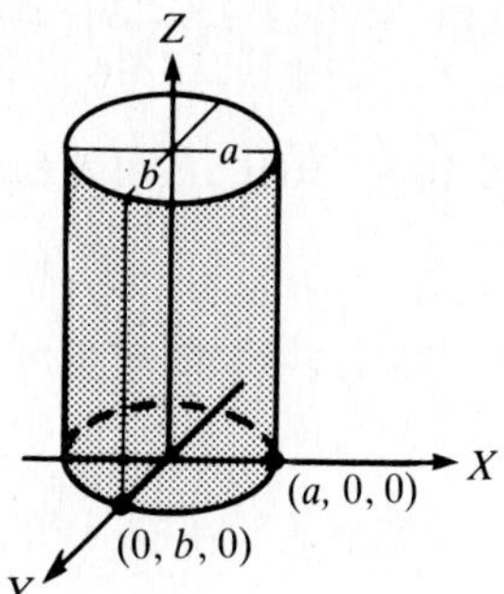

Figure 16-13

The Cone

PROBLEM 16-5 Identify the locus of a point $P(x, y, z)$ that moves so that the sum of the squares of its distances from the XY- and XZ-planes equals the square of its distance from the YZ-plane.

Solution: Writing the given information symbolically, you get $z^2 + y^2 = x^2$, or $z^2 + y^2 - x^2 = 0$, which is the equation of a cone with vertex at the origin and axis coincident with the X-axis.

PROBLEM 16-6 A point $P(x, y, z)$ moves so that its distance from the Z-axis is 4 times its distance from the X-axis. Find the locus.

Solution: From the data given, you have

$$\sqrt{x^2 + y^2} = 4\sqrt{y^2 + z^2}$$

$$x^2 + y^2 = 16y^2 + 16z^2$$

$$-x^2 + 15y^2 + 16z^2 = 0$$

This is the equation of a cone with vertex at the origin and axis coincident with the X-axis.

The Sphere

PROBLEM 16-7 Find the center and radius of the sphere whose equation is

$$4x^2 + 4y^2 + 4z^2 + 16x - 24y - 8z + 31 = 0$$

Solution: Write the equation in standard form by completing the squares in x and y:

$$4x^2 + 4y^2 + 4z^2 + 16x - 24y - 8z = -31$$

$$x^2 + y^2 + z^2 + 4x - 6y - 2z = -\frac{31}{4}$$

$$(x^2 + 4x + 4) + (y^2 - 6y + 9) + (z^2 - 2z + 1) = -\frac{31}{4} + 4 + 9 + 1$$

$$(x + 2)^2 + (y - 3)^2 + (z - 1)^2 = \left(\frac{5}{2}\right)^2$$

So the center is $(-2, 3, 1)$ and the radius is $r = 5/2$.

PROBLEM 16-8 Find the equation of the sphere with center at $(2, -3, 6)$ and radius 7.

Solution: Let $P(x, y, z)$ be any point on the sphere. Then, by the distance formula (eq. 13-1), you have

$$\sqrt{(x - 2)^2 + (y + 3)^2 + (z - 6)^2} = 7$$

$$(x - 2)^2 + (y + 3)^2 + (z - 6)^2 = 7^2$$

In this form (eq. 16-1) the center and radius are evident.

The Ellipsoid

PROBLEM 16-9 Identify and describe the quadric surface

$$2x^2 + 3y^2 + z^2 - 2x - 2y + 4z - 1 = 0$$

Solution: Complete the squares and simplify:

$$2x^2 + 3y^2 + z^2 - 2x - 2y + 4z = 1$$

$$2(x^2 - x + \tfrac{1}{4}) + 3(y^2 - \tfrac{2}{3}y + \tfrac{1}{9}) + (z^2 + 4z + 4) = 1 + \tfrac{1}{2} + \tfrac{1}{3} + 4$$

$$2(x - \tfrac{1}{2})^2 + 3(y - \tfrac{1}{3})^2 + (z + 2)^2 = 35/6$$

$$\frac{(x - \frac{1}{2})^2}{35/12} + \frac{(y - \frac{1}{3})^2}{35/18} + \frac{(z + 2)^2}{35/6} = 1$$

So the surface must be an ellipsoid with center at $(\frac{1}{2}, \frac{1}{3}, -2)$, because its equation has the form of eq. (16-4), which can be written in translated form as $(x - h)^2/a^2 + (y - k)^2/b^2 + (z - l)^2/c^2$.

PROBLEM 16-10 Show that line segment $P_1(-2, -2, -4)$, $P_2(8, -2, -4)$, line segment $Q_1(3, 0, -4)$, $Q_2(3, -4, -4)$, and line segment $R_1(3, -2, 0)$, $R_2(3, -2, -8)$ determine an ellipsoid with these line segments as axes. Write the equation of the ellipsoid.

Solution: From eq. (1-5), the midpoint of P_1P_2 is $(3, -2, -4)$. This point is also the midpoint of Q_1Q_2 and of R_1R_2; also P_1P_2, Q_1Q_2, and R_1R_2 are mutually perpendicular, as shown in Figure 16-14a. [Alternatively, the direction numbers of P_1P_2 are 10, 0, 0, and the direction numbers of Q_1Q_2 are 0, −4, 0. And since $(10)(0) + (0)(-4) + (0)(0) = 0$, the segments must be perpendicular.] Since these line segments are mutually perpendicular, they must determine an ellipsoid whose center is their mutual midpoint, as shown in Figure 16-14b. Thus, if the center of the ellipsoid is $(3, -2, -4)$, you can write its equation by eq. (16-4):

$$\frac{(x - 3)^2}{a^2} + \frac{(y + 2)^2}{b^2} + \frac{(z + 4)^2}{c^2} = \frac{(x - 3)^2}{5^2} + \frac{(y + 2)^2}{2^2} + \frac{(z + 4)^2}{4^2} = 1$$

where $2a = 10$ is the length of the major axis in the XY-plane, $2b = 4$ is the length of the minor axis in the XY-plane, and $2c = 8$ is the length of the major axis in the YZ-plane.

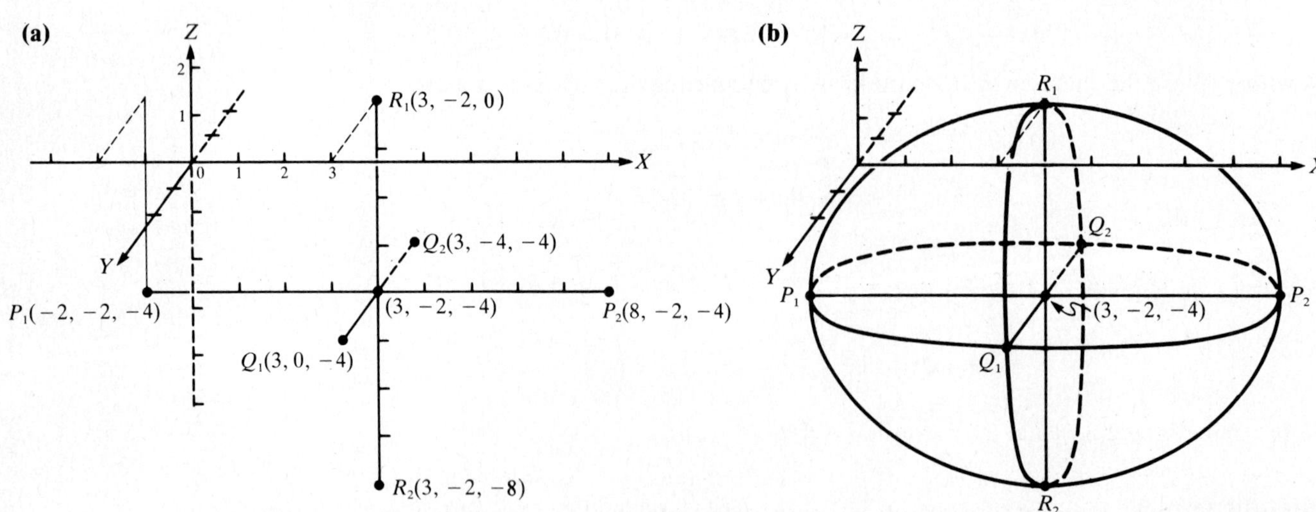

Figure 16-14

The Hyperboloid of One Sheet

PROBLEM 16-11 Find the equation of the surface obtained by revolving the hyperbola $x^2/4 - z^2/9 = 1$ about the Z-axis.

Solution: The equation for revolution about the Z-axis is

$$\frac{(\sqrt{x^2+y^2})^2}{4} - \frac{z^2}{9} = 1$$

So the surface is represented by

$$\frac{x^2}{2^2} + \frac{y^2}{2^2} - \frac{z^2}{3^2} = 1$$

This is a hyperboloid of one sheet, which you can see by comparing its equation with eq. (16-5): $x^2/a^2 + y^2/b^2 - z^2/c^2 = 1$.

PROBLEM 16-12 Describe the quadric surface $x^2 + 6x - y^2 + 2y - z^2 + 4z + 10 = 0$.

Solution: Completing the squares, you get the equation in standard form:

$$x^2 + 6x + 9 - (y^2 - 2y + 1) - (z^2 - 4z + 4) = -10 + 9 - 1 - 4$$

$$(x+3)^2 - (y-1)^2 - (z-2)^2 = -6$$

$$-\frac{(x+3)^2}{6} + \frac{(y-1)^2}{6} + \frac{(z-2)^2}{6} = 1$$

This is a hyperboloid of one sheet (see eq. 16-5) with center at $(-3, 1, 2)$ and axis parallel to the X-axis, so that the Y- and Z-intercepts are $1 \pm \sqrt{6}$ and $2 \pm \sqrt{6}$ and the X-intercepts are imaginary.

The Hyperboloid of Two Sheets

PROBLEM 16-13 Find the equation of the locus of a point $P(x, y, z)$ that moves so that its distance from $(1, 0, 0)$ equals its distance from $(-1, 0, 0)$ plus 1. Identify the surface.

Solution: From the given data you have

$$\sqrt{(x-1)^2 + y^2 + z^2} = \sqrt{(x+1)^2 + y^2 + z^2} + 1$$

$$x^2 - 2x + 1 + y^2 + z^2 = x^2 + 2x + 1 + y^2 + z^2 + 1 + 2\sqrt{(x+1)^2 + y^2 + z^2}$$

$$-4x - 1 = 2\sqrt{(x+1)^2 + y^2 + z^2}$$

So, squaring both sides, you can write

$$16x^2 + 8x + 1 = 4(x^2 + 2x + 1 + y^2 + z^2)$$

$$12x^2 - 4y^2 - 4z^2 = 3$$

$$\frac{x^2}{\frac{1}{4}} - \frac{y^2}{\frac{3}{4}} - \frac{z^2}{\frac{3}{4}} = 1$$

This is a hyperboloid of two sheets (see eq. 16-6) with center at the origin and X-axis as its transverse axis.

PROBLEM 16-14 Discuss the locus of the equation $x^2/9 - y^2/4 - z^2/16 = 1$.

Solution: Since x, y, and z can be replaced by their negatives without changing the value of the equation, this surface is symmetric about each of the coordinate axes and the origin. Its X-intercepts are ± 3, but it has no Y- or Z-intercepts. Sections of this surface by planes in or parallel to the XY- and XZ-planes are hyperbolas, $x^2/9 - y^2/4 = 1$ and $x^2/9 - z^2/16 = 1$, respectively. Sections by planes parallel to the YZ-plane, where $x = k$, are ellipses:

$$\frac{y^2}{4(k^2/9 - 1)} + \frac{z^2}{16(k^2/9 - 1)} = 1$$

Therefore the surface is a hyperboloid of two sheets with axis on the X-axis, center at the origin, and vertices $(\pm 3, 0, 0)$.

The Elliptic Paraboloid

PROBLEM 16-15 Identify and describe the surface represented by

$$\frac{(x-1)^2}{4} + \frac{(y-4)^2}{5} = 7z$$

Solution: This equation has the form of the standard equation (16-7), $x^2/a^2 + y^2/b^2 = cz$, so it must be an elliptic paraboloid with vertex at $(1, 4, 0)$ and axis parallel to the Z-axis.

PROBLEM 16-16 Identify and describe the surface $x^2 + z^2 - 3x - y + z - 1 = 0$.

Solution: Completing squares, you can write

$$(x - \tfrac{3}{2})^2 + (z + \tfrac{1}{2})^2 = y + \tfrac{7}{2}$$

which is in the standard form (16-7) of the equation of an elliptic paraboloid with vertex at $(\frac{3}{2}, -\frac{7}{2}, -\frac{1}{2})$, opening outward in the direction of the positive Y-axis.

The Hyperbolic Paraboloid

PROBLEM 16-17 Identify and describe the surface $y^2/4 - z^2/9 = 5x$.

Solution: By comparison with $x^2/a^2 - y^2/b^2 = cz$, the standard form (16-8), you see that this is a hyperbolic paraboloid with center at the origin and axis coincident with the X-axis.

PROBLEM 16-18 Identify and describe the surface $-x^2/4 + z^2/2 = 7y$.

Solution: By comparing this equation with the standard form (16-8), you recognize it as that of a hyperbolic paraboloid with center at the origin and axis coincident with the Y-axis.

Supplementary Exercises

PROBLEM 16-19 Find the general equation of the sphere determined by the four points $(1, 1, 1)$, $(-1, 0, 2)$, $(0, 4, 0)$, and $(-3, 1, 0)$.

PROBLEM 16-20 Find the center C and radius r of the sphere represented by $x^2 + y^2 + z^2 - 6x + 4z - 3 = 0$.

PROBLEM 16-21 Identify the surface $36x^2 + 9y^2 + 4z^2 - 72y + 72z + 432 = 0$.

PROBLEM 16-22 Identify the surface $6x^2 + 3y^2 + 2z^2 - 12x + 6y - 8z + 16 = 0$.

PROBLEM 16-23 Identify the surface $6x^2 + 6y^2 + 6z^2 - x + 17y + 3z - 7 = 0$.

PROBLEM 16-24 Identify the surface $4x^2 - y^2 + z^2 - 40x + 6z + 108 = 0$.

PROBLEM 16-25 Identify the surface $4x^2 + 12y^2 - 3z^2 + 48y + 6z + 44 = 0$.

PROBLEM 16-26 Identify the surface $x^2 + 4z^2 + 6x - 12y - 8z + 17 = 0$.

PROBLEM 16-27 Identify the surface $9x^2 - 4y^2 + 36z^2 + 36x + 8y + 68 = 0$.

PROBLEM 16-28 Identify the surface $6x^2 + 7y^2 - 3z^2 - 48x + 14y - 12z + 91 = 0$.

PROBLEM 16-29 Identify the surface $5y^2 - 6z^2 - 60x + 40y + 36z + 26 = 0$.

PROBLEM 16-30 Identify the surface $9x^2 + 4z^2 - 36 = 0$.

PROBLEM 16-31 Find the equations of the two planes that are parallel to the plane $x - 6y + 3z - 2 = 0$ and at a numerical distance of 3 units from it.

PROBLEM 16-32 Find the locus of a point $P(x, y, z)$ that moves so that the square of its distance from the Y-axis is 4 times its distance from the XY-plane.

PROBLEM 16-33 Find the locus of a point $P(x, y, z)$ that moves so that its distance from $(2, -3, 1)$ equals its distance from $(2, 3, 1)$ plus 4.

Answers to Supplementary Exercises

16-19: $15(x^2+y^2+z^2)+33x-63y-27z+12=0$

16-20: $C = (3, 0, -2)$; $r = 4$

16-21: ellipsoid: center at $(0, 4, -9)$

16-22: ellipsoid: center at $(1, -1, 2)$

16-23: sphere: center at $(\frac{1}{12}, -\frac{17}{12}, -\frac{1}{4})$

16-24: hyperboloid of one sheet: center at $(5, 0, -3)$, axis parallel to the Y-axis

16-25: hyperboloid of one sheet: center at $(0, -2, 1)$, axis parallel to the Z-axis

16-26: elliptic paraboloid: vertex at $(-3, 0, 1)$, axis parallel to the positive Y-axis

16-27: Hyperboloid of two sheets: center at $(-2, 1, 0)$, axis parallel to the Y-axis

16-28: Cone: vertex at $(4, -1, -2)$, axis parallel to the Z-axis

16-29: Hyperbolic paraboloid: saddle point at $(0, -4, 3)$

16-30: Elliptic cylinder: axis coincident with the Y-axis

16-31: $x - 6y + 3z - 2 \pm 3\sqrt{46} = 0$

16-32: $x^2 + z^2 = 4z$

16-33: $-\dfrac{(x-2)^2}{5} + \dfrac{y^2}{4} - \dfrac{(z-1)^2}{5} = 1$

FINAL EXAM (chapters 1–16)

CHAPTER 1

1. Find the distance d between the points (4, 1) and (3, 2).

2. Find the coordinates of the midpoint of the line segment (5, 8), (3, −2).

3. Find the tangent of the acute angle θ between the lines A and B if points (3, 7), (−6, 4) lie on line A and (−2, 8), (−7, 0) lie on line B.

CHAPTER 2

4. Identify the locus of the equation $x^2 + y^2 = r^2$. [See also Chapter 4.]

5. Discuss the symmetry of the curve whose equation is $x^2 + 4y^2 - 6 = 0$.

6. Find the equation of the set of all points $P(x, y)$ that are equidistant from $A(-4, 3)$ and $B(2, -2)$.

7. Translate axes to simplify the equation $y^2 - 6x - 10y + 19 = 0$.

CHAPTER 3

8. Find the equation of the line through (2, 1), (−3, 8).

9. Find the equation of the line with slope $m = 5$ and Y-intercept (0, 7).

10. Write the equation $3x - 4y + 2 = 0$ in normal form.

11. Find the distance from the line $6x - y - 3 = 0$ to the point (5, 2).

CHAPTER 4

12. Write the equation of the circle with center at (4, −3) and radius 8.

CHAPTER 5

13. Write the equation of the parabola whose directrix is $x = 3$ is and whose focus is (−3, 0).

CHAPTER 6

14. Find the center, vertices, and foci of the ellipse $x^2 + 4y^2 + 2x - 8y + 3 = 0$.

CHAPTER 7

15. Given the hyperbola

$$\frac{(x-3)^2}{25} - \frac{(y-1)^2}{36} = 1$$

write the equation of the conjugate hyperbola. Find the conjugate's center, vertices, foci, and eccentricity; write the equations of its asymptotes; and find the length of a latus rectum.

CHAPTER 8

16. Identify the conic $y^2 - 6y - 8x - 7 = 0$ and express the equation in standard form. Give the coordinates of the vertex, the focus, and the end points of the latus rectum. [See also Chapter 5.]

CHAPTER 9

17. Find the equation of the line tangent to the circle $(x - 5)^2 + (y + 2)^2 = 58$ at the point (−2, −5).

CHAPTER 10

18. Identify the conic $4x^2 + 12xy + 9y^2 - 2x - 3y - 20 = 0$ and simplify its equation.

19. Simplify $x^2 + xy + y^2 = 0$ by rotation of axes and identify the conic.

CHAPTER 11

20. Given the polar equation $r = 4/(1 + \sin\theta)$, identify the type of conic it represents and find the values of e and p.

21. Change $xy = 12$ to polar form.

CHAPTER 12

22. Give the rectangular (Cartesian) form of the equation for the curve represented by the parametric equations $x = t^2 - 1$ and $y = t^2$.

CHAPTER 13

23. Find the direction cosines of the line segment directed from point $P_1(4, -1, -3)$ to point $P_2(0, 1, 4)$.

24. Find $\cos\theta$ where θ is the acute angle between the line $P_1(-3, 1, -1)$, $P_2(1, 2, 0)$ and the line $P_3(0, 2, -1)$, $P_4(-3, -4, 1)$.

CHAPTER 14

25. Write the equation of the plane that

(**a**) is perpendicular to the line $\dfrac{x-1}{2} = \dfrac{y+3}{1} = \dfrac{z-5}{-3}$ and passes through point $(4, 2, -1)$

(**b**) is perpendicular to the plane $x - 3y + 3z - 8 = 0$ and passes through points $(0, 1, 0)$ and $(0, 0, 1)$.

26. Find the acute angle θ between the planes $x + y - z - 1 = 0$ and $3x + 2y + 3z + 4 = 0$.

CHAPTER 15

27. Write the symmetric form of the equations of the line determined by the intersection of the planes $x + 2y + z - 1 = 0$, $x - y - z + 2 = 0$.

28. Write the equation of the line joining $P_1(2, 3, 9)$, $P_2(-8, 5, 4)$.

CHAPTER 16

29. Identify the surface $3x^2 - 2y^2 + z^2 - 6x - 8y - 5 = 0$ and write its equation in standard form.

30. A point moves so that the difference between its distances from $(-2, 0, 0)$ and $(2, 0, 0)$ is unity. Find the equation of the locus and identify the surface.

Answers to Final Exam

1. $d = \sqrt{(x_2 - x_1)^2 + (y_2 - y_1)^2}$

$= \sqrt{(4-3)^2 + (1-2)^2} = \sqrt{2}$

2. $x = \dfrac{x_1 + x_2}{2} = \dfrac{5+3}{2} = 4$

$y = \dfrac{y_1 + y_2}{2} = \dfrac{8-2}{2} = 3$

3. $\tan\theta = \dfrac{m_B - m_A}{1 + m_B m_A} = \dfrac{\frac{8}{5} - \frac{1}{3}}{1 + (\frac{8}{5})(\frac{1}{3})} = \dfrac{19}{23}$

4. Closed curve—circle: radius r, center at $(0, 0)$

5. Since no change occurs in the equation when $-x$ and $-y$ are substituted for x and y, respectively, the curve is symmetric with respect to both axes and to the origin.

6. $\sqrt{(x+4)^2 + (y-3)^2} = \sqrt{(x-2)^2 + (y+2)^2}$

$12x - 10y + 17 = 0$

7. Complete the square on the y terms:

$$(y-5)^2 = 6(x+1)$$

Set $x' = x + 1$ and $y' = y - 5$: The simplified equation is

$$(y')^2 = 6x' \qquad \text{(a parabola)}$$

8. Use the two-point form of the equation:

$$\frac{y - y_1}{x - x_1} = \frac{y_1 - y_2}{x_1 - x_2}$$

$$\frac{y-1}{x-2} = \frac{1-8}{2+3}$$

$$-5y + 5 = 7x - 14$$

$$7x + 5y - 19 = 0$$

9. Use the slope-intercept form of the equation:

$$y = mx + b = 5x + 7$$

10. $$\frac{Ax + By + C}{-\sqrt{A^2 + B^2}} = \frac{3x - 4y + 2}{-5}$$

$$= -\frac{3x}{5} + \frac{4y}{5} - \frac{2}{5} = 0$$

11. Reduce the equation to normal form:

$$-\frac{6x}{\sqrt{37}} + \frac{y}{\sqrt{37}} + \frac{3}{\sqrt{37}} = 0$$

The distance from the line to (5, 2) is

$$d = \frac{Ax_1 + By_1 + C}{-\sqrt{A^2 + B^2}}$$

$$= -\left(\frac{6}{\sqrt{37}}\right)5 + \left(\frac{1}{\sqrt{37}}\right)2 + \frac{3}{\sqrt{37}} = -\frac{25}{\sqrt{37}}$$

12. $(x - h)^2 + (y - k)^2 = r^2$
$(x - 4)^2 + (y + 3)^2 = 64$

13. Here $a = -3$, and the equation is

$$y^2 = 4ax = -12x$$

14. Complete the squares:

$$x^2 + 2x + 1 + 4(y^2 - 2y + 1) = 1 + 4 - 3$$

$$\frac{(x + 1)^2}{2} + \frac{(y - 1)^2}{\frac{1}{2}} = 1$$

This is the standard form of an X-ellipse, $(x - h)^2/a^2 + (y - k)^2/b^2 = 1$, so $C(-1, 1)$; $V(-1+\sqrt{2}, 1)$, $V'(-1-\sqrt{2}, 1)$. Then $c = \frac{1}{2}\sqrt{6}$, so $F(-1 + \frac{1}{2}\sqrt{6}, 1)$, $F'(-1 - \frac{1}{2}\sqrt{6}, 1)$. [*Note:* For the ellipse, $c^2 = a^2 - b^2$.]

15. The conjugate hyperbola has the equation

$$-\frac{(x - 3)^2}{25} + \frac{(y - 1)^2}{36} = 1$$

for which $a = 6$ and $b = 5$, so $e = c/a = \sqrt{61}/6$. [*Note:* For the hyperbola, $c^2 = a^2 + b^2$.] Then $C(3, 1)$; $V(3, 7)$, $V'(3, -5)$; and $F(3, 1 + \sqrt{61})$, $F'(3, 1 - \sqrt{61})$. The equations of the asymptotes are $y - 1 = \pm\frac{6}{5}(x - 3)$, or $6x - 5y - 13 = 0$ and $6x + 5y - 23 = 0$. The length of the latus rectum is $|LR| = 2b^2/a = 2(25)/6 = 25/3$.

16. X-parabola: $(y - 3)^2 = 8(x + 2)$
$V(-2, 3)$; $F(0, 3)$; $L(0, 7)$, $R(0, -1)$

17. First note that $(-2, -5)$ is on the circle. Use the equation for the tangent at a point on a circle whose center is not at the origin:

$$(x - h)(x_1 - h) + (y - k)(y_1 - k) = r^2$$

$$(x - 5)(-2 - 5) + (y + 2)(-5 + 2) = 58$$

$$7x + 3y + 29 = 0$$

18. This equation represents a parabola since the discriminant $B^2 - 4AC = 0$. But the equation can be factored into

$$(2x + 3y - 5)(2x + 3y + 4) = 0$$

which represents two parallel lines, or a degenerate parabola.

19. The discriminant $B^2 - 4AC = -3 < 0$, so the conic is an ellipse. The center is at the origin since $h = k = 0$. Since $A = C$, rotate the axis through 45°:

$$\left(\frac{x'}{\sqrt{2}} - \frac{y'}{\sqrt{2}}\right)^2 + \left(\frac{x'}{\sqrt{2}} - \frac{y'}{\sqrt{2}}\right)\left(\frac{x'}{\sqrt{2}} + \frac{y'}{\sqrt{2}}\right) + \left(\frac{x'}{\sqrt{2}} + \frac{y'}{\sqrt{2}}\right)^2 = 0$$

$$3(x')^2 + (y')^2 = 0$$

20. Y-parabola: $e = 1$, $p = 4$

21. $$xy = 12$$

$$(r\cos\theta)(r\sin\theta) = 12$$

$$r^2 = \frac{12}{\sin\theta\cos\theta} = \frac{12}{\frac{1}{2}\sin 2\theta}$$

$$= 24\csc 2\theta$$

22. $x - y + 1 = 0$

23. Since $d = \sqrt{16 + 4 + 49} = \sqrt{69}$,

$$\cos\alpha = \frac{-4}{\sqrt{69}}, \cos\beta = \frac{2}{\sqrt{69}}, \cos\gamma = \frac{7}{\sqrt{69}}$$

24. Since

$$\cos\alpha_1 = \frac{4}{3\sqrt{2}}, \cos\beta_1 = \frac{1}{3\sqrt{2}}, \cos\gamma_1 = \frac{1}{3\sqrt{2}}$$

$$\cos\alpha_2 = \frac{-3}{7}, \cos\beta_2 = \frac{-6}{7}, \cos\gamma_2 = \frac{2}{7}$$

from eq. (13-8),

$$\cos\theta = \cos\alpha_1\cos\alpha_2 + \cos\beta_1\cos\beta_2 + \cos\gamma_1\cos\gamma_2$$

$$= -\frac{4}{7\sqrt{2}} - \frac{2}{7\sqrt{2}} + \frac{2}{21\sqrt{2}}$$

$$= \left|-\frac{16}{21\sqrt{2}}\right| = \frac{16}{21\sqrt{2}}$$

25. **(a)** $2x + y - 3z - 13 = 0$
(b) $y + z - 1 = 0$

26. $\cos\theta = \frac{1}{33}\sqrt{66}$

$\theta \cong 76°$

27. $\dfrac{x+1}{1} = \dfrac{y-1}{-2} = \dfrac{z-0}{3}$

28. $\dfrac{x-2}{-10} = \dfrac{y-3}{2} = \dfrac{z-9}{-5}$

29. The cone $\dfrac{(x-1)^2}{1/3} - \dfrac{(y+2)^2}{1/2} + \dfrac{z^2}{1} = 0$

30. $60x^2 - 4y^2 - 4z^2 = 15$

or

$$\frac{x^2}{1/4} - \frac{y^2}{15/4} - \frac{z^2}{15/4} = 1$$

hyperboloid of two sheets

APPENDIX A: SYMBOLS AND ABBREVIATIONS

$\angle$	angle	$>$	is greater than	sin	sine
$^\circ$	degree	$\geqslant$	is greater than or equal to	cos	cosine
$\lvert\ \rvert$	absolute value	$<$	is less than	tan	tangent
$\sim$	approximately	$\leqslant$	is less than or equal to	csc	cosecant
$=$	is equal to	$+$	plus	sec	secant
$\cong$	equals approximately	$-$	minus	cot	cotangent
$\neq$	is not equal to	$\pm$	plus or minus		

APPENDIX B: GREEK ALPHABET

Α	α	Alpha	Ι	ι	Iota	Ρ	ρ	Rho
Β	β	Beta	Κ	κ	Kappa	Σ	σ	Sigma
Γ	γ	Gamma	Λ	λ	Lambda	Τ	τ	Tau
Δ	δ	Delta	Μ	μ	Mu	Υ	υ	Upsilon
Ε	ε	Epsilon	Ν	ν	Nu	Φ	φ	Phi
Ζ	ζ	Zeta	Ξ	ξ	Xi	Χ	χ	Chi
Η	η	Eta	Ο	ο	Omicron	Ψ	ψ	Psi
Θ	θ	Theta	Π	π	Pi	Ω	ω	Omega

APPENDIX C: REVIEW OF ESSENTIAL MATHEMATICS

ALGEBRA

1. **Quadratic Equation**: The roots (solutions) of the quadratic equation $ax^2 + bx + c = 0$ are

$$x = \frac{-b \pm \sqrt{b^2 - 4ac}}{2a}$$

2. **Completing the Square**: The general solution of the quadratic equation is obtained by *completing the square.* First, we divide $ax^2 + bx + c = 0$ by a in order to reduce the coefficient of x^2 to 1:

$$x^2 + \frac{bx}{a} + \frac{c}{a} = 0 \qquad \text{or} \qquad x^2 + \frac{bx}{a} = -\frac{c}{a}$$

Next, we add the square of half the coefficient of x to each side of the equation:

$$x^2 + \frac{bx}{a} + \left(\frac{b}{2a}\right)^2 = \left(\frac{b}{2a}\right)^2 - \frac{c}{a}$$

This completes the square, since the left-hand side is now a perfect square, namely, $(x + b/2a)^2$. Then we take the square root of both sides,

$$x + \frac{b}{2a} = \pm\sqrt{\left(\frac{b}{2a}\right)^2 - \frac{c}{a}} = \pm\sqrt{\frac{b^2}{4a^2} - \frac{4ac}{4a^2}} = \pm\frac{\sqrt{b^2 - 4ac}}{2a}$$

Finally, we solve for x:

$$x = \frac{-b \pm \sqrt{b^2 - 4ac}}{2a}$$

The expression $b^2 - 4ac$ is called the **discriminant**:

- If $b^2 - 4ac > 0$, the roots are real and distinct.
- If $b^2 - 4ac = 0$, the roots are real and equal.
- If $b^2 - 4ac < 0$, the roots are imaginary.

3. **Logarithms:** If $a^b = x$ ($a \geq 0$, $a \neq 1$), then by definition,

$$\log_a x = b \qquad \text{and} \qquad \log_b a = \frac{1}{\log_a b}$$

To any base,

$$\log MN = \log M + \log N$$

$$\log M^A = A \log M$$

$$\log \frac{M}{N} = \log MN^{-1} = \log M - \log N$$

$$\log \sqrt[n]{M} = \log M^{1/n} = \frac{1}{n}\log M$$

4. **Determinants**: The left-hand member of the identity

$$\begin{vmatrix} a_1 & b_1 \\ a_2 & b_2 \end{vmatrix} = a_1 b_2 - a_2 b_1$$

is called a **determinant of the second order**. It is another—and often very useful—way of writing the algebraic quantity on the right. Similarly, we can write a determinant of the third order:

$$\begin{vmatrix} a_1 & b_1 & c_1 \\ a_2 & b_2 & c_2 \\ a_3 & b_3 & c_3 \end{vmatrix} = a_1\begin{vmatrix} b_2 & c_2 \\ b_3 & c_3 \end{vmatrix} - a_2\begin{vmatrix} b_1 & c_1 \\ b_3 & c_3 \end{vmatrix} + a_3\begin{vmatrix} b_1 & c_1 \\ b_2 & c_2 \end{vmatrix}$$

$$= a_1b_2c_3 - a_1b_3c_2 - a_2b_1c_3 + a_2b_3c_1 + a_3b_1c_2 - a_3b_2c_1$$

These two sets of determinants are said to be *expanded* into their equivalent algebraic forms.

5. Simultaneous Equations:

(a) For two linear equations in two unknowns,

$$a_1x + b_1y = c_1 \qquad \text{and} \qquad a_2x + b_2y = c_2$$

the solution in determinant form is

$$x = \frac{\begin{vmatrix} c_1 & b_1 \\ c_2 & b_2 \end{vmatrix}}{D}, \qquad y = \frac{\begin{vmatrix} a_1 & c_1 \\ a_2 & c_2 \end{vmatrix}}{D}, \qquad \text{where} \quad D = \begin{vmatrix} a_1 & b_1 \\ a_2 & b_2 \end{vmatrix} \neq 0$$

(b) For three linear equations in three unknowns,

$$a_1x + b_1y + c_1z = d_1$$

$$a_2x + b_2y + c_2z = d_2$$

$$a_3x + b_3y + c_3z = d_3$$

the solution in determinant form is

$$x = \frac{\begin{vmatrix} d_1 & b_1 & c_1 \\ d_2 & b_2 & c_2 \\ d_3 & b_3 & c_3 \end{vmatrix}}{D}, \qquad y = \frac{\begin{vmatrix} a_1 & d_1 & c_1 \\ a_2 & d_2 & c_2 \\ a_3 & d_3 & c_3 \end{vmatrix}}{D}, \qquad z = \frac{\begin{vmatrix} a_1 & b_1 & d_1 \\ a_2 & b_2 & d_2 \\ a_3 & b_3 & d_3 \end{vmatrix}}{D},$$

$$\text{where} \quad D = \begin{vmatrix} a_1 & b_1 & c_1 \\ a_2 & b_2 & c_2 \\ a_3 & b_3 & c_3 \end{vmatrix} \neq 0$$

(c) For one linear and one quadratic equation, each in two unknowns,

$$ax + by + c = 0$$

$$Ax^2 + Bxy + Cy^2 + Dx + Ey + F = 0$$

first solve the linear equation for one of the variables, say x, in terms of the other and substitute this value for x into the quadratic equation to get one quadratic equation in one variable (y) alone. Then solve the resulting quadratic equation by the quadratic formula (or completing the square), thus obtaining two possible values of y. Finally, substitute these values back into the linear equation to get two corresponding values of x.

GEOMETRY

6. Radian Measure:

(a) The measure of a central angle, subtended by an arc equal in length to the radius of the circle, is called a **radian**.

(b) If r is the radius of a circle and if θ, measured in radians, is the central angle subtended by an arc S, then

$$S = r\theta$$

(c) Relations between degree measure and radian measure:

$$360^\circ = 2\pi \text{ radians} = 1 \text{ revolution (or circumference)}$$

$$1^\circ \approx 0.017\,453 \text{ radian; } 1 \text{ radian} \approx 57.3^\circ$$

7. Mensuration Formulas: Let r denote radius; θ, a central angle in radians; S, an arc; h, altitude; b, length of base; and s, slant height. Then

	Circumference	Area	Volume
Circle	$2\pi r$	πr^2	
Triangle		$\frac{1}{2}bh$	
Trapezoid		$\frac{1}{2}(b_1 + b_2)h$	
Right circular cylinder		$2\pi rh$	$\pi r^2 h$
Right circular cone		πrs	$\frac{1}{3}\pi r^2 h$
Sphere		$4\pi r^2$	$\frac{4}{3}\pi r^3$

8. Pythagorean Theorem: The square of the hypotenuse of any right triangle is equal to the sum of the squares of the other two sides; that is,

$$c^2 = a^2 + b^2$$

TRIGONOMETRY

9. Definitions:

$$\sin\theta = \frac{y}{r} = \frac{\text{ordinate}}{\text{distance}} \qquad \csc\theta = \frac{r}{y} = \frac{\text{distance}}{\text{ordinate}}$$

$$\cos\theta = \frac{x}{r} = \frac{\text{abscissa}}{\text{distance}} \qquad \sec\theta = \frac{r}{x} = \frac{\text{distance}}{\text{abscissa}}$$

$$\tan\theta = \frac{y}{x} = \frac{\text{ordinate}}{\text{abscissa}} \qquad \cot\theta = \frac{x}{y} = \frac{\text{abscissa}}{\text{ordinate}}$$

10. Signs of the Trigonometric Functions:

Quadrant	sin	cos	tan	csc	sec	cot
I	+	+	+	+	+	+
II	+	−	−	+	−	−
III	−	−	+	−	−	+
IV	−	+	−	−	+	−

11. Functions of Special Angles:

θ	0°	30°	45°	60°	90°
$\sin\theta$	0	1/2	$\sqrt{2}/2$	$\sqrt{3}/2$	1
$\cos\theta$	1	$\sqrt{3}/2$	$\sqrt{2}/2$	1/2	0
$\tan\theta$	0	$\sqrt{3}/3$	1	$\sqrt{3}$	∞

12. Fundamental Identities:

$$\sin x = \frac{1}{\csc x} \qquad \cos x = \frac{1}{\sec x} \qquad \sin^2 x + \cos^2 x = 1$$

$$\tan x = \frac{1}{\cot x} \qquad \tan x = \frac{\sin x}{\cos x} \qquad 1 + \tan^2 x = \sec^2 x$$

$$1 + \cot^2 x = \csc^2 x$$

13. Functions of the Sum and Difference of Two Angles:

$$\sin(x \pm y) = \sin x \cos y \pm \cos x \sin y$$

$$\cos(x \pm y) = \cos x \cos y \mp \sin x \sin y$$

$$\tan(x \pm y) = \frac{\tan x \pm \tan y}{1 \mp \tan x \tan y}$$

14. Multiple-Angle Formulas:

$$\sin 2x = 2 \sin x \cos x \qquad \sin\frac{x}{2} = \sqrt{\frac{1 - \cos x}{2}}$$

$$\cos 2x = \cos^2 x - \sin^2 x \qquad \cos\frac{x}{2} = \sqrt{\frac{1 + \cos x}{2}}$$

$$= 2\cos^2 x - 1$$

$$= 1 - 2\sin^2 x$$

$$\tan 2x = \frac{2 \tan x}{1 - \tan^2 x} \qquad \tan\frac{x}{2} = \sqrt{\frac{1 - \cos x}{1 + \cos x}} = \frac{1 - \cos x}{\sin x} = \frac{\sin x}{1 + \cos x}$$

15. Sum and Product Formulas:

$$\sin x + \sin y = 2 \sin \tfrac{1}{2}(x + y) \cos \tfrac{1}{2}(x - y)$$

$$\sin x - \sin y = 2 \cos \tfrac{1}{2}(x + y) \sin \tfrac{1}{2}(x - y)$$

$$\cos x + \cos y = 2 \cos \tfrac{1}{2}(x + y) \cos \tfrac{1}{2}(x - y)$$

$$\cos x - \cos y = -2 \sin \tfrac{1}{2}(x + y) \sin \tfrac{1}{2}(x - y)$$

$$\sin x \sin y = \tfrac{1}{2}\cos(x - y) - \tfrac{1}{2}\cos(x + y)$$

$$\sin x \cos y = \tfrac{1}{2}\sin(x - y) + \tfrac{1}{2}\sin(x + y)$$

$$\cos x \cos y = \tfrac{1}{2}\cos(x - y) + \tfrac{1}{2}\cos(x + y)$$

16. Formulas for Plane Triangles: Let a, b, c be sides; A, B, C, opposite angles; and $s = (a + b + c)/2$, the semi-perimeter. Then

$$r = \sqrt{\frac{(s - a)(s - b)(s - c)}{s}}$$

is the radius of the inscribed circle. And if R is the radius of the circumscribed circle and K is the area,

Law of sines: $\dfrac{a}{\sin A} = \dfrac{b}{\sin B} = \dfrac{c}{\sin C} = 2R$

Law of cosines: $a^2 = b^2 + c^2 - 2bc \cos A$

Law of tangents: $\dfrac{a + b}{a - b} = \dfrac{\tan \frac{1}{2}(A + B)}{\tan \frac{1}{2}(A - B)}$

Tangent of half angle: $\tan \frac{1}{2}A = \dfrac{r}{s - a}$

Area: $\frac{1}{2}ab \sin C = \sqrt{s(s - a)(s - b)(s - c)} = rs = \dfrac{abc}{4R}$

INDEX

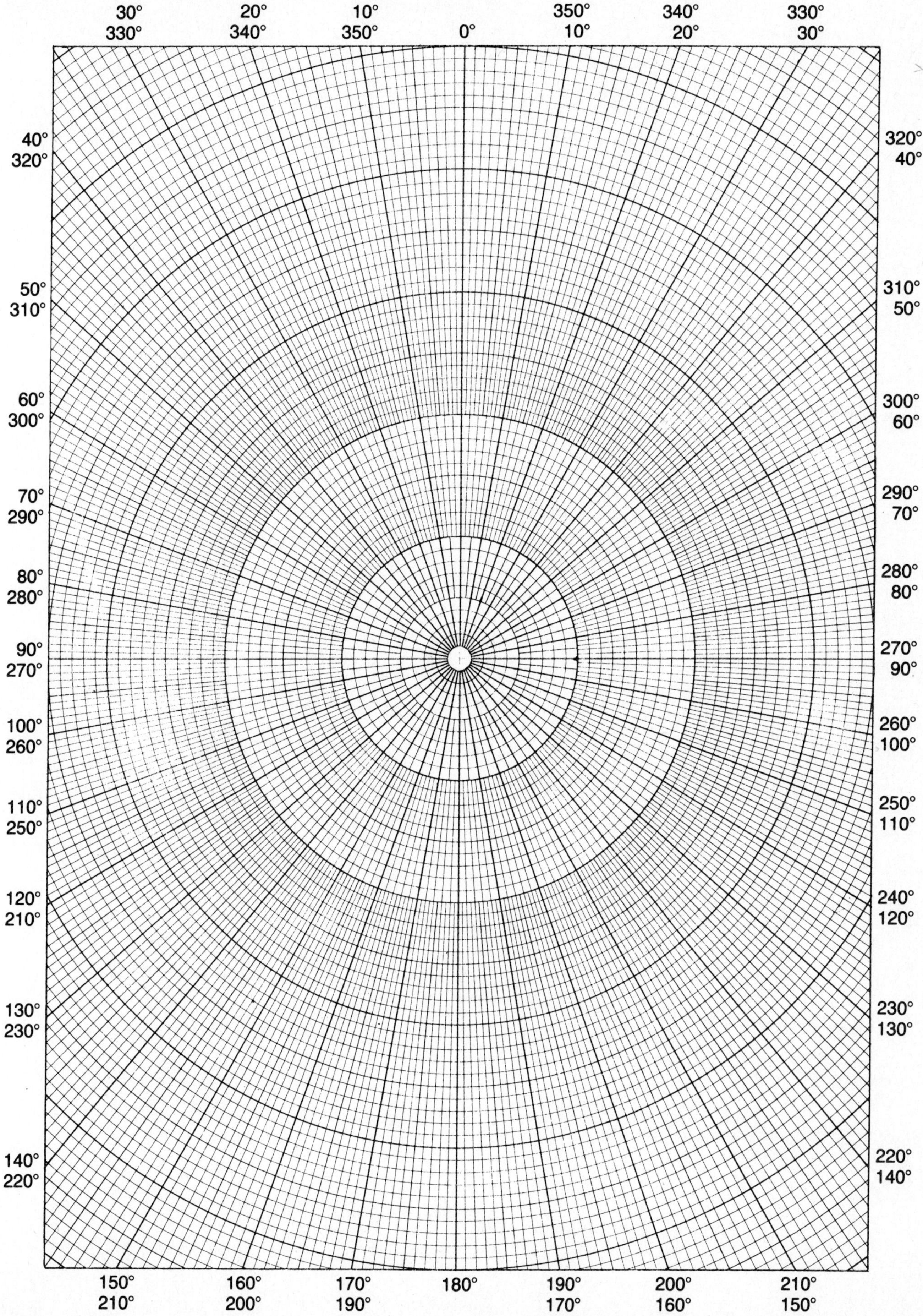

30°
330°
20°
340°
10°
350°
0°
350°
10°
340°
20°
330°
30°
40°
320°
320°
40°
50°
310°
310°
50°
60°
300°
300°
60°
70°
290°
290°
70°
80°
280°
280°
80°
90°
270°
270°
90°
100°
260°
260°
100°
110°
250°
250°
110°
120°
210°
240°
120°
130°
230°
230°
130°
140°
220°
220°
140°
150°
210°
160°
200°
170°
190°
180°
190°
170°
200°
160°
210°
150°

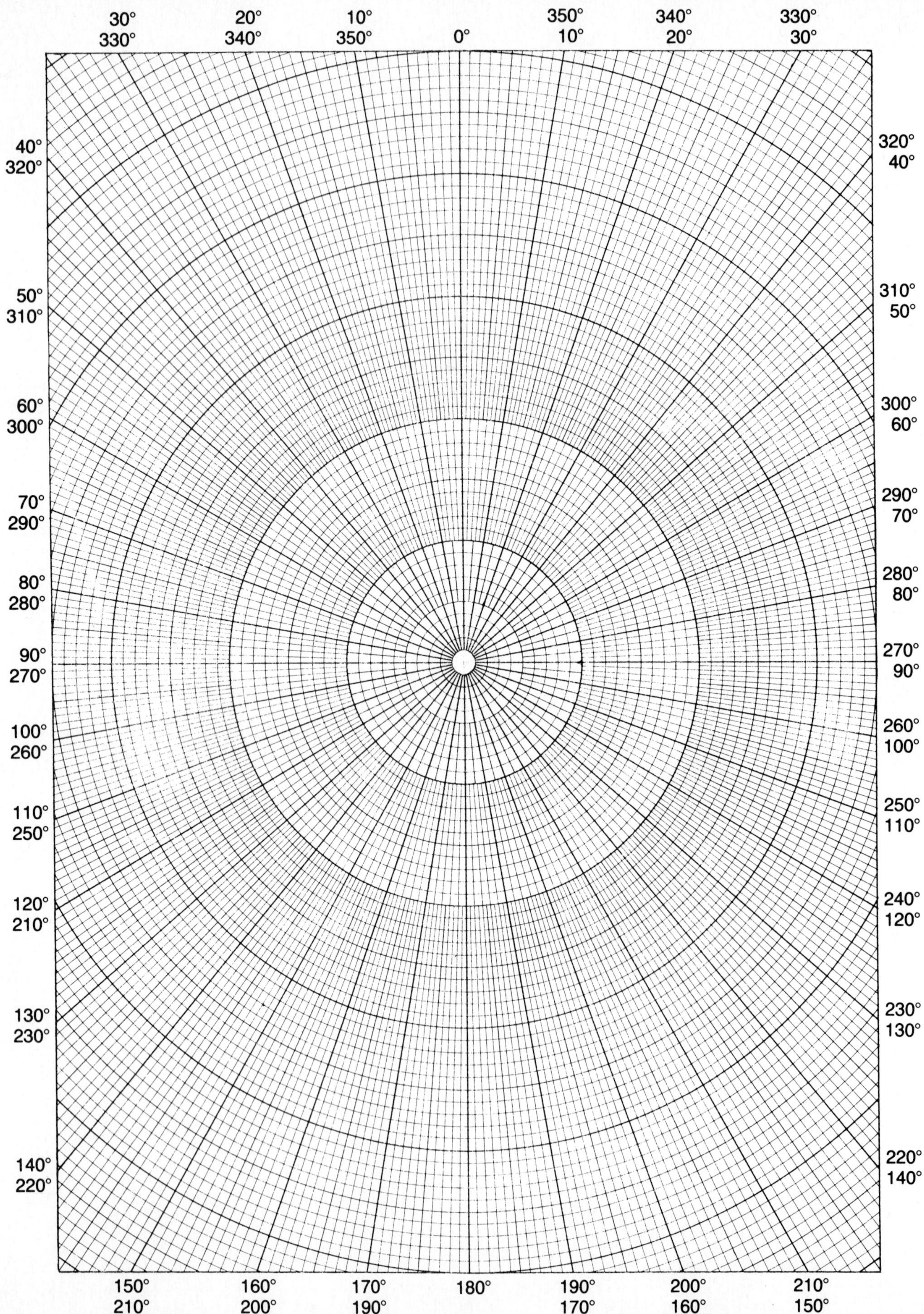
30° 330°
20° 340°
10° 350°
0°
350° 10°
340° 20°
330° 30°
40° 320°
50° 310°
60° 300°
70° 290°
80° 280°
90° 270°
100° 260°
110° 250°
120° 210°
130° 230°
140° 220°
320° 40°
310° 50°
300° 60°
290° 70°
280° 80°
270° 90°
260° 100°
250° 110°
240° 120°
230° 130°
220° 140°
150° 210°
160° 200°
170° 190°
180°
190° 170°
200° 160°
210° 150°

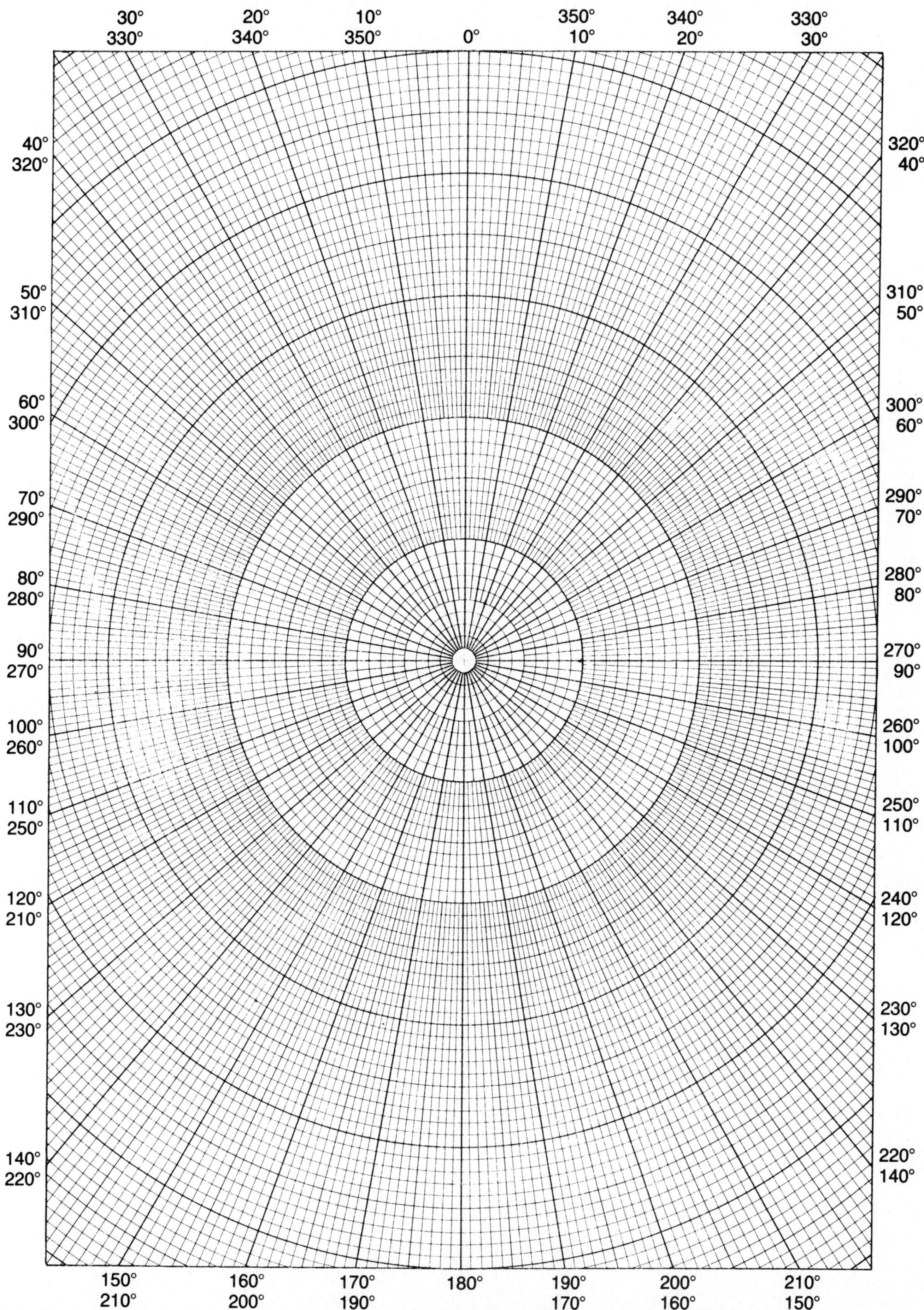
30° 330°
20° 340°
10° 350°
0°
350° 10°
340° 20°
330° 30°
40° 320°
50° 310°
60° 300°
70° 290°
80° 280°
90° 270°
100° 260°
110° 250°
120° 210°
130° 230°
140° 220°
320° 40°
310° 50°
300° 60°
290° 70°
280° 80°
270° 90°
260° 100°
250° 110°
240° 120°
230° 130°
220° 140°
150° 210°
160° 200°
170° 190°
180°
190° 170°
200° 160°
210° 150°

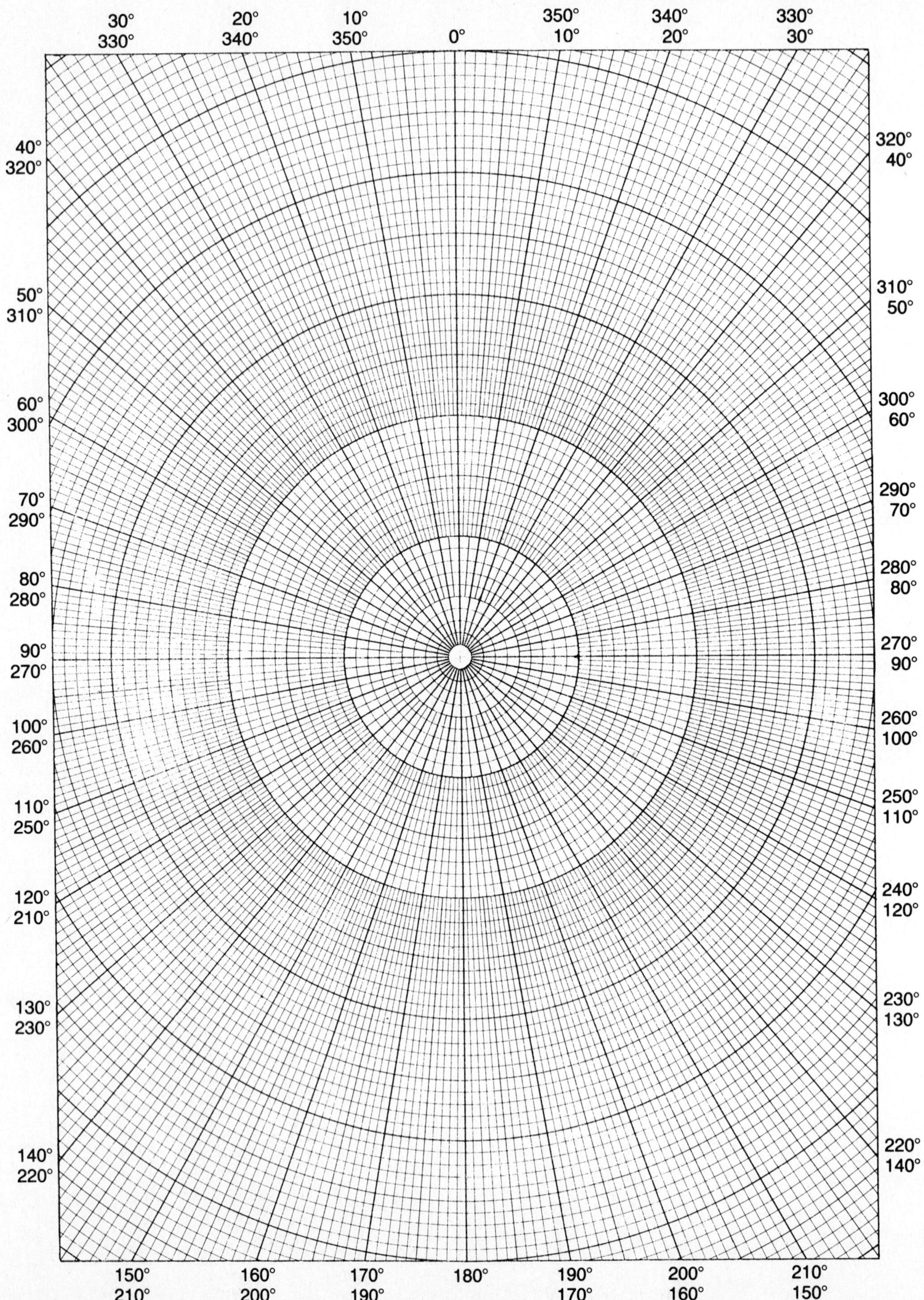

30° 330°
20° 340°
10° 350°
0°
350° 10°
340° 20°
330° 30°
40° 320°
320° 40°
50° 310°
310° 50°
60° 300°
300° 60°
70° 290°
290° 70°
80° 280°
280° 80°
90° 270°
270° 90°
100° 260°
260° 100°
110° 250°
250° 110°
120° 210°
240° 120°
130° 230°
230° 130°
140° 220°
220° 140°
150° 210°
160° 200°
170° 190°
180°
190° 170°
200° 160°
210° 150°

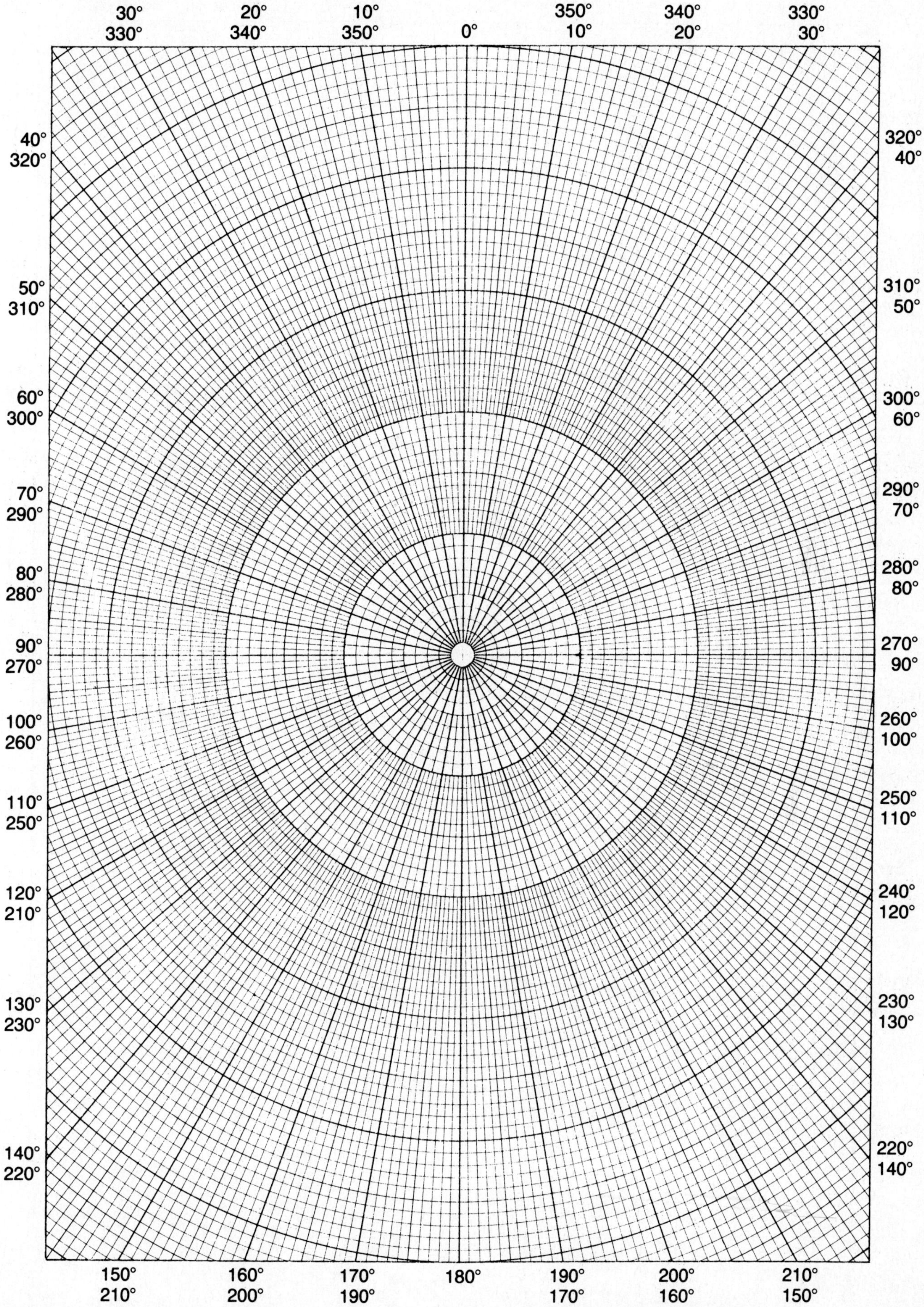
30° 330°
20° 340°
10° 350°
0°
350° 10°
340° 20°
330° 30°
40° 320°
320° 40°
50° 310°
310° 50°
60° 300°
300° 60°
70° 290°
290° 70°
80° 280°
280° 80°
90° 270°
270° 90°
100° 260°
260° 100°
110° 250°
250° 110°
120° 210°
240° 120°
130° 230°
230° 130°
140° 220°
220° 140°
150° 210°
160° 200°
170° 190°
180°
190° 170°
200° 160°
210° 150°

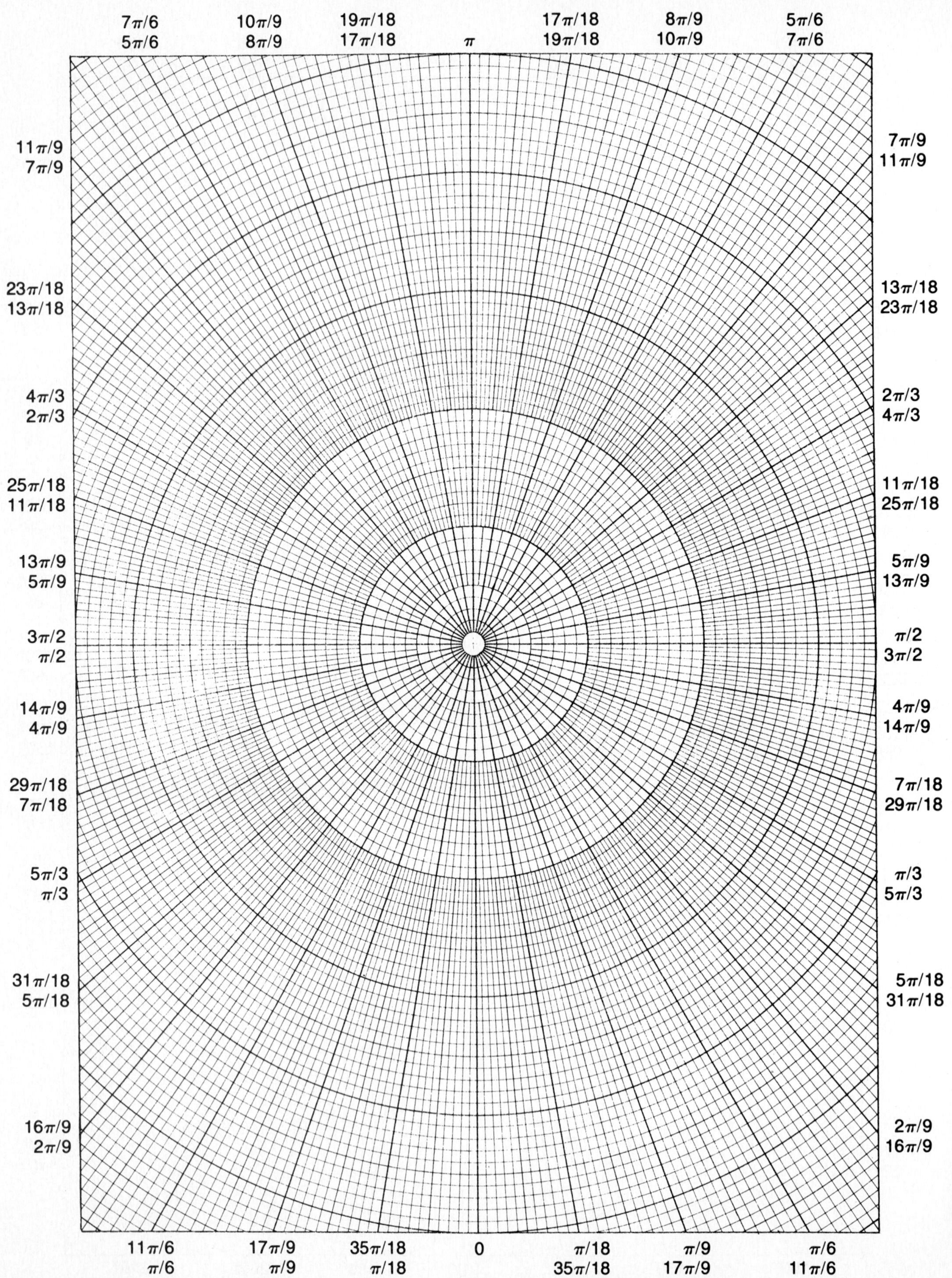

7π/6 5π/6
10π/9 8π/9
19π/18 17π/18
π
17π/18 19π/18
8π/9 10π/9
5π/6 7π/6
11π/9 7π/9
7π/9 11π/9
23π/18 13π/18
13π/18 23π/18
4π/3 2π/3
2π/3 4π/3
25π/18 11π/18
11π/18 25π/18
13π/9 5π/9
5π/9 13π/9
3π/2 π/2
π/2 3π/2
14π/9 4π/9
4π/9 14π/9
29π/18 7π/18
7π/18 29π/18
5π/3 π/3
π/3 5π/3
31π/18 5π/18
5π/18 31π/18
16π/9 2π/9
2π/9 16π/9
11π/6 π/6
17π/9 π/9
35π/18 π/18
0
π/18 35π/18
π/9 17π/9
π/6 11π/6

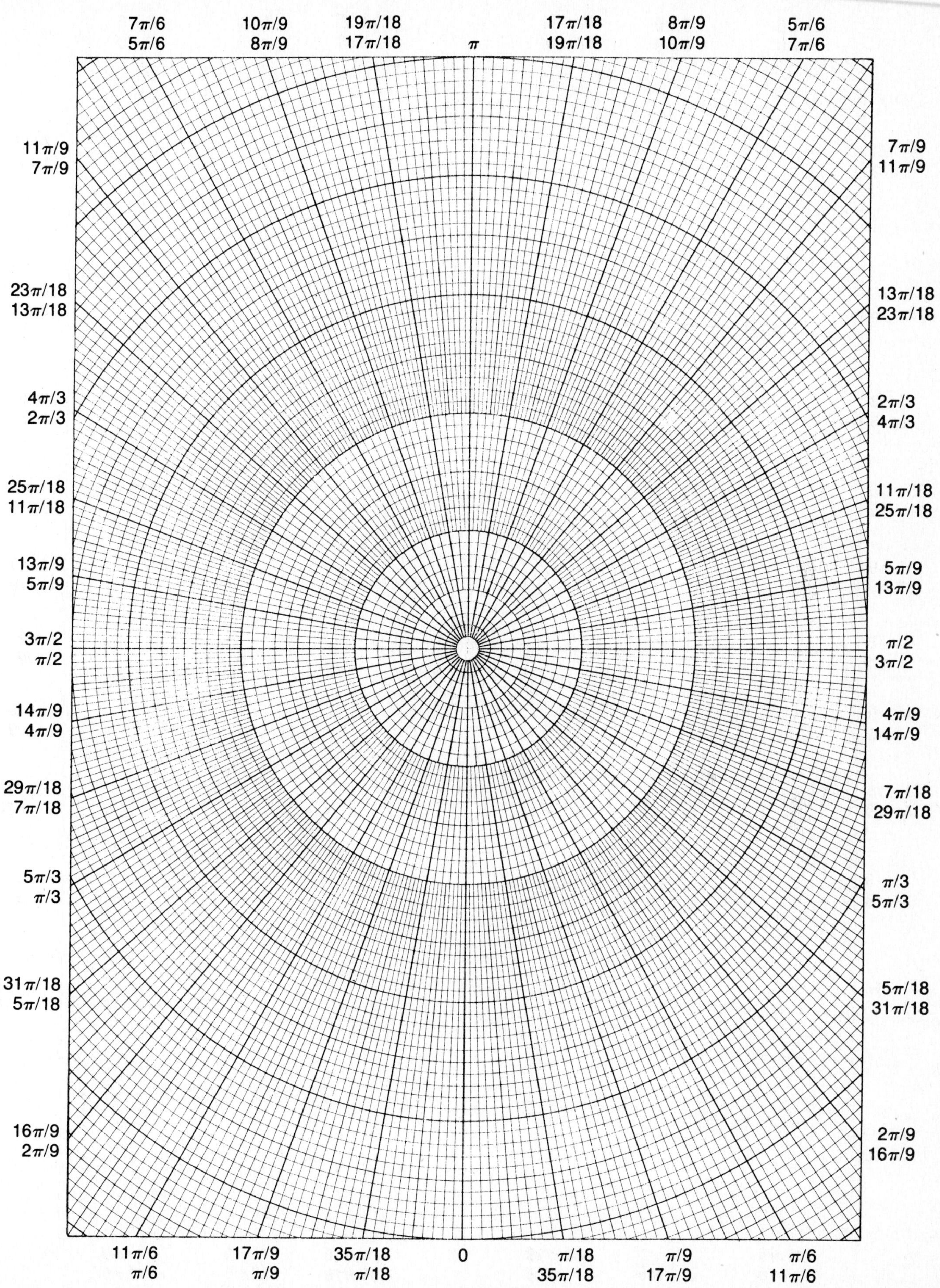

7π/6
5π/6
10π/9
8π/9
19π/18
17π/18
π
17π/18
19π/18
8π/9
10π/9
5π/6
7π/6
11π/9
7π/9
7π/9
11π/9
23π/18
13π/18
13π/18
23π/18
4π/3
2π/3
2π/3
4π/3
25π/18
11π/18
11π/18
25π/18
13π/9
5π/9
5π/9
13π/9
3π/2
π/2
π/2
3π/2
14π/9
4π/9
4π/9
14π/9
29π/18
7π/18
7π/18
29π/18
5π/3
π/3
π/3
5π/3
31π/18
5π/18
5π/18
31π/18
16π/9
2π/9
2π/9
16π/9
11π/6
π/6
17π/9
π/9
35π/18
π/18
0
π/18
35π/18
π/9
17π/9
π/6
11π/6

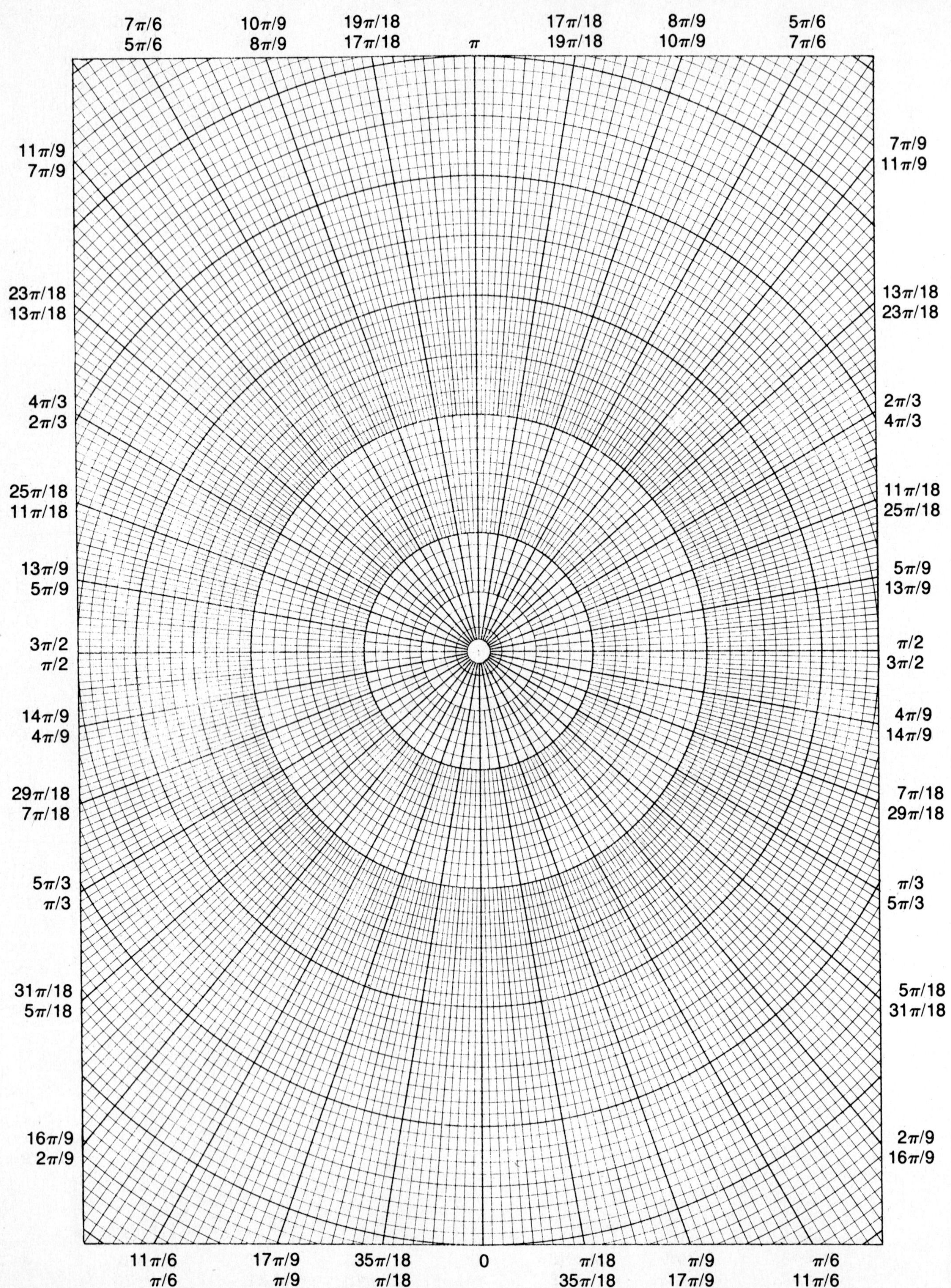
7π/6
5π/6
10π/9
8π/9
19π/18
17π/18
π
17π/18
19π/18
8π/9
10π/9
5π/6
7π/6
11π/9
7π/9
7π/9
11π/9
23π/18
13π/18
13π/18
23π/18
4π/3
2π/3
2π/3
4π/3
25π/18
11π/18
11π/18
25π/18
13π/9
5π/9
5π/9
13π/9
3π/2
π/2
π/2
3π/2
14π/9
4π/9
4π/9
14π/9
29π/18
7π/18
7π/18
29π/18
5π/3
π/3
π/3
5π/3
31π/18
5π/18
5π/18
31π/18
16π/9
2π/9
2π/9
16π/9
11π/6
π/6
17π/9
π/9
35π/18
π/18
0
π/18
35π/18
π/9
17π/9
π/6
11π/6

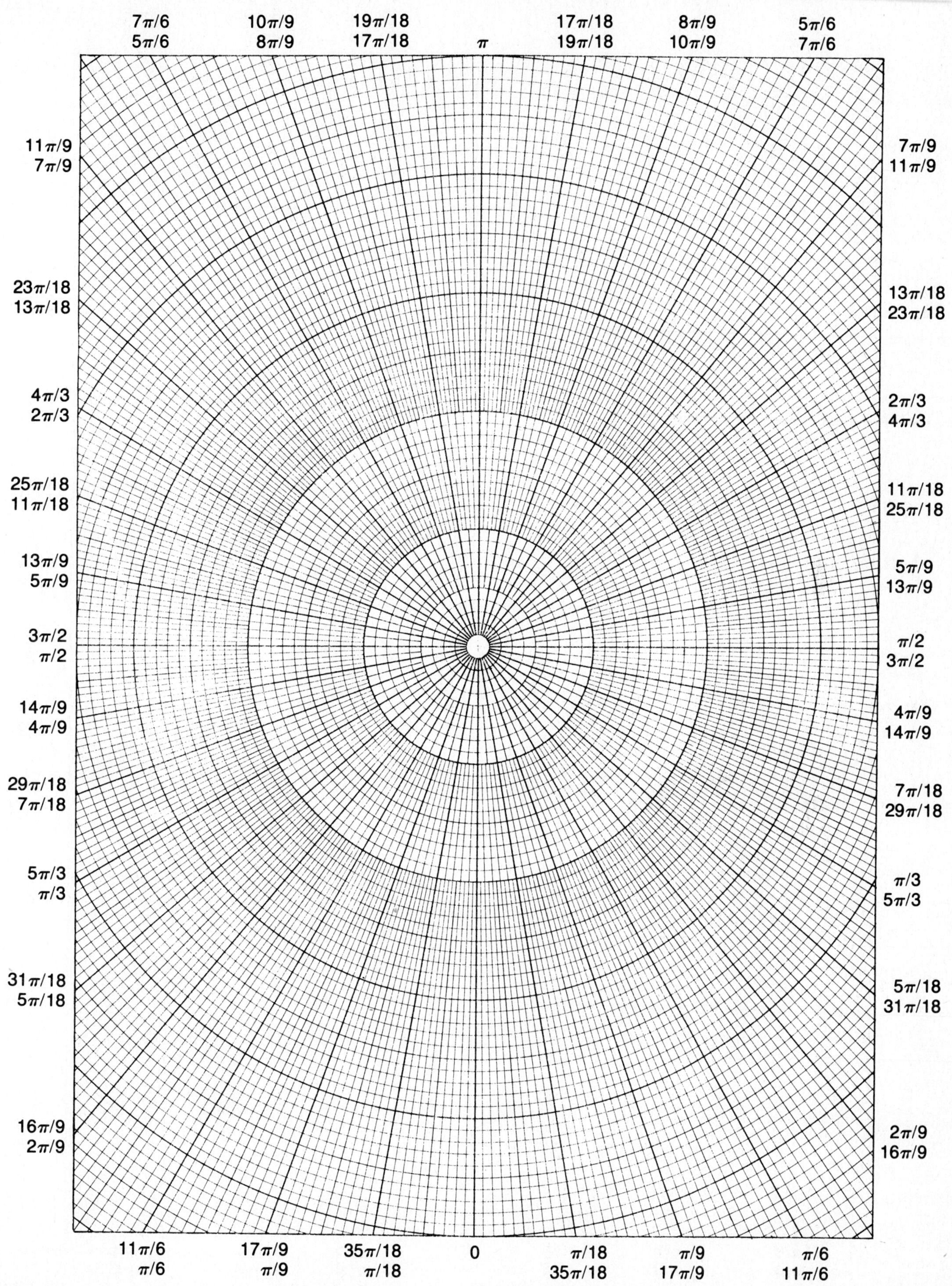
7π/6
5π/6
10π/9
8π/9
19π/18
17π/18
π
17π/18
19π/18
8π/9
10π/9
5π/6
7π/6
11π/9
7π/9
7π/9
11π/9
23π/18
13π/18
13π/18
23π/18
4π/3
2π/3
2π/3
4π/3
25π/18
11π/18
11π/18
25π/18
13π/9
5π/9
5π/9
13π/9
3π/2
π/2
π/2
3π/2
14π/9
4π/9
4π/9
14π/9
29π/18
7π/18
7π/18
29π/18
5π/3
π/3
π/3
5π/3
31π/18
5π/18
5π/18
31π/18
16π/9
2π/9
2π/9
16π/9
11π/6
π/6
17π/9
π/9
35π/18
π/18
0
π/18
35π/18
π/9
17π/9
π/6
11π/6

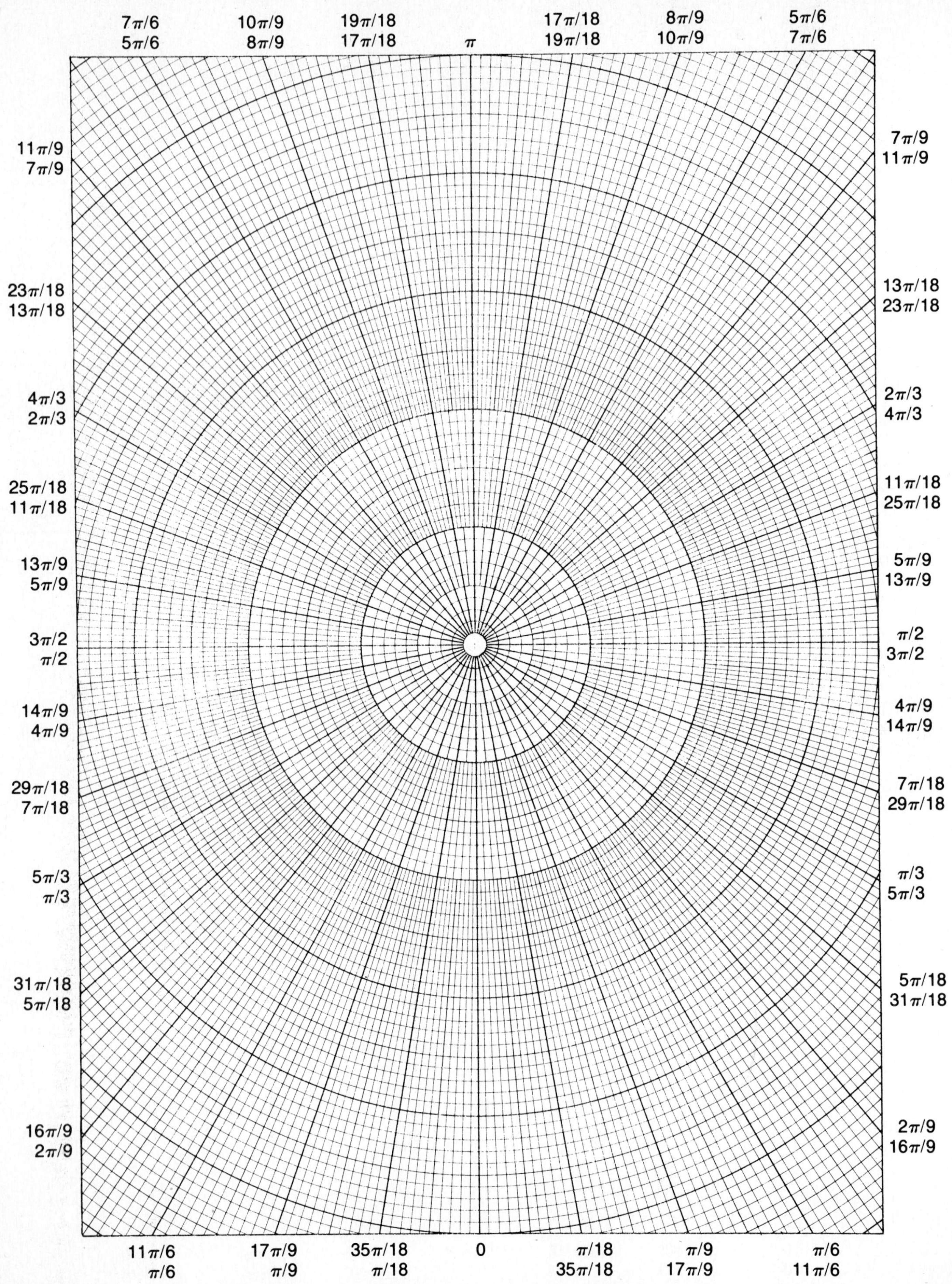

7π/6 5π/6
10π/9 8π/9
19π/18 17π/18
π
17π/18 19π/18
8π/9 10π/9
5π/6 7π/6
11π/9 7π/9
7π/9 11π/9
23π/18 13π/18
13π/18 23π/18
4π/3 2π/3
2π/3 4π/3
25π/18 11π/18
11π/18 25π/18
13π/9 5π/9
5π/9 13π/9
3π/2 π/2
π/2 3π/2
14π/9 4π/9
4π/9 14π/9
29π/18 7π/18
7π/18 29π/18
5π/3 π/3
π/3 5π/3
31π/18 5π/18
5π/18 31π/18
16π/9 2π/9
2π/9 16π/9
11π/6 π/6
17π/9 π/9
35π/18 π/18
0
π/18 35π/18
π/9 17π/9
π/6 11π/6